Y0-CBI-036

16.95

INTRODUCTION TO VLSI DESIGN

McGraw-Hill Series in Electrical Engineering

Consulting Editor
Stephen W. Director, *Carnegie-Mellon University*

Circuits and Systems
Communications and Signal Processing
Control Theory
Electronics and Electronic Circuits
Power and Energy
Electromagnetics
Computer Engineering
Introductory
Radar and Antennas
VLSI

Previous Consulting Editors
Ronald N. Bracewell, Colin Cherry, James F. Gibbons, Willis W. Harman, Hubert Heffner, Edward W. Herold, John G. Linvill, Simon Ramo, Ronald A. Rohrer, Anthony E. Siegman, Charles Susskind, Frederick E. Terman, John G. Truxal, Ernst Weber, and John R. Whinnery

Electronics and Electronic Circuits

Consulting Editor
Stephen W. Director, *Carnegie-Mellon University*

Colclaser and Diehl-Nagle: Materials and Devices for Electrical Engineers and Physicians
Fabricius: Introduction to VLSI Design
Franco: Design with Operational Amplifiers and Analog Integrated Circuits
Grinich and Jackson: Introduction to Integrated Circuits
Hamilton and Howard: Basic Integrated Circuits Engineering
Hodges and Jackson: Analysis and Design of Digital Integrated Circuits
Long and Butner: Gallium Arsenide Digital Integrated Circuit Design
Millman and Grabel: Microelectronics
Millman and Halkias: Integrated Electronics: Analog, Digital Circuits, and Systems
Millman and Taub: Pulse, Digital, and Switching Waveforms
Paul: Analysis of Linear Circuits
Roulston: Bipolar Semiconductor Devices
Schilling and Belove: Electronic Circuits: Discrete and Integrated
Smith: Modern Communication Circuits
Sze: VLSI Technology
Taub: Digital Circuits and Microprocessors
Taub and Schilling: Digital Integrated Electronics
Wait, Huelsman, and Korn: Introduction to Operational and Amplifier Theory Applications
Yang: Microelectronic Devices
Zambuto: Semiconductor Devices

VLSI

Consulting Editor
Stephen W. Director, *Carnegie-Mellon University*

Elliott: Microlithography: Process Technology for IC Fabrication
Fabricius: Introduction to VLSI Design
Geiger, Allen, and Strader: VLSI Design Techniques for Analog and Digital Circuits
Long and Butner: Gallium Arsenide Digital Integrated Circuit Design
Offen: VLSI Image Processing
Ruska: Microelectronic Processing: An Introduction to the Manufacture of Integrated Circuits
Seraphim: Principles of Electronic Packaging
Sze: VLSI Technology
Tsividis: Operation and Modeling of the MOS Transistor
Walsh: Choosing and Using CMOS

INTRODUCTION TO VLSI DESIGN

Eugene D. Fabricius
California Polytechnic State University

McGraw-Hill Publishing Company

New York   St. Louis   San Francisco   Auckland   Bogotá   Caracas
Hamburg   Lisbon   London   Madrid   Mexico   Milan   Montreal
New Delhi   Oklahoma City   Paris   San Juan   São Paulo
Singapore   Sydney   Tokyo   Toronto

INTRODUCTION TO VLSI DESIGN
INTERNATIONAL EDITION

Copyright © 1990
Exclusive rights by McGraw-Hill Book Co.– Singapore for
manufacture and export. This book cannot be re-exported
from the country to which it is consigned by McGraw-Hill.

1 2 3 4 5 6 7 8 9 0 BJE UPE 9 5 4 3 2 1 0

Copyright © 1990 by McGraw-Hill, Inc.
All rights reserved. Except as permitted under the United States Copyright
Act of 1976, no part of this publication may be reproduced or distributed in
any form or by any means, or stored in a data base or retrieval system,
without the prior written permission of the publisher.

This book was set in Times Roman.
The editors were Alar E. Elken and John M. Morriss.
The production supervisor was Louise Karam.
The cover was designed by Rafael Hernandez.
Project supervision was done by Harley Editorial Services.

Library of Congress Cataloging-in-Publication Data

Fabricius, Eugene D.
    Introduction to VLSI design / Eugene D. Fabricius.
       p. cm. – (McGraw-Hill series in electrical engineering.
    Electronics and electronic circuits. VLSI.)
     ISBN 0-07-019948-5
     1. Integrated circuits--Very large scale integration--Design and
    construction--Data processing. 2. Computer-aided design.
    I. Title. II. Series.
    TK7874.F33   1990
    621.39'5--dc20   89-49699

When ordering this title use ISBN 0-07-100727-X

Printed in Singapore

To
Peggy
with love

CONTENTS

12 Testability of VLSI

Appendixes

PREFACE

This textbook is meant to be an introduction to the design and layout of VLSI circuits for undergraduate electrical engineering, computer engineering, or computer science students. The reader is presumed to have a knowledge of basic boolean algebra and elementary circuit theory. While an introductory course in device physics would be desirable it is not necessary. The essential physics is covered as needed in the text.

The text is designed to be used with an activity period which allows the students to work with Magic or a similar interactive software program. Suggested design layouts to be done during the activity period are listed at the end of each chapter. In my classes the students spend the last two or three weeks doing a suitable circuit layout.

A brief introduction is included at the beginning of each chapter, and a short summary at the end of each chapter. These are intended to assist the reader in determining the contents of each chapter, and/or give the main topics covered in that chapter.

The text contains many worked examples which are used to illustrate the concepts. At the conclusion of each chapter are a number of problems which cover the subject matter of that chapter. A Solutions Manual is available which gives solutions to these problems.

An outline of the text is given below. Depending upon the background of the students and the time available some material may have to be omitted. There should be sufficient time in a one-semester course to cover all the material. In a one-quarter course some material will have to be omitted.

Chapter 1 offers an introduction to and overview of the field of VLSI.

Chapter 2 gives background information on the physics of MOS devices, FET modeling, and some reliability problems associated with VLSI design.

Chapter 2 can be skipped if a course of solid-state or device physics is prerequisite for the VLSI class. The results of Chapter 2 are used throughout the text.

Chapter 3 introduces the student to device processing and process limitations, reliability, photolithographic processes, scaling, input protection, and substrate pumping. Sections 3.1 through 3.4 inclusive can be skipped if device processing is not of interest, or if it is prerequisite for the class.

Chapter 4 discusses design rules for laying out NMOS and CMOS circuits. This chapter could be relegated to the activity period, during which the student is laying out circuits. Magic will automatically warn the student of design rule violations, whereas this chapter will explain the purpose of the rules.

Chapter 5 is an introduction to NMOS and CMOS inverters, and covers inverter rise times, transit and switching times, output voltages, loading, and fanout.

Chapter 6 introduces the reader to superbuffers, BiCMOS circuits, the concepts of pass-transistor logic, and general function blocks.

Chapter 7 compares the common CMOS technologies, and static and dynamic CMOS design. Latchup, charge sharing, and clocking are discussed, and methods of avoiding latchup and undesired charge-sharing are covered.

Chapter 8 introduces the reader to unique approaches to tally circuits, two-level logic circuits, multiplexers, and barrel shifters, as well as wire routing, layout, and clock distribution.

Chapter 9 introduces the general topics of charge storage, and regular arrays of logic via the programmable logic array or PLA. Subsets of PLA logic include programmed read only memories or PROMs, programmable array logic or PALs, and dynamic logic arrays. Feedback and finite state machines are also covered.

Chapter 10 continues the discussion of PLAs with advanced and special techniques involving input and output circuitry, driving circuitry for the OR plane, and reduction techniques such as PLA folding and feedback reduction.

Chapter 11 offers an introduction to Weinberger arrays, gate matrices, and boolean algebra for multilevel minimization and multioutput minimization of boolean expressions. Topics include boolean cubes, kernels and cokernels and their determination, boolean trees, binary decision diagrams, directed acyclic graphs, and if-then-else operators.

Chapter 12 discusses the basics of VLSI testability, and includes testing of stuck-at faults and PLA crosspoint faults. The major topics covered are boolean difference algebra and PLA testability.

Students with a previous course in device physics can omit Chapters 2 and 5. Chapters 11 and 12 can be omitted if time does not permit covering them, although these chapters cover important topics in VLSI design. Thus, a quarter sequence for students with a previous course in device physics could consist of Chapter 3, Sections 3.5 through 3.8, Chapters 4, 6, 7, 8, and 9. This allows just over one-and-a-half weeks per chapter, and might give the instructor the option of covering some topics in Chapters 10, 11, and/or 12. Students with no background in field-effect transistors would have to stick to the basic topics in Chapters 1 through 9, and may have to forgo the last three chapters.

ACKNOWLEDGEMENTS

The author wishes to thank the following people:

Peggy Rodriguez for installing the Magic software with X-windows on the SUN workstations.

Joseph Codispoti for photographing the color plates.

James Harris for his support of the VLSI program at Cal Poly with funding and release time.

Lynn Conway for graciously making her class notes from MIT available to teachers of VLSI. My debt to her and to the Mead-Conway text are evident in every page.

Alar Elken for many discussions and recommendations.

All my students who have struggled through the VLSI classes over the years.

My wife, Peggy, for helping with all the endless hours of proofreading and for her constant encouragement and support.

McGraw-Hill and the author would like to thank the following reviewers for their comments and suggestions: Steve Bibyk, The Ohio State University; Paul M. Chau, University of California-San Diego; William Eisenstadt, University of Florida; Yu Hen Hu, University of Wisconsin-Madison; H. C. Lin, University of Maryland; M. A. Littlejohn, University of North Carolina; Wantai Liu, North Carolina State University-Raleigh; Barry M. Pangrele, University of California-Santa Barbara; and Resve Saleh, University of Illinois-Urbana-Champaign.

Eugene D. Fabricius

INTRODUCTION TO VLSI DESIGN

CHAPTER
1

INTRODUCTION TO VLSI LAYOUT

1.1 INTRODUCTION

This text is an introduction to the design and implementation of very large scale integration or VLSI, including devices, circuits, and digital subsystems. The procedures for designing and implementing digital integrated systems will be covered, including the Mead and Conway structured design approach consisting of the use of stick diagramming, scaling of NMOS and CMOS design rules, and techniques for estimating time delays.

1.2 COMPUTER-AIDED-DESIGN TOOLS

The complexity and capability of present-day VLSI technology is extraordinary, but current design techniques are still inadequate to meet all the challenges of VLSI. Techniques that may be satisfactory for high-volume applications will not be financially competitive for small custom jobs, and future increases in the number of active devices per chip require highly refined and sophisticated approaches.

To achieve the full potential of VLSI technology it is necessary to develop and use computer aids that provide significant assistance in the design and analysis of complex VLSI systems. The emphasis of this text is on an understanding of the design and layout of integrated circuits, as well as accurate simulations of the resultant designs, and the testing of manufactured circuits.

1

Computer-aided design (CAD) approaches make use of cell libraries consisting of tested and debugged field-effect and bipolar transistor circuits. The complete design cycle must be accomplished with minimum artwork generation time. Analysis and design verification tools are needed to achieve correct designs before chips are manufactured. This requires system designers who can specify IC designs without a detailed knowledge of integrated-device physics.

Conventional CAD systems use graphic design tools to capture, edit, and output the detailed physical description of the IC mask in a form that the fabrication house can use. Artwork generation and testing attracts the most attention, but the complete design cycle must be addressed for a design philosophy to be truly effective. A graphic interface between a designer and data is both convenient and useful, but manipulating the design at the mask level does not guarantee that the resulting hardware will be an optimum design in terms of chip area or performance.

The IC designer and the process designer should interact during process development, because the process designer's objective should be compatible with the chip-design methodology. The smallest layout often results from optimizing the overall design concept, rather than from minimizing design rules.

Capturing the physical, structural, and behavioral representations of a VLSI circuit is vital to correct design. A good artwork system uses graphic design descriptions and symbolic representations of components and interconnects, along with basic layout information, to modify the data representation by minimizing superfluous physical information. With unnecessary information suppressed, the designer can zoom in on part of the design to examine detail, or he/she can reduce the scale to enable a better overall perspective of the system design. The conversion from symbolic layout to final artwork is done after design, editing, and verification have been completed.

With a structured design approach one can create a library of basic functional blocks that have matching cell height and bus structure in the vertical layout dimension, and vary in width to accommodate a complete family of structured cells.

Computer-aided design has advanced sufficiently for design centers to have been created that link the work of professionals across many functional boundaries. This provides the advantages of improved design tools, as well as improved productivity. The work can be correlated, documented, and traced throughout the entire project.

A language such as the *Caltech Intermediate Form* (CIF) is required to convert the designed projects into hardware chips. The effects of future scaling of the dimensions of devices and systems must also be kept in mind as processing limitations on device size shrink, and fundamental physical limitations come into play.

The goal of this text is to assist the student in becoming familiar with the design of NMOS and CMOS circuits and their simulation and testing. To this end, an understanding of the behavior of NMOS and CMOS circuits is necessary, as is familiarization with the CAD tools and techniques in common use in industry.

Nothing replaces doing layouts in an interactive environment. In keeping with the basic Cal Poly hands-on approach, the text is designed to incorporate an activity period for doing layout designs on a color terminal each week as the student progresses in capability. This activity is designed to augment the weekly lectures.

1.3 THE PHILOSOPHY OF VLSI

Most introductory digital courses are devoted to small-scale integrated chips, usually in *transistor-transistor logic* (TTL), *emitter-coupled logic* (ECL), and *metal-oxide-semiconductor* (MOS) logic. This text assumes a working familiarity with TTL, ECL, and MOS small-scale integration, as well as basic boolean logic and digital design.

TTL flip-flops are edge-triggered and can get by with a single system clock. Level-triggered devices predominate in CMOS design, and require at least two-phase clocking schemes. For this reason, the text will follow the basic two-phase clocking scheme proposed by Carver Mead and Lynn Conway (1) whenever possible.

There are two basic sequencing techniques, synchronous and self-timed. A *synchronous sequential system* uses a fixed global clock with a period that is longer than the worst-case propagation delay. The major disadvantages inherent in this approach are loss of efficiency, problems in interfacing to the asynchronous world, and problems in routing the clock circuitry.

In a *self-timed system*, events are initiated by completion signals from other events. Timing is dependent on wiring delays, but the sequence of events is guaranteed by adherence to protocol and there is no upper limit to the size of a functional system. The disadvantages to this approach are that more hardware is needed, and there exist fewer formal design tools.

All synchronous digital systems are composed of *finite-state machines* controlling register-to-register data transfer paths. Thus, we need only two basic types of building blocks; *registers* that store data and can be clocked, and *combinational-logic blocks*, or modules, containing no data storage elements.

Consider a stored-program computer as shown in Fig. 1.1. With two-phase clocking the data path can be constructed of blocks of *combinational logic* (C/L), clocked by storage registers, as shown in Fig. 1.2.

The finite-state machine is also composed of combinational-logic blocks, clocked by storage registers, as shown in Fig. 1.3. The only structural difference between the data path and the finite-state machine is the presence of feedback in the latter.

Storage registers, combinational logic, and the associated interconnections are very easy to design and implement in both NMOS and CMOS. The challenge is to take advantage of this ease of design to create new architectures and design large digital structures in an efficient and reasonably systematic way, so as to contain their complexity; and to formally describe and quickly implement these structures.

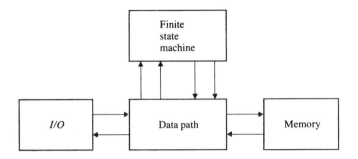

FIGURE 1.1
A simple stored-program computer.

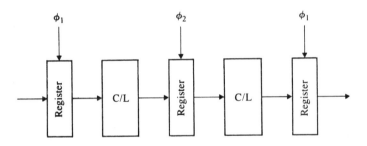

FIGURE 1.2
A two-phase clocked data path.

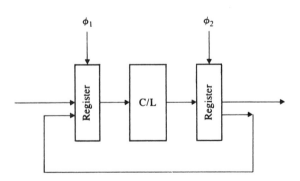

FIGURE 1.3
A two-phase clocked finite-state machine.

The design method developed by Carver Mead and Lynn Conway (1) capitalizes on the inherent advantages of NMOS processing by systematizing the NMOS design rules to be pattern- and process-independent. Their approach has been extended to include CMOS design rules by many authors. This text will use the NMOS and CMOS rules as specified by MOSIS (2, 3), the MOS Implementation System of the University of Southern California Information Sciences Institute.†

1.4 NMOS AND PMOS TRANSISTOR STRUCTURES

VLSI layout design consists of creating appropriate masks that define the sizes and locations of sources, drains, gates, and the necessary interconnections. To facilitate design and checking, different colors are used for each separate mask required.

Diffusions for *n*-channel (NMOS) and *p*-channel (PMOS) devices involve different masks and must be distinguishable. Green is used for NMOS source and drain regions, and brown is used for PMOS source and drain regions, as shown in Figs. 1.4, 1.5, and 1.6. The substrate must be *p* type for NMOS transistors and *n* type for PMOS devices.

The NMOS and PMOS single-metal processes are each analogous to a three-level printed-circuit board, consisting of three levels of conducting material, each layer electrically isolated from the layers immediately above and below by silicon dioxide, as shown in Fig. 1.4. These layers are color coded according to the different photolithographic masks needed to manufacture the devices. The top layer consists of *metallization (blue)*, followed by a layer of *polysilicon (red)*, followed by a layer *diffused (green* for NMOS and *brown* for PMOS) into the silicon substrate. Contacts between layers are shown in *black*.

---

† MOSIS no longer supports NMOS design.

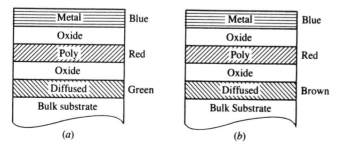

FIGURE 1.4
The three-level MOS, single-metallization process. (*a*) *n*-channel FET; (*b*) *p*-channel FET.

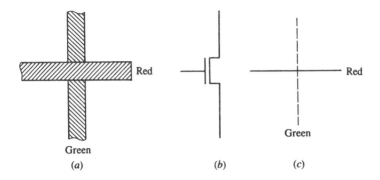

FIGURE 1.5
(a) Layout, (b) circuit symbol, and (c) stick representation for an NMOS FET.

The Three-level NMOS and PMOS structures shown in Fig. 1.4 can be expanded to two or more metal or polysilicon layers by adding more mask steps and by assigning different colors to the other metal and/or polysilicon layers, which are also isolated by oxide insulation, giving rise to four or more levels of structure. Purple or a different shade of blue can be used for a second metal mask, and a different color or shade of red can be used for a second polysilicon mask.

Metal can cross polysilicon or diffused areas with no functional effect other than to produce a parasitic capacitance. Thus blue conductive layers can cross red and green conductive layers, and connect to them at black. Polysilicon crossing a diffused area creates a FET switch; wherever red crosses green an n-channel transistor is formed, and a p-channel transistor is formed wherever red crosses brown, as shown in Figs. 1.5a and 1.6a.

The NMOS transistor is an active-high switching device which conducts and acts as a closed switch when its gate voltage is high. The PMOS FET is an active-low switching device that conducts when its gate voltage is low. This is

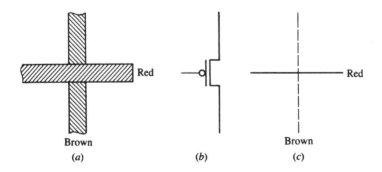

FIGURE 1.6
(a) Layout, (b) circuit symbol, and (c) stick representation for a PMOS FET.

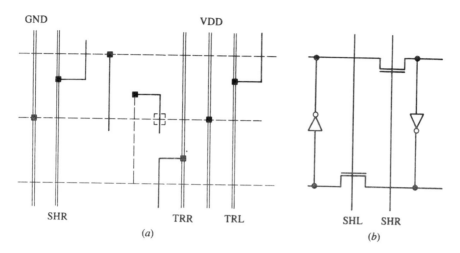

FIGURE 1.7
Representation of a shift-right/shift-left register cell in (*a*) a stick drawing, and (*b*) logic notation.

shown by the circuit symbols in Figs. 1.5*b* and 1.6*b*. The "bubble" at the gate of the PMOS transistor means that its gate must be at a low voltage in order for it to turn on. The absence of a bubble at the gate of the NMOS device means it conducts when its gate is at a high potential.

The symbols in Figs. 1.5*c* and 1.6*c* are referred to as *stick diagrams* or *stick drawings*. They convey color-coded or black-and-white-coded information that reflects the actual layout topology of a circuit to the designer, and when augmented with vital information such as the size of the transistor gates, the stick diagram contains sufficient information to lay out the circuit.

In this text, black and white drawings will portray metal with two parallel solid lines, polysilicon with one solid line and diffusion with dotted lines. Transistors will then have to be identified as *p*-channel or as *n*-channel. Contacts can be denoted by small solid squares as shown in Fig. 1.7. A small "X" can also be used to represent a contact.

To design complex layouts, one needs to understand the basics of the NMOS process as well as the CMOS process, and the electrical properties of both NMOS and PMOS transistors. A study of the basic electrical properties of MOSFET design will allow us to do "stick" layouts of circuits, and then "flesh out" the stick diagrams with the help of design rules, to form the geometrical layouts of transistors and wires that will implement working circuits.

1.5 SCALABILITY

VLSI is a rapidly changing technology, and the goal is to design chips in a manner that facilitates the transition to smaller layouts and more complex chips in the future. Microcircuit design differs from previous digital design in the attention that must be given, at every level, to the physical design or layout of a system.

The good design engineer of the future must understand the basics of patterning, processing, and fabrication technologies as used in industry. To do all the above jobs, the engineer must have a minimum working knowledge of all levels of design, so that he or she will feel comfortable working with *systems*, *processors*, *bit slices*, *registers*, *gates*, *devices*, and *features* of the design. This is to be contrasted with design engineers of the past, who traditionally have specialized in subsets of these hierarchies, such as devices and features, gates and registers, or bit-slice design, etc.

1.6 DESIGN REQUIREMENTS

A VLSI circuit is designed to implement a specific function which is required by a larger system in order to achieve some specified result. The circuit must perform its designed function properly, and *validation* is the process by which it is established that the circuit does, or does not, correctly implement the specified function.

For validation to be successful an appropriately defined standard of reference must be specified and a testable design must be provided. To accomplish this the functional requirements of the circuit must be described in a complete and unambiguous manner. Through each stage of design the engineer must keep in mind the *verifiability* and *testability* of the system.

The potential reliability of an IC depends upon the design, and can be maximized through the careful definition of, and strict adherence to, design rules associated with various design levels. The ability to effectively accomplish this depends upon the overall design method that is followed.

1.6.1 Structured Design

Because of the degree of complexity of VLSI circuits, the design process must be very highly organized and more formal than was previously necessary. Structured programming techniques that have been very successful in the development of complex software systems are being successfully applied to the design of hardware systems in silicon. Such a structured design process can be described by a hierarchy of design levels, each level corresponding to a progressively lower level of abstraction and more highly detailed description of the design.

The phrase *levels of design* (or *levels of abstraction*) is used to refer to the concept that, to manage the complexity of VLSI at each level, one uses models that are devised to abstract away all those details that are not essential to understanding the structure and behavior of the system at that level.

There is no unique list of levels of design or abstraction. A typical breakdown according to engineering speciality might consist of architectures and algorithms, followed by digital system organization, logical design, electrical circuits and semiconductor devices and processes. To create suitable design rules requires an understanding of the *pattern, mask,* and *fabrication* information needed by the commercial firms that will implement hardware.

CAD tools are essential to VLSI designers, and their designs are only as good as the CAD tools allow. Designing a VLSI chip or a system consisting of several chips is similar to designing on the medium-scale integration (MSI) level or large-scale integration (LSI) level, except that the functions of several MSI chips can be incorporated into a single VLSI chip. There are advantages, though, to designing the entire system on a single chip.

The major advantage occurs due to the shortening of communication paths internal to a given circuit design, and the reduction of interconnection buses off chip to a printed-circuit board. In both cases, the shorter wires have lower parasitic capacitances, leading to much faster circuit performance.

At the *architectural level,* the design engineer is concerned with functional organization, instruction-set architecture and interfacing requirements, as well as subsystem functions at the register transfer level.

At the *logic level,* the digital structures needed to implement the architectural design are studied. At the *physical level,* the design engineer is concerned with the circuit elements necessary to implement the digital or analog function. Finally, at the *geometrical level,* the networks of circuit elements must be translated into the topographical layout that is to be reproduced in silicon.

The description of the design at each level must be transformed into a description at the next lower level in a format or language appropriate to that level. The new description must then be evaluated against the requirements and constraints placed upon it, and for behavioral or structural completeness. *Validation* is employed to ascertain the system behavior at different levels, and *verification* is used to demonstrate structural equivalence.

A successful design ideally would start with the complete functional description of the IC, with all the input and output characteristics specified. This description would provide the basic standard of reference for validation of the design at all levels of development.

1.6.2 Design Evaluation

Before manufacturing a VLSI chip, the circuit performance should be evaluated by simulating the behavior of the chip. In doing this, problems arise due to both inadequate software models and the processing time required to run algorithms on a computer. The complexity of modern VLSI design requires development of the necessary tools to communicate with computers at a much greater level of sophistication than was previously possible.

VLSI implementation consists of all the tasks involved in going from a set of design files to packaged chips ready to test: collecting and merging design files into starting frames, converting merged files into pattern format, testing for logical and design-rule errors, making masks, fabricating wafers, packaging chips, and testing the finished product.

The Mead-Conway structured approach to VLSI System Design converts the numerous VLSI design rules into a comprehensive, general, compact, and straightforward science, and makes the performance of standard MOS circuit blocks and composites of these blocks as predictable and reliable as TTL circuits. Effective design tools and proper technique can ensure the primary goal of obtaining a working chip in the shortest possible time.

1.7 HIERARCHICAL REPRESENTATIONS

Very large and complex systems require a hierarchically structured approach, and abstract representations are needed. Interconnections can be symbolic rather than pin-to-pin, layout can be topological rather than exact geometry, and signaling can proceed in a sequential manner instead of requiring absolute timing.

Systems design can be from the top down, starting with the design goals in terms of inputs/outputs, states and functional subsystems, with the designer then iterating until the design is completed.

The design can also proceed from the bottom up, starting with basic building blocks, such as programmable logic arrays (PLAs), read only memories (ROMs), multiplexers, decoders, registers, buses, and input/output pads. From these the designer can construct larger subsystems such as arithmetic logic units (ALUs), again iterating until a satisfactory design is reached. The most suitable solution may require iterating between top-down and bottom-up designs.

A good *stick drawing* is topologically equivalent to the proposed circuit design, and gives a quick representation of how the layout will appear. The stick drawing forms a bridge between the circuit diagram and the final layout. An example of a shift-register cell is shown in circuit notation and in stick form in Fig. 1.7. This circuit is discussed and explained in Sec. 9.3, and shown in Figs. 9.8 and 9.9.

1.8 TESTABILITY ENHANCEMENT

One of the most important steps in VLSI design is the incorporation of measures to enhance testability. The rationale behind such measures is to provide circuitry that is well behaved, simple to simulate, easy to interrogate by test equipment, and offers access to internal circuit nodes in a convenient manner, thereby satisfying the twin criteria of *observability* and *controllability*.

Testability can be enhanced by using synchronous circuit sequencing whenever possible, and isolating the clocking circuitry from the logic circuitry. Level-sensitive circuits permit a more disciplined approach to clocking than edge-triggered circuits, and will be used whenever possible. Provision must also be made for the initialization of all sequential logic.

The use of regular circuit structures throughout the design tends both to reduce the likelihood of design errors and to produce a more easily testable circuit. The concept includes not only logic elements such as gates and memory cells, but also regular interconnect structures and communication paths (4). The human eye has great pattern-recognition capability and can often detect design errors in a regular structure, especially errors such as broken lines which violate no design rules and might be difficult if not impossible to detect by a computer.

Simulation and testing can be assisted by proper partitioning of the design, which can take place at several design levels. Partitioning circuitry dealing with data flow from that dealing with control flow allows one to simulate and test each separately. A circuit that has been partitioned into functional units allows the simulation and testing of each unit individually.

Combinational circuitry is much easier to test than sequential circuitry, and a test mode during which the circuitry can be reconfigured into a purely combinational logic network often greatly expedites matters.

1.9 COMBINATIONAL LOGIC

Combinational-logic (C/L) modules contain no data storage elements. In IC design, C/L may be broadly lumped into three categories based on the level of complexity.

Functions that require a small amount of simple logic are amenable to traditional NAND/NOR gate design which can be realized by a direct implementation of a sum-of-products or product-of-sums representation of the function. The design involves few gates and can be done by inspection.

Second, some complex functions lend themselves to implementation with clever, regular structural topologies. These solutions can be placed in a cell library, to be reused when needed. Examples of this type of realization will be discussed when appropriate throughout the text.

Third, there are many complex and inherently irregular functions which may often be best implementated with a ROM or with a PLA configured as a finite-state machine. This also allows the designer to maintain flexibility by postponing the details of the logic functions realized in the ROM or PLA until most of the design is complete.

1.10 CHIP REGULARIZATION

A major problem at present is the devising of new design techniques and methods to make the rapidly changing VLSI technology widely usable by the electronics industry. Design methods have not always kept pace with the increased on-chip complexity the technology is capable of, and it keeps taking more time and effort to design, debug, and bring a complex VLSI system to production.

Layout is one of the more expensive and time-consuming portions of the design cycle and is in constant need of improvement. The complexity of VLSI at the chip level has grown exponentially for several years. This ever-increasing number of devices per chip will continue to make the layout portion of the design cycle more costly, until it becomes the dominant factor in development cost, and perhaps even the limiting factor in chip design.

Simultaneously, layout productivity is decreasing with increasing chip complexity, and can be as low as five or ten devices per layout designer per day, including the time to draw, check, and correct a layout.

A method to keep logic chip complexity from becoming unwieldy has been proposed by Sutherland and Mead (4). It is a concept whereby random logic layout with its inherent interconnect problems is structured by a set of well-defined communication paths. These structures are usually implemented with very regular cells such as ROMs, RAMs, and PLAs, but it is the geometric regularity of the interconnections between elements that provides the greatest benefit in reducing complexity.

A second major benefit of designing VLSI with regular structures is a decrease in layout time and effort, because the use of regular structures reduces the total number of devices that must be individually drawn. Also, more structured layouts are easier to debug.

A measure of the effectiveness of regular structuring in reducing layout time can be obtained by defining the *chip regularization*, the degree of regularization on a given chip, as the total devices on a chip divided by the number of drawn devices. Total devices includes all possible ROM and PLA placements, and drawn devices are all the devices that require layout effort. The regularization of recent microprocessors is given by Bill Lattin (5) as:

$$8080: \quad 4.6/4.3 = 1.07$$
$$8085: \quad 6.2/2.0 = 3.10$$
$$8086: \quad 29.0/6.6 = 4.39$$

The regularization parameter is now in the range of 10 to 100 allowing designers to use VLSI technology to a far greater extent than was once possible, while simultaneously reducing layout efforts (6).

REFERENCES

1. C. A. Mead and L. A. Conway, *Introduction to VLSI Systems*, Addison-Wesley Publishing Company, Reading, Mass., 1980.
2. "MOSIS Scalable NMOS Process, Version 1.0," USC Information Sciences Institute, USC, November 1984.
3. "MOSIS Scalable & Generic CMOS Design Rules, Revision 6," USC Information Sciences Institute, USC, February 1988.
4. I. Sutherland and C. Mead, "Microelectronics and Computer Science," *Scientific American*, September 1977.
5. B. Lattin, "VLSI Design Methodology, the Problem of the 80's for Microprocessor Design," Proceedings of the Caltech Conference on VLSI, Caltech, January 1979, pp. 247–252.
6. D. A. Hodges and H. G. Jackson, *Analysis and Design of Digital Integrated Circuits*, 2d ed., McGraw-Hill, Inc., New York, N.Y., 1988, p.397.

DESIGN PROBLEM

1.1. Become familiar with the log-on and log-off procedures and the basic commands used to create layouts on the computer color-graphics terminal. For Magic users this would be Magic Tutorials 1: Getting Started, and 2: Basic Painting and Selection.

CHAPTER
2

THE PHYSICS
OF FIELD-EFFECT
TRANSISTORS

2.1 INTRODUCTION

An introduction to the device physics of field-effect transistors is necessary in order to understand device design and behavior. The channel conductivity of a FET is modulated by charges induced at the semiconductor surface as a result of a voltage applied to the gate terminal of the device. This voltage also determines the transconductance and capacitances of the FET.

NMOS and PMOS enhancement-mode and depletion-mode devices will be studied, and equations governing device behavior will be derived. Linear and saturated regions of operation will be investigated, and equations for computing drain current will be derived. Capacitive behavior that determines time constants and device speed will also be studied.

The chapter will conclude with a discussion of the physical causes of reliability problems due to hot-electron effects, thermal effects, electromigration, aluminum spiking, and contact resistance.

2.2 GENERAL PHYSICAL CONSIDERATIONS

Crucial to a study of FET behavior is an understanding of the behavior of silicon-silicon dioxide interfaces. The presence of an oxide layer on a silicon surface gives rise to what are called *surface states*. These are energy levels that are not present in pure bulk silicon and exist both throughout the silicon dioxide and at the oxide-silicon interface. The energy states within the oxide layer are usually caused by positive ions of sodium, potassium, lithium, etc., as shown in Fig. 2.1, sodium being the worst offender. Silicon dioxide has a very wide forbidden energy gap and is an excellent insulator. Electrons and holes have very low mobilities in the bulk oxide, and these surface states charge or discharge very slowly, with extremely long time constants. They are referred to as slow states, and for practical purposes can be treated as a dc phenomenon.

The fixed charge at the silicon-silicon dioxide interface is always positive and can quickly and easily be neutralized by electrons from the bulk silicon. This fixed charge is usually referred to as the *oxide charge* or the *surface-state charge*. Q_{ox} and Q_{ss} are the commonly used symbols for these states. Their presence produces a bending of the energy levels at the oxide-semiconductor interface,

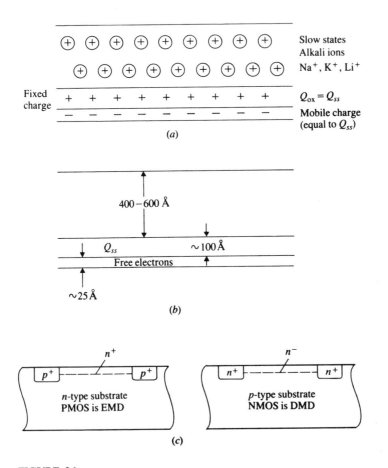

FIGURE 2.1
The Si-SiO$_2$ interface. (*a*) Surface states and mobile surface charge; (*b*) typical dimensions; (*c*) effect of Q_{ss} on substrate conductivity.

which has a profound effect upon the conductivity of channels formed at the interface.

Vacancies, interstitial silicon atoms, and other physical defects, as well as various chemical impurities at the silicon surface, can and do give rise to energy levels not present at an ideal interface. There would still be fast states at a perfectly clean, uncontaminated surface, due to the abrupt termination of the crystal lattice structure. These states are due to the fact that surface atoms have only two nearest neighbors to bond with and two of the four tetrahedral chemical bonds are "dangling," meaning that they are unpaired, and thus not saturated.

The surface atom desires to acquire two additional electrons, in order to satisfy its bonding with eight valence electrons in the sp_3 state. However, the acquisition of a first electron changes the surface atom to a negative ion, and tends to repel the second electron. These electrons, whether one or two per surface atom, are in energy levels that do not exist in a perfect bulk material. These states have small trapping energies and can be charged or discharged quickly by small changes in temperature or bias voltage. For this reason they are referred to as fast states.

The effect of fast surface states is to produce a shift in conductivity of the silicon material at the surface, caused by the attracted electrons. The result is that the surface of the wafer is more *n*-type than the bulk, as shown in Fig. 2.1*c*. PMOS FETs thus tend to be *enhancement-mode devices* (EMD) due to the surface charge, while NMOS FETs tend to be *depletion-mode devices* (DMD).

In the early days of MOS manufacture, process steps were not well controlled, and the chemicals used were not sufficiently purified of alkali ions. This led to large surface-state densities and *n*-type surfaces regardless of the bulk conductivity, and drove the industry to manufacture PMOS devices since NMOS enhancement-mode devices could not be constructed.

Improved manufacturing capability and "MOS-grade" chemicals gave process engineers better control of surface states and threshold voltages. This led to the manufacture of NMOS enhancement-mode devices, which are about twice as fast as PMOS devices due to the higher mobility of electrons in silicon, and made low-power CMOS design practical.

An NMOS device is shown in cross section in Fig. 2.2. The device is an enhancement-mode FET if the channel is absent with no external gate bias, and a depletion-mode FET if the channel is present with no external gate bias.

The following parameters and symbols are defined, along with the usually specified units.

L	Channel length from source to drain, in microns
W	Channel width (not shown in Fig. 2.2) in microns
N_{ss}	Density of surface states, in atoms/cm^3
Q_{ss}	Surface-state charge density, in nanocoulombs/cm^2
t_{ox}	Oxide thickness, in angstroms or microns
x_j	Junction depth below the silicon surface, in microns
x_d	Depletion-region width, in microns
V_{GN}	Bias, gate to ground, in volts

V_{SN} Bias, source to ground, in volts
V_{DN} Bias, drain to ground, in volts
V_{BN} Bias, body (substrate) to ground, in volts
V_{TH} Threshold voltage, in volts
V_{THO} Threshold voltage with no gate-to-body bias, in volts
V_{THE} Threshold voltage of an enhancement-mode FET, in volts
V_{THD} Threshold voltage of a depletion-mode FET, in volts
V_{THN} Threshold voltage of an NMOS enhancement FET, in CMOS
V_{THP} Threshold voltage of a PMOS enhancement FET, in CMOS
Q Mobile charge density in thickness x_d of the depletion region, in C/cm^2 of cross-sectional area

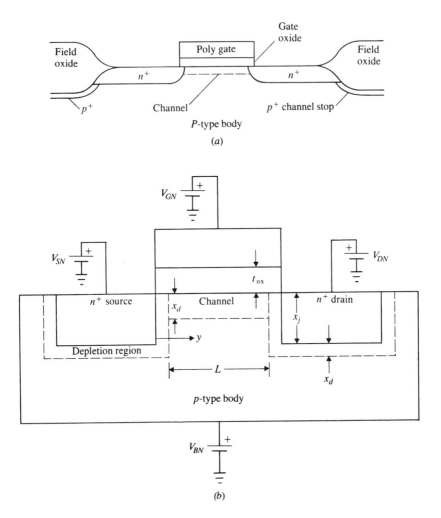

FIGURE 2.2
Cross section of an n-channel FET. (a) Physical; (b) idealized.

N_a Acceptor impurity concentration density, in atoms/cm^3
N_d Donor impurity concentration density, in atoms/cm^3
n Free electron concentration density, in electrons/cm^3
p Free hole concentration density, in holes/cm^3

n (p) used as a subscript refers to n-type (p-type) material.
Some necessary physical parameters and constants are (1,2):

Boltzmann's constant $k = 1.38 \times 10^{-23}$ J/K
Electronic charge $q = 1.60 \times 10^{-19}$ C
Thermal voltage $V_T = kT/q = 25.9$ mV at 27°C = 300 K
     $V_T = T(\text{K})/11{,}600$ in general

Intrinsic electron (hole) concentration: $n_i = p_i = 1.45 \times 10^{10}$ electrons-(holes)/cm^3 at room temperature.

Formulas that are also needed and are derived in most texts on semiconductor device physics are (1,2,3):

Fermi level in p-type material, assuming 100 percent ionization of acceptor atoms: $\phi_{fp} = V_T \ln (n_i/p_p) = V_T \ln (n_i/N_a)$

Fermi level in n-type material, assuming 100 percent ionization of donor atoms: $\phi_{fn} = V_T \ln (n_n/n_i) = V_T \ln (N_d/n_i)$

The pn junction built-in barrier potential:

$$\phi_0 = \phi_{fn} - \phi_{fp} = V_T \ln (N_a N_d / n_i^2)$$

Dielectric constant, silicon: $k_{si} = 11.7$, silicon dioxide: $k_{ox} = 3.9$

Dielectric permittivity, free space: $\epsilon_0 = 88.5$ fF/cm, silicon: $\epsilon_{si} = 1.035$ pF/cm, silicon dioxide: $\epsilon_{ox} = 0.345$ pF/cm

Process transconductance parameter: $k' = \mu C_{ox}$

Device transconductance parameter: $k = k'(W/L)$

Channel mobility† 1 in silicon (1,4,5):

NMOS technology $\mu_n = 600$ to 800 cm^2/V·s†
CMOS technology $\mu_n = 400$ to 800 cm^2/V·s
     $\mu_p = 200$ to 400 cm^2/V·s

Bulk mobility in silicon: $\mu_n = 1350$ cm^2/V·s, $\mu_p = 480$ cm^2/V·s

---

† Channel mobility depends upon many factors, one of the principal ones being the amount of impurities in the channel region. Silicon CMOS/SOS and twin-tub silicon/bulk have low electron and hole mobilities. Electron mobility in p-type substrate material and hole mobility in n-type substrate material are the maximum values obtainable with a specific technology. Channel mobility is discussed in more detail in Sec. 5.10.1.

2.3 MOSFET THRESHOLD VOLTAGE

Electrons and holes in semiconductors obey the laws of Fermi-Dirac statistics. The *Fermi level* is defined as that electron energy level in thermodynamic equilibrium at which the probability of occupation of an energy state by an electron is one-half.

Calculation of the threshold voltage of an NMOS FET is simplified by examining each term separately. First, ground the source, drain and substrate (body), and apply a bias $V_{GN} = V_{GS}$ to the gate. The equilibrium electrostatic potential (Fermi level) in the p-type bulk silicon is given by

$$\phi_f = V_T \ln \left(\frac{n_i}{N_a} \right) \qquad \text{V} \tag{2.1}$$

The charge density in the channel region can be approximated by a step function distribution, with a constant value of $-qN_a$ over the channel region width of x_d, as shown in Fig. 2.3. In an infinitesimal volume of thickness dx, the differential charge per cross-sectional area is

$$dQ = -qN_a dx \qquad \text{C/cm}^2 \tag{2.2}$$

The electric field and the electrostatic potential can be calculated from either Gauss' law or Poisson's equation, as follows:

$$\frac{dE}{dx} = \frac{\rho_v}{\epsilon_{si}} \qquad \text{or} \qquad dE = \frac{\rho_v}{\epsilon_{si}} dx \tag{2.3}$$

Integrate both sides of Eq. (2.3) to obtain the field

$$E = \frac{\rho_v}{\epsilon_{si}} (x + C_1)$$

The constant of integration, C_1, is evaluated by observing that the electric field goes to zero at the channel-bulk interface, or $E = 0$ at $x = x_d$. One then obtains $C_1 = -x_d$, and

$$E = \frac{\rho_v}{\epsilon_{si}} (x - x_d) = -\frac{d\phi}{dx} \tag{2.4}$$

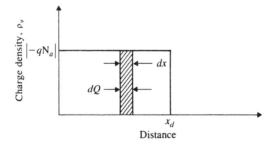

FIGURE 2.3
The charge density in the channel region of an NMOS FET.

All electric field lines start on positive charges and end on negative charges. Since all the positively charged ions are on the n side of the pn junction and all the negatively charged ions are on the p side of the junction, it follows that the maximum electric field is at the pn junction where $x = 0$. Hence, $E_{max} = -\rho_v x_d / \epsilon_{si}$.

The Fermi level has the value ϕ_f, in the bulk of the substrate, and the value ϕ_s at the oxide-channel interface. Thus:

$$\int_{\phi_s}^{\phi_f} d\phi = -\frac{\rho_v}{\epsilon_{si}} \int_0^{x_d} (x - x_d)\, dx = -\frac{\rho_v}{\epsilon_{si}} \left(\frac{x^2}{2} - x_d x \right) \Big|_0^{x_d}$$

$$\phi_f - \phi_s = \frac{\rho_v}{\epsilon_{si}} \left(\frac{x_d^2}{2} \right) \tag{2.5}$$

The charge density, $\rho = -qN_a$, is obtained from Fig. 2.3 and

$$\phi_s - \phi_f = \frac{qN_a x_d^2}{2\epsilon_{si}} \tag{2.6}$$

If the absolute value of $\phi_s - \phi_f$ is used, Eq. (2.6) can be applied to either NMOS or PMOS devices. The depletion-region depth, x_d, is given by

$$x_d = \sqrt{\frac{2\epsilon_{si}|\phi_s - \phi_f|}{qN_a}} \tag{2.7}$$

The ionized charge in the depletion region of the channel is

$$Q = -qN_a x_d = -\sqrt{2qN_a \epsilon_{si}|\phi_s - \phi_f|} \tag{2.8}$$

Strong surface inversion is defined to occur when $\phi_s = -\phi_f$, and the surface-to-bulk voltage required to accomplish this is $V_{GS} = -2\phi_f$. From Fig. 2.4 it is seen that ϕ_f is negative for n-channel devices, requiring a positive voltage, V_{GS}, to produce the channel.

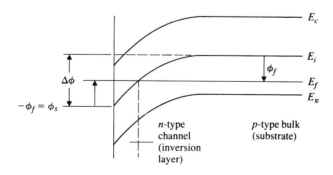

FIGURE 2.4
The final condition of the energy bands of an NMOS FET.

Define the onset of strong inversion as the *threshold voltage*, V_{TH1}. Further increases in V_{GS} will increase the conductivity of the channel without greatly changing ϕ_s. Electrons flowing into the channel from source and/or drain regions cause this increased conductivity. Thus

$$V_{TH1} = -2\phi_f > 0 \text{ for NMOS} \quad (<0 \text{ for PMOS}) \quad \text{devices} \quad (2.9)$$

Define Q_{B0} as the value of the charge density Q in the depletion region of the channel at the onset of strong inversion, and:

$$Q_{B0} = -\sqrt{2qN_a\epsilon_{si}|-2\phi_f|} \quad (2.10)$$

Next, let $V_{BN} = 0$, so that $V_{SN} = V_{SB}$ is the source-to-body voltage of the FET. $V_{SB} \geq 0$ normally for NMOS devices. The surface potential required to produce inversion is now $-2\phi_f + V_{SB}$, and the charge stored in the depletion region is obtained from Eq. (2.8) and is given by

$$Q_B = -\sqrt{2qN_a\epsilon_{si}|-2\phi_f + V_{SB}|} \quad (2.11)$$

The *gate-oxide specific capacitance* is defined as:

$$C_{ox} = \frac{\epsilon_{ox}}{t_{ox}} \quad (2.12)$$

and a voltage Q_B/C_{ox} is required to produce the charge Q_B.

The *work function difference* between the bulk silicon and the gate oxide is the difference in Fermi levels of the silicon and gate materials. This work-function difference, labeled ϕ_{GC}, contributes a term to the threshold voltage. For silicon-gate devices

$$\phi_{GC} = \phi_{f(\text{substrate})} - \phi_{f(\text{gate})} \quad (2.13a)$$

For metal-gate devices

$$\phi_{GC} = \phi_{f(\text{substrate})} - \phi_{m(\text{metal})} \quad (2.13b)$$

The metal work function for aluminum is $\phi_m = 0.6$ V.

$Q_{ox} = Q_{ss}$ is the surface-state charge at the bulk-oxide interface. Q_{ss} charges the surface states, and is positive always. This contributes a term Q_{ox}/C_{ox} to the threshold voltage.

The threshold voltage obtained by combining the above factors is seen to consist of the work-function difference between the gate and the channel, the potential required to produce strong inversion, charge the channel to Q_B, and charge the surface states.

$$V_{TH} = \phi_{GC} - 2\phi_f - \frac{Q_B}{C_{ox}} - \frac{Q_{ox}}{C_{ox}}$$

$$= \phi_{GC} - 2\phi_f - \frac{Q_{B0}}{C_{ox}} - \frac{Q_{ox}}{C_{ox}} - \frac{Q_B - Q_{B0}}{C_{ox}} \quad (2.14)$$

When the source of the FET is not at the same potential as the substrate, the substrate or body acts as a "back-gate" on the transistor and changes the threshold voltage seen by the front gate. The effect of this back gate can be accounted for by defining a factor called the *body factor*, or *body-effect coefficient*, given by

$$\gamma = \frac{\sqrt{2q\epsilon_{si}N_a}}{C_{ox}} \tag{2.15}$$

When the source and body of a FET are at the same potential ($V_{SB} = 0$), the threshold voltage is defined as

$$V_{THO} = V_{TH}(V_{SB} = 0) = \phi_{GC} - 2\phi_f - \frac{Q_{ox}}{C_{ox}} - \frac{Q_{BO}}{C_{ox}} \tag{2.16}$$

The threshold voltage can then be expressed as

$$V_{TH} = V_{THO} + \gamma\left[\sqrt{|-2\phi_f + V_{SB}|} - \sqrt{|-2\phi_f|}\right] \tag{2.17}$$

Example 2.1. Find the depletion-layer width, x_d, the depletion-region charge, Q_{BO}, the threshold voltage with no source-to-body voltage, V_{THO}, and the body factor, γ, of a device with the following physical parameters: $t_{ox} = 400$ angstroms (gate oxide thickness); $N_a = 1.5 \times 10^{16}/cm^3$ (substrate acceptor doping); $N_d = 10^{18}/cm^3$ (gate donor doping); $N_{ss} = 5 \times 10^{10}/cm^2$ (density of singly charged positive surface ions).

Solution. From Sec. 2.2, the Fermi level is

$$\phi_f = V_T \ln\left(\frac{n_i}{N_a}\right) = (0.0259) \ln\left(\frac{1.45 \times 10^{10}}{1.5 \times 10^{16}}\right)$$

$$= -0.3587 \, V, \quad \text{and} \quad 2\phi_f = -0.7174 \, V.$$

From Eq. (2.7), the depletion-region width is given by

$$x_d = \sqrt{\frac{2\epsilon_{si}|\phi_s - \phi_f|}{qN_a}}$$

$$= \sqrt{\frac{2(1.035 \times 10^{-12})0.717}{1.6 \times 10^{-19}(1.5 \times 10^{16})}} = 0.518 \text{ microns}$$

From Eq. (2.10), the charge in the channel at the onset of strong inversion is given by

$$Q_{BO} = -\sqrt{2qN_a\epsilon_{si}|-2\phi_f|}$$

$$= -\sqrt{2(1.6 \times 10^{-19})1.5 \times 10^{16}(1.035 \times 10^{-12})0.717} = -59.7 \text{ nC/cm}^2$$

Also from Sec. 2.2, the Fermi level in the *n*-type gate material is given by

$$\phi_{f(gate)} = V_T \ln\left(\frac{N_d}{n_i}\right) = 0.0259 \ln\left(\frac{10^{18}}{1.45 \times 10^{10}}\right) = 0.4675 \, V$$

The work function gate-to-channel is

$$\phi_{GC} = \phi_{f(\text{substrate})} - \phi_{f(\text{gate})} = -0.3587 - 0.4675 = -0.826 \text{ V}$$

Also

$$C_{\text{ox}} = \frac{\epsilon_{\text{ox}}}{t_{\text{ox}}} = \frac{0.345 \times 10^{-12}}{4 \times 10^{-6}} = 86 \text{ nF/cm}^2$$

$$Q_{\text{ox}} = qN_{ss} = 1.6 \times 10^{-19}(5 \times 10^{10}) = 8 \text{ nC/cm}^2$$

$$\frac{Q_{\text{ox}}}{C_{\text{ox}}} = \frac{8}{86} = 0.093 \text{ V}$$

$$\frac{Q_{BO}}{C_{\text{ox}}} = \frac{-59.7}{86} = -0.692 \text{ V}$$

Thus, the threshold voltage, V_{THO} is

$$V_{THO} = \phi_{GC} - 2\phi_f - \frac{Q_{\text{ox}}}{C_{\text{ox}}} - \frac{Q_{BO}}{C_{\text{ox}}}$$

$$= -0.826 + 0.717 - 0.093 + 0.692 = 0.490 \text{ V}$$

The body factor is given by Eq. (2.15) as

$$\gamma = \frac{\sqrt{2q\epsilon_{\text{si}}N_a}}{C_{\text{ox}}}$$

$$= \frac{\sqrt{3.2 \times 10^{-19}(1.035 \times 10^{-12})(1.5 \times 10^{16})}}{86 \times 10^{-9}} = 0.817 \text{ V}^{1/2}$$

Typical values of surface charge density for the three commonly used semiconductor surfaces are given in Table 2.1.

Every year, improved fabrication processing lowers the typical values of N_{ss} or Q_{ss}. However, the relative values of surface states remain the same, with $Q_{ss}(100) < Q_{ss}(110) < Q_{ss}(111)$.

When the FET is a pull-up device and the output voltage is high, the body effect or back-gate effect changes the threshold voltages. V_{THE} and V_{THD} are shifted more positive by about 0.5 V when the FET source is about 3.5 V above the substrate value.

TABLE 2.1
Typical surface-state charge

Surface	Q_{ss}, nC/cm^2	N_{ss}, ions/cm^2
(111)	40–80	2.5–5.0 × 10^{11}
(110)	16–32	1.0–2.0 × 10^{11}
(100)	6–12	0.4–0.8 × 10^{11}

2.3.1 Flatband Conditions

An alternative way to determine the components of threshold voltage is to calculate the gate bias required to establish *flatband* conditions, and then the added bias required to achieve strong surface inversion. The flatband condition is shown in Fig. 2.5. As the name implies, the conduction and valence bands are flat when $V_{GS} = V_{FB}$. The voltage required to establish the flatband condition, V_{FB}, is the difference in work function between the gate and the channel plus the voltage required to charge the surface states

$$V_{FB} = V_{GS} = \phi_{GC} - \frac{Q_{ss}}{C_{ox}} \tag{2.18}$$

Additional bias is required to bend the bands through a potential of $2\phi_f$ and to offset the depletion-layer charge. Call this voltage V_{TH2}, given by

$$V_{TH2} = -2\phi_f - \frac{Q_{BO}}{C_{ox}} \tag{2.19}$$

The threshold voltage is now the sum of V_{FB} and V_{TH2}.

Example 2.2. Find the flatband voltage V_{FB} and the voltage V_{TH2} of the device of Example 2.1. Find the threshold voltage of this device with $V_{SB} = 0$ V.

Solution. From Example 2.1

$Q_{ox} = 8$ nC/cm^2, $\phi_{GC} = -0.826$ V, and $C_{ox} = 86$ nF/cm^2. Thus,

$$V_{FB} = \phi_{GC} - \frac{Q_{ox}}{C_{ox}} = -0.826 - \frac{8}{86} = -0.919 \text{ V}$$

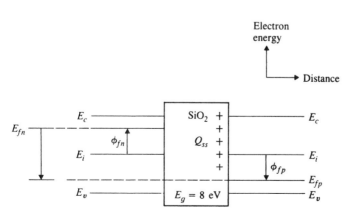

FIGURE 2.5
Silicon-silicon dioxide flatband condition.

From Example 2.1, $2\phi_f = -0.7174$ V and $Q_{B0} = -59.7$ nC/cm^2, giving

$$V_{TH2} = -2\phi_f - Q_{B0}/C_{ox} = 0.717 + 59.7/86 = 1.409 \text{ V}$$
$$V_{TH0} = V_{FB} + V_{TH2} = -0.919 + 1.409 = 0.490 \text{ V}$$

2.3.2 Threshold Adjustment

The calculated threshold voltage may not be the desired value, and a method of adjusting it is required. Breakdown voltage and junction capacitance determine the specifications for N_a, N_d, and C_{ox}, so another degree of freedom is needed. An ion implant in the channel region can be used to obtain the needed independent control over the threshold voltage.

The desired threshold voltage with zero bias across the source to body, V_{TH0}, is typically between $+0.5$ and $+1.5$ V for NMOS enhancement-mode devices, -0.5 and -1.5 V for PMOS enhancement-mode devices, and from -1.0 to -4.0 V for NMOS depletion-mode devices. The change in threshold voltage due to an ion implant (assuming 100 percent ionization of the implanted atoms) is given by the ion-implant charge density N_I divided by the oxide capacitance. Calculations of the ion-implant doses required to obtain typical enhancement-mode and depletion-mode thresholds are given in Example 2.3.

Example 2.3. Calculate the ion-implant dose necessary to change the threshold voltage V_{TH0} of the device in Example 2.1 to $+1$ V or to -4 V. Assume 100 percent ionization of implanted material.

Solution. For $V_{THE} = +1.0$ V:

$$N_I = \frac{Q_I}{q} = \frac{C_{ox}}{q}(V_{THE} - V_{TH0}) = \left(\frac{86 \times 10^{-9}}{1.6 \times 10^{-19}}\right)(1 - 0.49) = 0.275 \times 10^{12} \text{ ions/cm}^2$$

For $V_{THD} = -4.0$ V:

$$N_I = \frac{Q_I}{-q} = \frac{C_{ox}}{-q}(V_{THD} - V_{TH0}) = \left(\frac{86 \times 10^{-9}}{-1.6 \times 10^{-19}}\right)(-4 - 0.49)$$
$$= 2.425 \times 10^{12} \text{ ions/cm}^2$$

In summary, the threshold voltage, V_{TH}, is seen to consist of five components. A voltage ϕ_{GC} is required to overcome the work function difference between the oxide and the bulk silicon in the channel, and a voltage $-2\phi_f$ is needed to produce strong inversion of the energy bands. A voltage Q_B/C_{ox} is required to charge the depletion layer, a voltage Q_{ss}/C_{ox} is needed to neutralize the surface-state charge, and finally, an ion implant may be needed to shift the threshold voltage by an amount Q_I/C_{ox}.

The above calculations are not exact due, among other things, to lack of precise control of the oxide charge, variations in bulk doping near the oxide interface, variations in oxide thickness and dielectric constant due to process fluctuations, and the assumption of room temperature in calculations involving the thermal voltage. A computer circuit simulation program such as SPICE will give more accurate results if one measures all the parameters necessary to the calculations.

2.4 LINEAR AND SATURATED OPERATION

There are two basic regions of operation of a FET. For small drain-to-source voltage, V_{DS}, the output *I-V* characteristics are linear, and the device behaves as a *voltage-controlled resistor*, with V_{GS} controlling the resistance. This is normally referred to as the *linear region of operation* of the FET.‡

For sufficiently large V_{DS}, and a constant channel length, the transistor current saturates at a value that is almost independent of the bias drain-to-source. In this mode of operation, the FET behaves as a *voltage-controlled current source*, with V_{GS} controlling the current. This is normally referred to as the *saturated region of operation*.

To determine the output characteristics in both regions of operation, refer to the basic MOSFET of Fig. 2.2, with $V_{SN} = 0$. If $V_{GS} > V_{TH}$, a conducting channel exists, and if $V_{DS} > 0$, I_D is from the drain to the source as shown in Fig. 2.6. Begin by assuming that V_{DS} is small, and a uniform channel exists under the gate, from the source to the drain of the FET. Let the distance along the channel be y, with y measured from the source toward the drain, as shown in Fig. 2.2*b*. At any distance y, the voltage between the gate and the channel is $V_{GS} - V(y)$, where $V(y)$ is the voltage drop in the channel from y to the source of the FET.

The induced charge of free electrons per unit area in the channel at a distance y from the source is

$$Q(y) = C_{ox}[V_{GS} - V(y) - V_{TH}] \qquad C/cm^2 \qquad (2.20)$$

---

‡ The linear region is also referred to as the ohmic, triode, nonsaturation, or resistive region.

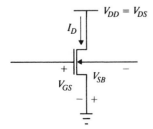

FIGURE 2.6
NMOS FET with terminal voltages and drain current indicated.

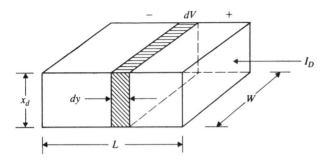

FIGURE 2.7
Cross section of channel conducting current I_D.

The cross-sectional area of the channel is Wx_d, as shown in Fig. 2.7, and the resistance of a differential length dy of the channel is

$$dR = \frac{\rho \, dy}{W x_d} = \frac{dy}{\sigma W x_d} \tag{2.21}$$

where ρ is the channel resistivity, and $\sigma = 1/\rho = q\mu_n n$ is the channel conductivity. Thus, the differential resistance of the channel can be written as

$$dR = \frac{dy}{q\mu_n n W x_d} = \frac{dy}{(qnx_d)\mu_n W} = \frac{dy}{Q(y)\mu_n W} \tag{2.22}$$

The differential voltage drop along the length dy is given by

$$dV = I_D \, dR = \frac{I_D \, dy}{W\mu_n Q(y)}$$

The drain current can be determined as follows:

$$I_D \, dy = W\mu_n Q(y) \, dV = W\mu_n C_{ox}[V_{GS} - V(y) - V_{TH}] \, dV \tag{2.23}$$

Under the assumption that V_{DS} is small there is no back-gate bias along the channel, and the threshold voltage is independent of distance along the channel, or $dV_{TH}/dy = 0$.

Define a *process transconductance parameter*, also referred to as the *process gain factor*, k', by

$$k' = \mu_n C_{ox} \qquad \mu\text{A/V}^2 \tag{2.24}$$

Then, for $V_{GS} \geq V_{TH}$ and $V_{DS} \leq V_{GS} - V_{TH}$, the drain current is

$$I_D \int_0^L dy = Wk' \int_0^{V_{DS}} [V_{GS} - V - V_{TH}] \, dV$$

$$I_D = k'\left(\frac{W}{L}\right)\left[(V_{GS} - V_{TH})V_{DS} - \frac{V_{DS}^2}{2}\right] \tag{2.25}$$

Define the *device transconductance parameter* k (sometimes called the gain, β, as

$k'W/L$, and the drain current in the linear region is given by the expression

$$I_D(\text{LIN}) = \frac{k}{2}[2(V_{GS} - V_{TH})V_{DS} - V_{DS}^2]$$ (2.26)

with $V_{GS} \geq V_{TH}$ and $V_{DS} \leq V_{GS} - V_{TH}$.

Some typical values for the process transconductance parameter, obtained by assuming $t_{ox} = 400$ angstroms $= 0.04$ microns, $\mu_n = 800$ cm²/V·s, $\mu_p = 400$ cm²/V·s and $\epsilon_{ox} = 0.345$ pF/cm are, for an n-channel FET,

$$k' = 800\left(\frac{0.345 \times 10^{-12}}{4 \times 10^{-6}}\right) = 69.0 \ \mu\text{A/V}^2$$

and for a p-channel FET

$$k' = 400\left(\frac{0.345 \times 10^{-12}}{4 \times 10^{-6}}\right) = 34.5 \ \mu\text{A/V}^2$$

As V_{DS} approaches $V_{GS} - V_{TH}$, the drain current given by Eq. (2.26) approaches a constant saturation value, given by:

(2.27)
$$I_D(\text{SAT}) = \frac{k}{2}[V_{GS} - V_{TH}]^2$$

with $V_{GS} \geq V_{TH}$ and $V_{DS} \geq V_{GS} - V_{TH}$.

This is current saturation. For the saturation condition, the charge at the drain end of the channel, $y = L$, goes to zero, namely,

$$Q = C_{ox}[V_{GS} - V_{TH} - V_{DS}] = 0,$$

when $V(y) = V_{DS} = V_{GS} - V_{TH}$.

Further increases in V_{DS} have little effect on the drain current as calculated above. However, as V_{DS} increases, the drain depletion region extends primarily into the lightly doped channel region, shortening the "effective channel length." As can be seen from the device transconductance parameter k, as the value of L decreases the drain current increases.

Unless otherwise specified, it will be assumed that the channel is sufficiently long to neglect the changes in channel length with drain-to-source bias. Then I_D as a function of V_{DS} is as shown in Fig. 2.8. Modifications due to short channel effects are discussed in Sec. 2.6.2.

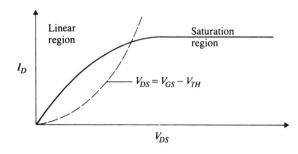

FIGURE 2.8
Output characteristics for a FET with constant channel length.

2.5 FET CAPACITANCES

The capacitances associated with a FET device are shown in Fig. 2.9. Source/drain impurity profiles of modern FETs approximate step-junction distributions whether they are obtained by diffusion or by ion implantation. Equations for the depletion-region width of a step junction, as well as the electric field through, and the potenial across, a step pn junction as a function of doping concentration are given in App. A. If the source/drain conductivity is much higher than the bulk conductivity, which is normally the case, the depletion region extends mostly into the substrate material and the junction width is approximately equal to the extension into the p-type substrate material, x_p. The depletion width at the drain-bulk interface is labeled x_{dd}, and the depletion width at the source-bulk interface is labeled x_{ds}.

The positive charge per unit area of a step junction is

$$Q_j = qN_a x_p \quad \text{C/cm}^2 \tag{2.28}$$

The small-signal, specific capacitance of the junction is defined by

$$C_j = \left| \frac{dQ_j}{dV} \right| \quad \text{F/cm}^2 \tag{2.29}$$

Therefore, assuming the depletion region extends only into the p type substrate,

$$C_j = \left| \frac{d(qN_a x_p)}{dV} \right| = qN_a \left| \frac{dx_p}{dV} \right| \tag{2.30}$$

Define the *built-in potential* of the depletion region as ϕ_0, and the external bias as V. The value of x_p (and therefore x_p^2) is given in App. A, Eq. (A.18), as

$$x_p^2 = \left[\frac{2\epsilon_{si} N_d}{qN_a(N_a + N_d)} \right] (\phi_0 - V) \tag{2.31}$$

It simplifies the mathematics to operate upon x_p^2. Upon differentiating both sides of Eq. (2.31), one obtains

$$2x_p \, dx_p = \left[\frac{2\epsilon_{si} N_d}{qN_a(N_a + N_d)} \right] (-dV)$$

$$\left| \frac{dx_p}{dV} \right| = \left[\frac{\epsilon_{si} N_d}{qN_a(N_a + N_d)} \right] \left(\frac{1}{x_p} \right) \tag{2.32}$$

Substitute Eq. (2.32) into Eq. (2.30) to get the junction capacitance per unit area, C_j

$$C_j = \left[\frac{qN_a \epsilon_{si} N_d}{qN_a(N_a + N_d)} \right] \left(\frac{1}{x_p} \right) = \frac{\epsilon_{si} N_d}{(N_a + N_d)x_p} \tag{2.33}$$

Substitute x_p from Eq. (A.18) in Eq. (2.33) to get

$$C_j = \left[\frac{\epsilon_{si} N_d}{(N_a + N_d)} \right] \sqrt{\frac{qN_a(N_a + N_d)}{2\epsilon_{si} N_d(\phi_0 - V)}}$$

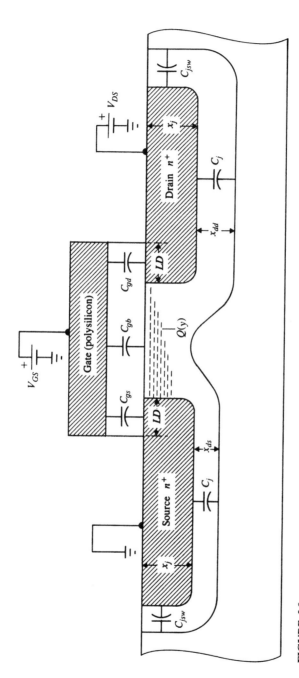

FIGURE 2.9
FET capacitances. (a) Cross-sectional view.

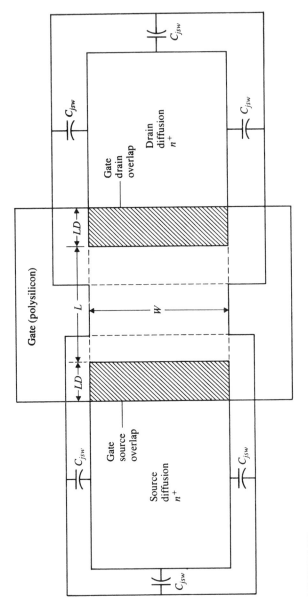

FIGURE 2.9
FET capacitances. (*b*) Top view.

when $N_d \gg N_a$, $N_a N_d/(N_a + N_d) \approx N_a$ and $x_d \approx x_p$. Then

$$C_j = \sqrt{\frac{q\epsilon_{si} N_a}{2(\phi_0 - V)}} = \frac{\epsilon_{si}}{x_d} \quad \text{F/cm}^2 \tag{2.34}$$

The capacitance derived above is a specific capacitance, given in units of farads per cross-sectional area. To obtain the capacitance of a silicon *pn* junction, the specific capacitance must be multiplied by the area of the junction.

The source or drain junction specific capacitance with no external bias is obtained from Eq. (2.34) by setting $V = 0$. Represent this capacitance as C_{j0}, given by

$$C_{j0} = \sqrt{\frac{q\epsilon_{si} N_a}{2\phi_0}} \quad \text{F/cm}^2 \tag{2.35}$$

The specific capacitance of the source or drain *pn* junction can then be written as

$$C_j = \frac{C_{j0}}{\sqrt{1 - V/\phi_0}} \quad \text{F/cm}^2 \tag{2.36}$$

C_j is the *small-signal specific capacitance* of the FET source or drain junction under bias.

The *large-signal switching capacitance*, C_{LS}, when the input is a step function from V_1 volts to V_2 volts is, approximately,

$$C_{LS} = \frac{\Delta Q}{\Delta V} = \frac{Q_j(V_2) - Q_j(V_1)}{V_2 - V_1} \tag{2.37}$$

The total charge per unit area on the positive side of the depletion region is given by substituting for x_p from Eq. (A.18) and C_{j0} from Eq. (2.35).

$$Q_j = qN_a x_p = qN_a \sqrt{\frac{2\epsilon_{si} N_d}{qN_a(N_a + N_d)}} \sqrt{\phi_0 - V}$$

Again, when $N_d \gg N_a$

$$Q_j = \sqrt{2\epsilon_{si} qN_a}\sqrt{\phi_0 - V} = 2\phi_0 C_{j0}\sqrt{1 - V/\phi_0} \quad \text{C/cm}^2$$

Thus, the large-signal switching capacitance per unit area is approximately

$$C_{LS} = \left| \left[\frac{2C_{j0}\phi_0}{V_2 - V_1} \right] [\sqrt{1 - V_2/\phi_0} - \sqrt{1 - V_1/\phi_0}] \right| \tag{2.38}$$

There is also a capacitance associated with the sidewalls of the source and drain regions, call it the *sidewall capacitance*, C_{jsw}. The units of C_{jsw} are farads per centimeter of perimeter of the source or drain.

The impurity concentration varies in a complicated manner along the sidewalls of the source and drain regions. Three sides of the source and drain regions abut a thick oxide called the field oxide, and the fourth side abuts the active channel region. The side facing the channel sees an impurity concentration that can vary from the substrate bulk value due to ion implants used to adjust the threshold voltage, as was discussed in Sec. 2.3.2. The other three sides of the source and drain regions face a complicated impurity profile which is determined by the channel stop impurity concentration, and its interaction with the field oxide.§

The ion implant used to form the channel stop is redistributed by the growth of the field oxide, and by the interaction of the field oxide and the boron used for the channel-stop implant. A diagram of the boron impurity profile after growth of the field oxide and before the source/drain impurity deposition is given by Sze (6). Following the source/drain implant or diffusion the picture becomes more complicated.

A general statement can be made that the impurity concentrations on the lateral sides of the source and drain regions are much higher than the concentrations found under the source/drain regions. Also, the voltage dependence of the sidewall capacitances may differ from that of the junction capacitance due to the fact that the channel-stop and threshold-adjustment implants give rise to heavily doped impurity concentrations on both sides of the pn junction. When the impurity concentrations on each side of the pn junction are of the same order of magnitude, Eqs. (A.14), (A.15), and (A.16), with ϕ_0 replaced by $\phi_0 - V$, are applicable.

Finally, the sidewalls of the source/drain regions are curved, and an accurate calculation of the sidewall capacitance requires two-dimensional modeling. From Eq. (2.35) it is seen that the impurity concentration of the junction is under the radical sign. For a default value, the sidewall capacitance can be, and often is, approximated by

$$C_{jsw} = x_j \sqrt{Z} C_j \tag{2.39}$$

where Z is the ratio of the average value of impurity concentration along the junction sidewalls to the substrate doping, and x_j is the approximate vertical height of the sidewall. For typical diffusions, the surface doping of the channel-stop (field doping) is much higher than the doping of the substrate at the bottom of the source/drain region. For lack of a better estimate, the average doping of the sidewalls can be assumed to be 10 times the doping level under the source and drain regions, giving a default value of $Z = 10$. If an impurity concentration is increased by 10, the capacitance is increased by the square root of 10. The sidewall capacitance is then approximately given by

$$C_{jsw} \approx 3.16 x_j C_j \quad \text{F/cm} \tag{2.40}$$

The sidewalls facing the field oxide have a different capacitance associated with them than does the sidewall facing the channel. In view of all the approximations and assumptions involved in deriving Eq. (2.40), this distinction is not warranted, and the specific sidewall capacitance can be multiplied by the pe-

---

§ A more accurate cross-sectional drawing of a FET is shown in Fig. 3.2. Channel stop implant and field oxide are discussed in Sec. 3.4.1.

rimeter of the source or drain region to obtain an estimate of the total sidewall capacitance. The total capacitance of a source or drain region of area A and perimeter P is approximated by

$$C_T = C_j A + C_{jsw} P = C_j[A + 3.16 x_j P]$$

Example 2.4. A FET is designed to have source and drain regions that are square in plan view. Let the area of the regions be L^2 and the perimeter be $4L$. What portion of the total source or drain capacitance does the sidewall capacitance constitute, if the average sidewall doping concentration is ten times higher than the bulk doping concentration and $x_j = 0.1L$? If $x_j + 0.4L$?

Solution. For $x_j = 0.1L$: $C_T = C_j[L^2 + 3.16(0.1)4L] = C_j[L^2 + 1.26L^2]$

The sidewall capacitance is 26 percent larger than C_j, and the total capacitance is $2.26C_j$, or 126 percent larger than estimated by ignoring the sidewall contribution.

For $x_j = 0.4L$: $C_T = C_j[L^2 + 3.16(0.4)4L] = 6.06C_j L^2$

The sidewall capacitance is five times more important in this case. As device surface dimensions shrink, sidewall capacitance can dominate the source and drain capacitances unless the diffusion or implant depth is also scaled down.

Source and drain regions, self-registered by an ion-implantation step after deposition of the polysilicon gate material, give a very small *gate-overlap capacitance*. Self-registration helps greatly with diffused source and drain regions also, but diffusion is isotropic, and the metallurgical junction will be located a lateral distance under the gate, as shown in Fig. 2.9.

The *lateral diffusion distance* will be less than the vertical junction depth, x_j, due primarily to the fact that the background doping concentration is higher on the sidewalls, as discussed above. Sze reports a range of lateral diffusion distances ranging from about 65 to 80 percent of the vertical junction depth (7). Call this gate-drain or gate-source overlap capacitance, due to lateral diffusion, $C_{ox LD}$, with units of farads per centimeter of gate width. Using x_j as a default value of LD gives a conservative estimate of the *diffusion overlap capacitance*.

$$C_{ox LD} \approx x_j C_{ox} \quad \text{F/cm} \quad \text{and} \quad C_{gd} \approx x_j C_{ox} W \quad \text{F} \quad (2.41)$$

Ion implanting is more directional than diffusion. If the source and drain regions are implanted, the lateral junction displacement is much less than the junction depth, x_j, and the overlap capacitances are much smaller.

The capacitances of a FET can be summarized in terms of the above individual capacitances, as shown in Figs. 2.9 and 2.10. Let DA be the drain area, SA be the source area, DP be the drain perimeter, and SP be the source perimeter of the FET. The capacitances source-to-body and drain-to-body are then given by:

$$C_{sb} = C_{j0}(SA) + C_{jsw}(SP) \quad (2.42)$$

$$C_{db} = C_j(DA) + C_{jsw}(DP) \quad (2.43)$$

where the value of C_j is determined by the drain-to-body voltage, and C_{j0} is used

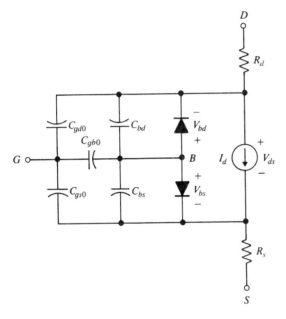

FIGURE 2.10
A simple model of a FET for hand calculations.

to calculate C_{sb} with $V_{GS} = 0$.

$$C_{gs} = C_{gd} = C_{ox}(x_j W) = C_{ox\,LD} W \tag{2.44}$$

$$C_{gb} = C_{ox}(WL) \tag{2.45}$$

and the lumped, approximate gate capacitance of the FET is given by:

$$C_g = C_{gs} + C_{gd} + C_{gb} \tag{2.46}$$

Example 2.5. A FET is to be designed with a substrate doping concentration of $N_a = 1.5 \times 10^{16}/\text{cm}^3$ and source and drain doping concentrations of $N_d = 10^{20}/\text{cm}^3$. The source and drain regions are squares with side dimensions of 5 microns, and the junction depth is 0.5 micron. Calculate C_{LS} from 0 to -5 V, C_{jsw}, and C_j, Q_j, $E_{\max}$, and x_d for voltages of -5 and $+0.5$ V. Let DA = drain area, DP = drain perimeter, SA = source area, and SP = source perimeter.

Solution.

$$\phi_0 = V_T \ln\left(\frac{N_a N_d}{n_i^2}\right) = 0.0259 \ln\left(\frac{10^{20}(1.5 \times 10^{16})}{(1.45 \times 10^{10})^2}\right) = 0.945 \text{ V}$$

$$\text{For } N_a \ll N_d \qquad \frac{N_a N_d}{N_a + N_d} \approx N_a$$

$$C_{jo} = \sqrt{\frac{q\epsilon_{si} N_a}{2\phi_0}} = \sqrt{\frac{(1.6 \times 10^{-19})(1.035 \times 10^{-12})(1.5 \times 10^{16})}{2(0.945)}}$$

$$= 36.24 \text{ nF/cm}^2$$

$$C_{j0}\,\text{DA} = 25 \times 10^{-8}(36.24 \times 10^{-9}) = 9.06 \text{ fF}$$

$$C_{LS}\,\text{DA}(V_1 = 0 \text{ V}, V_2 = -5 \text{ V}) = \frac{2(9.06)(0.945)}{5}\left[\sqrt{1 + \frac{5}{0.945}} - 1\right]$$

$$= 5.165 \text{ fF}$$

$$C_{jsw}\,\text{DP} = 3.16x_j C_{j0}\,\text{DP}$$

$$= 3.16(5 \times 10^{-5})(36.24 \times 10^{-9})(20 \times 10^{-4})$$

$$= 11.45 \text{ fF}$$

$$C_j\text{DA} = \frac{C_{j0}\,\text{DA}}{\sqrt{1 - V/\phi_0}}$$

$$C_j(-5 \text{ V})\text{DA} = \frac{9.06}{\sqrt{1 + 5/0.945}} = 3.61 \text{ fF}$$

$$C_j(0.5 \text{ V})\text{DA} = \frac{9.06}{\sqrt{1 - 0.5/0.945}} = 13.20 \text{ fF}$$

$$Q_j\text{DA} = \text{DA}\sqrt{2\epsilon_{\text{si}}qN_a}\sqrt{\phi_0 - V}$$

$$= 25 \times 10^{-8}\sqrt{2(1.03 \times 10^{-12})(1.6 \times 10^{-19})(1.5 \times 10^{16})}\sqrt{\phi_0 - V}$$

$$= 1.762 \times 10^{-14}\sqrt{\phi_0 - V}$$

$$\sqrt{\phi_0 + 5} = 2.438 \quad \text{and} \quad \sqrt{\phi_0 - 0.5} = 0.667$$

$$Q_j(-5 \text{ V})\text{DA} = 1.762 \times 10^{-14}(2.438) = 42.96 \text{ fC}$$

$$Q_j(0.5 \text{ V})\text{DA} = 1.762 \times 10^{-14}(0.667) = 11.75 \text{ fC}$$

$$E_{\max} = -\sqrt{\frac{2qN_a}{\epsilon_{\text{si}}}}\sqrt{\phi_0 - V}$$

$$= -\sqrt{\frac{2(1.6 \times 10^{-19})(1.5 \times 10^{16})}{1.035 \times 10^{-12}}}\sqrt{\phi_0 - V}$$

$$= -68.1 \times 10^3 \sqrt{\phi_0 - V}$$

$$E_{\max}(-5 \text{ V}) = -68.1(2.438) = -145 \text{ kV/cm}$$

$$E_{\max}(0.5 \text{ V}) = -68.1(0.667) = -45 \text{ kV/cm}$$

$$x_d = \sqrt{\frac{2\epsilon_{\text{si}}(\phi_0 - V)}{qN_a}}$$

$$= \sqrt{\frac{2(1.035 \times 10^{-12})}{1.6 \times 10^{-19}(1.5 \times 10^{16})}}\sqrt{\phi_0 - V}$$

$$= 2.937 \times 10^{-5}\sqrt{\phi_0 - V}$$

$$x_d(-5 \text{ V}) = 2.937 \times 10^{-5}(2.438) = 0.716 \text{ }\mu\text{m}$$

$$x_d(0.5 \text{ V}) = 2.937 \times 10^{-5}(0.667) = 0.196 \text{ }\mu\text{m}$$

2.6 MODELING FETS

The simple model shown in Fig. 2.10 is sufficient for most hand calculations. The model is seen to consist of two back-to-back diodes, a current source that is controlled by the gate bias of the FET, and interelectrode capacitances. More complex models are most useful when built into a circuit simulator if more accuracy is desired and/or if some errors are cumulative.

As feature size is reduced below one micron, device models need to be modified to include such phenomena as mobility saturation and short-channel effects.

2.6.1 Mobility Saturation and Thermal Variations

Mobility is a function of both high electric fields and temperature. Electron and hole mobilities saturate at high electric fields, causing the process transconductance to saturate also. Thermal variations in mobility cause the process transconductance parameter to vary with temperature. Since mobility varies as temperature to the negative 3/2 power, the process transconductance k', at absolute temperature T, is related to the value k'_0 at 300 K by:

$$k' = k'_0 \left(\frac{T}{300} \right)^{-1.5}$$

Since $k' = \mu C_{ox}$, variations in mobility, μ, produce the same result as variations in specific oxide capacitance, C_{ox}, would. In particular, a device operating at $100°C = 373$ K, will have an effective transconductance that is $(373/300)^{-1.5} = 0.72$, or 72 percent of the value at room temperature. In terms of effective speed, a system designed to operate at 10 MHz at room temperature will only operate to about 7 MHz when the devices in the system are at $100°C$.

2.6.2 Short-Channel Effects

Tolerances on channel length and width are the least controlled parameters of a device. The result of errors in L and W is that a transistor designed to be twice as wide as another device will not source or sink twice the current. Variations in length and width, as well as in threshold voltage and oxide thickness, cause variations in currents from the calculated values, including current drawn from supply. Both channel length and width are affected by bloats and shrinks applied to masks, over- and under-etching in the lithography, and lateral diffusion.

As FETs approach smaller and smaller sizes, once satisfactory one-dimensional problems become two-dimensional problems, and second-order effects that were once negligible become important. One of the major corrections for small FETs is due to the effects of very short channel lengths. In modeling short-channel FETs, one can modify long-channel models, or resort to two-dimensional numerical approaches. Much work is being done on two-dimensional modeling (8).

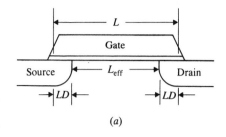

(a)

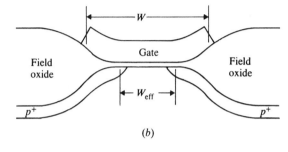

(b)

FIGURE 2.11
(a) Effective length and (b) effective width of a short-channel device.

The default value or zeroth-order approximation is to assume that the ratio of W to L is given by the designed width divided by the designed length. The first-order correction would be to replace W/L by W_{eff}/L_{eff}, where:

$$W_{eff} = W - \Delta W \qquad \text{and} \qquad L_{eff} = L - 2(\Delta L + LD) \qquad (2.47)$$

where ΔW is the width reduction of the actually manufactured FET gate due to manufacturing errors, such as the field oxide growing under the nitride protective layer, and the high-conductivity channel-stop diffusion or implant. ΔL is the length reduction of the FET channel due to errors, and LD is the lateral diffusion distance under the gate due to the source/drain diffusion or implant step. See Fig. 2.11.

An empirical approximation to the drain current in saturation, which accounts for the increase in drain current with shortening of the effective length of the channel is (9):

$$I_D(\text{SAT}) = \frac{k}{2}(V_{GS} - V_{TH})^2\left(1 + \frac{V_{DS}}{V_a}\right) \qquad (2.48)$$

where $10 \text{ V} \leq V_a \leq 100 \text{ V}$.

The best value of V_a for given operating conditions is determined by fitting the experimental output curves in the saturation region. V_a is often referred to as the *Early-effect voltage*, since it measures the effect of the drain depletion-region widening. SPICE models the reciprocal of the Early voltage, and calls the parameter lambda.

The correction factor

$$\left(1 + \frac{V_{DS}}{V_a}\right)$$

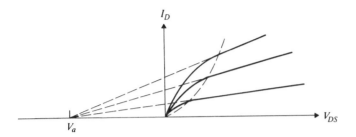

FIGURE 2.12
Output characteristics for a short-channel FET.

can be added to the linear equation for drain current given by Eq. (2.26). It will have little effect on the drain current in the linear region and it makes the linear and saturation drain-current curves continuous at $V_{DS} = V_{GS} - V_{TH}$.

The output characteristics of a FET with a constant channel length and a fixed bias gate-to-source were shown in Fig. 2.8. The output characteristics of a typical short-channel FET are shown in Fig. 2.12.

Additional short-channel effects can be treated as second-order corrections obtained from the basic equations by considering the effects of channel-length modulation on velocity saturation and linear-to-saturation region mobility differences, as well as the effect of V_{GS} and V_{DS} upon the mobility of channel carriers. Subthreshold leakage currents and bulk resistances of the source and drain regions, especially for lightly doped drain devices, must also be considered.

Figure 2.13 shows the influence of short-channel parameters on the output current-voltage characteristics of an ideal MOS device. Curve 1 is for an ideal MOSFET with $I_D(LIN)$ given by Eq. (2.26), and $\dot{I}_D(SAT)$ given by Eq. (2.27). In this case the onset of saturation is given by

$$V_{DS} = V_{GS} - V_{TH}.$$

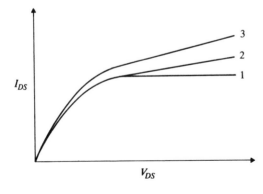

FIGURE 2.13
The effect of short-channel parameters on the FET output characteristics.

Curve 2 is for a MOS device with channel-length modulation accounted for by the Early-voltage correction factor. The drain voltage causes the drain depletion region to move toward the source, effectively reducing the channel length L, and causing the device transconductance k to increase. The primary effect of channel-length modulation is to give the device in the saturation region a finite output impedance, given by the reciprocal slope of the I-V characteristics.

As the drain depletion region extends into the channel region it acts as a back-gate bias. This bias has the effect of decreasing the front-gate threshold voltage V_{TH} and increasing the Early effect, causing the drain current to increase even more rapidly with V_{DS}.

When the linear-to-saturation region mobility ratio and the velocity saturation factor are taken into account, the effect is to decrease the drain current in the linear region, and cause I_D to saturate at a lower drain-to-source voltage, V_{DS}. As the device enters current saturation the carrier drift velocity saturates at a critical field value. In short-channel devices this field is reached a very short distance from the source, and both velocity and current saturation occur at a low value of V_{DS}, which is independent of V_{GS}. The net result is to shift the output characteristic upward to higher drain current, and to the left to lower drain-to-source voltage. The combination of these items gives curve 3 in Fig. 2.13.

Mobility degradation occurs due to the vertical electric field caused by the gate-to-source bias V_{GS}, which in turn causes surface charge carriers to scatter. This reduces mobility in the channel region, which reduces the device gain in both the saturation and linear regions, and tends to lower the curves. The effect is more severe at higher values of V_{GS}, and is high for thin-oxide devices and short-channel devices with higher transconductance values. For very long channel devices surface scattering is due only to surface roughness and surface state charge.

Sakurai (10,11) has investigated the effects of velocity saturation upon device transconductance. His results modify Eq. (2.27) by changing the exponent in the drain current equation from 2 to α.

$$I_D(\text{SAT}) = \frac{k}{2}[V_{GS} - V_{TH}]^{\alpha} \qquad (2.49)$$

Working with channel widths of 10 μm and channel lengths of 1 μm, his data agree better with calculations based upon $\alpha = 1.2$ for NMOS devices and $\alpha = 1.5$ for PMOS devices. A transconductance curve based upon the usually assumed quadratic dependence of drain current upon gate bias is compared with curves for $\alpha = 1.2$ and $\alpha = 1.5$ in Fig. 2.14.

Bulk series resistance is important in lightly doped drain/source regions, which have lower peak electric fields caused by the depletion region (and electric field) at pinchoff extending into the drain region. This improves short-channel performance, but causes a voltage drop across the source and drain regions, which increases $V_{DS}(\text{SAT})$ and lowers channel conductance in both the saturation

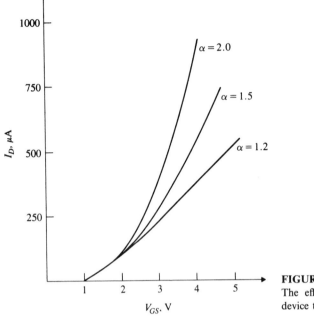

FIGURE 2.14
The effect of velocity saturation on device transconductance.

and linear regions of operation. For conventional FETs this resistance is negligible, but for lightly doped drain (LDD) devices, as shown in Fig. 2.15, it can be as high as 2500 $\Omega \cdot \mu m$.

For short-channel devices the effective doping level under the gate is reduced due to the fact that electric field lines near the source and drain terminate on the source or drain instead of on the gate. This makes V_{TH} strongly dependent upon L_{eff}, as shown in Fig. 2.16.

The body-effect factor γ also depends on W_{eff} since, for narrow-width devices ($W < 5\ \mu m$) the channel-stop implant encroachment into the channel region significantly increases the body effect.

Narrow-width effects are observed to a lesser extent even in the absence of channel-stop implants, since the relatively narrower depletion region under the field oxide distorts the depletion region under the gate oxide, and prevents inversion from occurring at the true boundary regions.

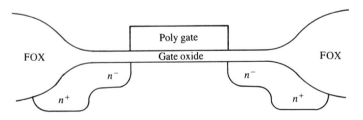

FIGURE 2.15
The cross section of a lightly doped drain device.

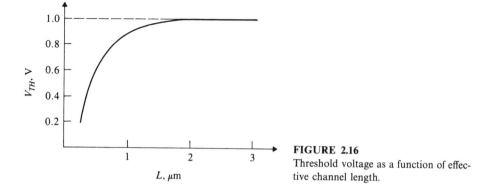

FIGURE 2.16
Threshold voltage as a function of effective channel length.

Combined short-channel and narrow-width effects are complicated. The depletion-region width under the gate increases with substrate bias V_{SB}, and enters the constant-doping level of the bulk region for a substrate bias of about 1 V. At this critical voltage, γ drops to about 1/2 or 1/3. V_{TH} and γ are process-dependent and must be extracted carefully when modeling the device behavior.

For very short channels, subthreshold current is also important. The leakage current at turn-on, when $V_{GS} = V_{TH}$, can be as large as 1 or 2 μA and is dependent upon the device temperature.

2.7 HOT-ELECTRON EFFECTS

If the maximum value of the electric field accelerating electrons in the channel of a FET is not large, the temperature of the electron distribution is the same as that of the lattice. As the drain bias is increased and the field becomes larger, electrons acquire more energy between scattering events than they dissipate to the lattice, and their effective temperature exceeds the lattice temperature. When this happens the electron velocity saturates, impact ionization gives rise to a substrate current, and the most energetic electrons are emitted into the gate oxide region.

Substrate *hot electrons* are thermally generated in the depletion region as leakage current, or diffuse from the bulk substrate into the channel and drift toward the Si-SiO$_2$ interface. They acquire their energy from the high electric field of the depletion region (12), and some electrons can obtain sufficient energy to overcome the Si-SiO$_2$ energy barrier and be injected into the gate insulator.

When the drain voltage exceeds the gate voltage, the field reverses somewhere along the channel, and a retarding field exists in the gate oxide near the drain. Some injected electrons are still collected by the gate electrode, while others are pulled back into the channel and collected at the drain.

The gradual channel approximation was assumed in deriving the drain current equations for long-channel devices. In short-channel FETs the electric field can be sufficient to cause velocity saturation, especially at high gate drive (13). This causes the channel current to be less than that predicted from a simple

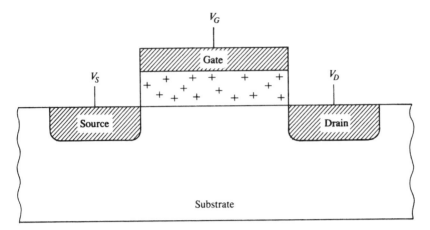

FIGURE 2.17
Alkali ions distributed randomly throughout the gate oxide of an NMOS FET.

scaling of the channel width-to-length ratio from the long-channel case. The drain voltage for channel current saturation decreases with decreasing channel length too, and velocity saturation is usually accompanied by an increase in the small-signal output conductance.

At higher field values, impact ionization at the drain of a FET produces an easily measurable substrate current consisting of the secondary holes created (14). This substrate current contributes to parasitic bipolar problems, results in additional power loss, and can cause catastrophic junction breakdown (15).

At sufficiently high electric fields, emission of channel hot electrons occurs. Once electrons escape from the channel region, their motion depends upon the electric field in the gate oxide. When the gate voltage exceeds the drain voltage, an accelerating field exists everywhere along the channel, attracting the hot electrons to the gate electrode. A small fraction of the hot carriers will be trapped in the oxide layer, and the remainder are collected at the gate electrode, giving rise to a gate current.

When the gate and drain potentials are equal, the transverse electric field at the drain is approximately zero, whereas there is an accelerating transverse field throughout the rest of the channel. All injected electrons that are not trapped are collected by the gate electrode. Apart from the effects of residual charge in the oxide, the emission for a given drain voltage is maximum when $V_{GD} = 0$. Any further increase in gate bias increases channel conductance and reduces the peak electric field in the channel, resulting in less injection.

For gate voltages well above threshold, the change in output characteristics can be attributed to a positive shift in threshold voltage, while for gate voltages near threshold, a combination of threshold shift and transconductance reduction is necessary to obtain a correct curve fit. When FETs are driven hard in high-speed circuits, describing the hot-electron trapping effects as a positive threshold shift is a good approximation, but near threshold, such an approximation underestimates the channel current that actually flows (14).

The worst-case generation of hot electrons occurs when $V_{DS} = 0$, $V_{GS} > 0$ and a large source-to-substrate bias, V_{SB}, exists. This condition usually occurs in bootstrap circuits. For a given applied bias, the substrate hot electron effect is a strong function of substrate conductivity and channel-doping profile, and is only a weak function of channel length and width (15).

Hot electron effects are also greater in devices with high concentrations of positive ions in the oxide layer, as these ions have large electron capture cross sections (16). Alkali ions (Na^+, Li^+, K^+) distributed uniformly within a gate oxide prior to the application of a positive gate bias, as shown in Fig. 2.17, are driven toward the silicon channel surface by the applied gate bias as shown in Fig. 2.18. The electric field in the oxide points vertically downward and attracts electrons to the gate.

The "capture cross section" is a measure of the probability of electron capture by a trap center. The electric field in a typical gate oxide with a gate-to-source bias of 5 V and an oxide thickness of 500 angstroms is $V_{GS}/t_{ox} = 1$ MV/cm. At fields of this size, the capture cross section for the oxide-charge traps is of the order of 2.4×10^{-13} cm^2 (16).

In general, electron trapping cross sections are in the range of 10^{-12} to 10^{-14} cm^2 for Coulomb attractive centers and in the range of 10^{-15} to 10^{-18} cm^2 for neutral trapping centers (16,17).

Shown in Fig. 2.19 is an n-channel FET in the conduction mode. Those electrons which acquire more than 3.1 eV of energy can overcome the energy barrier at the oxide-silicon interface and be injected into the gate oxide. This occurs predominantly near the drain, and a strong vertical field due to V_{GD} is required to pull these electrons to the gate electrode.

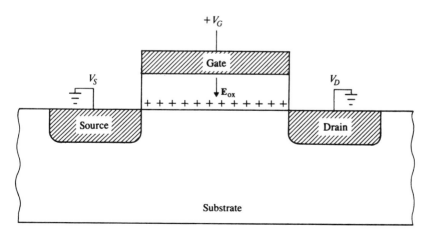

FIGURE 2.18
Alkali ions shift due to the electric field, E_{ox}, in the gate oxide of an NMOS device.

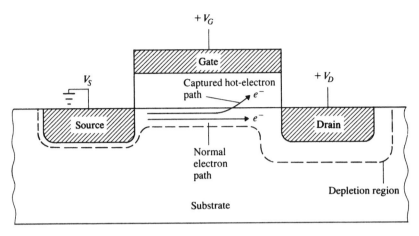

FIGURE 2.19
NMOS device in conduction can generate hot electrons as shown.

If the gate bias is greater than the drain bias, the hot electrons tend to remain in the gate oxide; whereas, if the drain bias is greater than the gate bias, they can be pulled back out of the oxide and collected at the drain. This is shown in Fig. 2.20.

In the absence of a channel, hot electrons can acquire 3.1 eV of energy and cross from the substrate into the gate oxide. These electrons can come from forward biased junctions or from the thermal generation of electrons in the substrate, as shown in Fig. 2.21.

If voltage is not scaled, hot electron effects become more critical as VLSI devices continue to shrink in size, leading to transconductance degradation and threshold-voltage shifting (14).

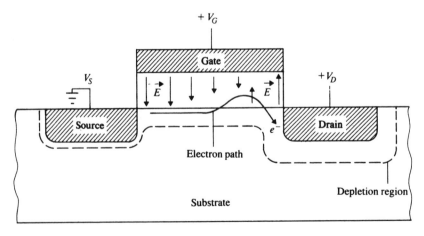

FIGURE 2.20
Hot electrons can be pulled out of the oxide and collected by the drain if $V_{DS} > V_{GS}$.

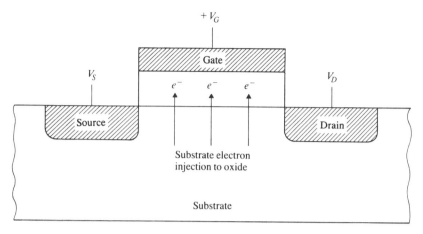

FIGURE 2.21
Substrate electron injection into the oxide.

The superposition of positive ionic charges in the gate oxide will affect electron conduction in the channel region. The close proximity of the charges after a positive gate bias is applied causes a negative shift in the threshold voltage as shown in Fig. 2.22 (i.e., the gate voltage appears to be greater due to the positive charge in the oxide).

The density of injected electrons varies with temperature, being proportional to the concentration of minority carriers, which increases exponentially with temperature. At low temperatures all trapping centers can acquire and hold electrons. Shallow traps have small activation energies, and lose their ability to retain electrons at higher temperatures, whereas deep traps with energy levels near the center of the oxide forbidden gap are more difficult to neutralize. Thus, the density of effective trapping centers, N_T, decreases with increasing temperature, typical values being approximately 2×10^{12} traps/cm^2 at $-40°C$, 10^{12} traps/cm^2 at $30°C$, and 5×10^{11} traps/cm^2 at $100°C$ (18).

Electrons that are captured in traps in the oxide will increase the threshold voltage of the device. Typical changes in threshold voltage, with time and

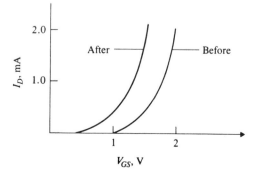

FIGURE 2.22
Transconductance curves before and after gate-charge migration.

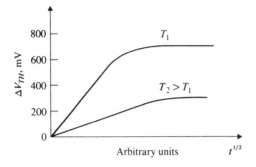

FIGURE 2.23
Variation in threshold voltage with time and temperature in an *n*-channel FET.

temperature, are shown in Fig. 2.23. Initially, changes in threshold voltage increase linearly with the square root of time, until all the ionic charge in the gate oxide has been swept to the oxide-channel interface, at which time the curves reach saturation.

Since the effective trap density decreases as a function of temperature, the saturation value of the threshold-voltage shift decreases due to temperature, and the shift can be described in terms of a trapping-center activation energy as follows:

$$(\Delta V_{TH})^2 = Ate^{-2\Delta H/kT}$$

where A is a constant, a property of the oxide and the ion concentration, t is time, ΔH is the trapping center activation energy, k is Boltzmann's constant, and T is the absolute temperature.

Under zero field in the gate oxide, thermal activation will cause the ions to redistribute uniformly throughout the oxide, and cause the threshold voltage to return to the original value.

2.8 ELECTROMIGRATION, ALUMINUM SPIKES, AND CONTACT RESISTANCE

The exchange of momentum between electrons and metal lattice atoms can cause physical voids or cracks at grain boundaries. These defect regions can grow under stress and eventually cause an open ciruit. When voids form in an aluminum bus line, the reduced cross-sectional area at that location increases the current density at the site of the void. This is positive feedback, and leads to a discontinuity in the aluminum bus line.

Another problem associated with scaled-down structures is the making of contacts which can withstand the necessary postfabrication annealing procedures. In the fabrication of shallow-junction aluminum-silicon contacts, the aluminum can penetrate the shallow junction due to interdiffusion of aluminum and silicon during annealing of process-induced trapping centers and interfacial states at or above 400°C. This short circuiting to the substrate is referred to as *aluminum spiking*.

As device sizes are shrunk vertical dimensions must also shrink, and the use of deeper junction depths in the contact region is not an acceptable solution. Lowering the annealing temperature reduces the penetration depth of spiking, but can result in high-resistivity ohmic contacts. The use of aluminum which is presaturated with about 2 or 3 percent silicon by weight, or the use of Al-Cu-Si alloys with about 3 percent by weight of copper and silicon, not only minimize spiking effects, but help minimize aluminum migration also (18).

A metallurgical barrier can be interposed between the aluminum and the contact region. A layer of platinum between 500 and 1000 angstroms thick can be deposited on the silicon surface where the contacts are to be made, and heat-treated at 600 to 650°C for about 10 minutes in a nonoxidizing atmosphere, to form platinum silicide, PtSi. About 500 angstroms of platinum mixed with 665 angstroms of silicon creates a 1000-angstrom PtSi layer. The PtSi makes a good contact to silicon and does not spike as aluminum does (19). Palladium can be deposited more easily than platinum, is easily etched, and is converted to Pd_2Si at 200°C.

Aluminum conductors may also corrode cathodically in the presence of phosphorus ions, or anodically in the presence of chlorine ions. Contact resistance represents a fundamental limit as device dimensions continue to shrink. The resistance of a μm contact to silicon could range from 1 to 10 kΩ provided the contact interfacial resistivity is in the range of 10^{-5} to 10^{-7} Ω·cm². Contact resistances as low as 10 to 20 Ω are obtainable with present technology, but contact resistance is still a potential limit to device scaling.

2.9 SUMMARY

Part of the necessary groundwork for designing physical layouts in VLSI consists of a minimal knowledge of device physics. In this chapter the necessary device physics required to predict circuit performance is discussed, and the basic device equations are derived.

The silicon/silicon-dioxide interface, the origin of fast and slow surface states, and their effect upon the conduction and valence energy bands are discussed, followed by a derivation of the factors determining the threshold voltage of a field-effect device. The intrinsic threshold voltage, V_{TH0} is derived, a parameter referred to as the body-effect coefficient which accounts for the back-gate effect of the substrate is defined, and the effect of the substrate bias upon device threshold voltage is discussed.

The output characteristics of FETs in the linear and saturated regions of operation and the effect of short channels upon the output characteristics are derived.

The capacitances of a FET which determine switching speed are analyzed, and appropriate equations to calculate these capacitances and estimate the device time constants are derived.

Mobility saturation, short-channel effects, hot-electron effects, electromigration, aluminum spikes, and contact resistance are also discussed.

REFERENCES

1. A. S. Grove, *Physics and Technology of Semiconductor Devices*, John Wiley and Sons, Inc., New York, N.Y., 1967.
2. D. A. Hodges and H. G. Jackson, *Analysis and Design of Digital Integrated Circuits*, 2d ed. McGraw-Hill Book Co., New York, N.Y., 1988.
3. S. M. Sze, *Semiconductor Devices, Physics and Technology*, John Wiley & Sons, New York, N.Y., 1985, Apps. E and F.
4. "The MOSIS User's Manual," USC Information Sciences Institute, USC, 1987.
5. L. A. Glasser and D. W. Dobberpuhl, *The Design and Analysis of VLSI Circuits*, Addison-Wesley Publishing Company, Reading, Mass., 1985, App. D.
6. *VLSI Technology*, S. M. Sze (ed.), McGraw-Hill Book Co., New York, N.Y., 1983, p. 407.
7. S. M. Sze, *Semiconductor Devices, Physics and Technology*, John Wiley & Sons, New York, N.Y., 1985, pp. 401–402.
8. "Computer-Aided Design of IC Fabrication Processes," Integrated Circuits Laboratory, Stanford University, Aug. 5–7, 1987.
9. B. Hoefflinger, "Output Characteristics of Short-Channel Field-Effect Transistors," *IEEE Transactions on Electron Devices*, vol. ED-28, no. 8, August 1981, pp. 971–976.
10. T. Sakurai, "Optimization of CMOS Arbiter and Synchronizer with Sub-Micron MOSFETs," *IEEE J. Solid State Circuits*, SC-23, no. 4, August 1988, pp. 901–906.
11. T. Sakurai, "CMOS Inverter Delay and Other Formulas Using α-Power Law MOS Model," IEEE International Conference on CAD, ICCAD-88, Santa Clara, CA., Nov. 7–10, 1988, pp. 74–77.
12. T. H. Ning, P. W. Cook, R. H. Dennard, C. M. Osburn, S. E. Schuster, and H. N. Yu, "1 μm MOSFET VLSI Technology: Part IV Hot-Electron Design Constraints," *IEEE Transactions on Electron Devices*, vol. ED-26, 1979, pp. 346–353.
13. A. Popa, "An Injection Level Dependent Theory of the MOS Transistor in Saturation," *IEEE Transactions on Electron Devices*, vol. ED-19, 1972, pp. 774–781.
14. R. R. Troutman, T. V. Harroun, P. E. Cottrell, and S. N. Chakravarti, "Hot-Electron Design Considerations for High-Density RAM Chips," *IEEE Transactions on Electron Devices*, vol. ED-27, no. 8, 1980, pp. 1629–1639.
15. D. P. Kennedy and A. Phillips, Jr., "Source-Drain Breakdown in an Insulated Gate Field-Effect Transistor," *IEEE International Electron Devices Conference Technical Digest*, 1973, pp. 160–163.
16. T. H. Ning, "High-Field Capture of Electrons by Coulomb-Attractive Centers in Silicon Dioxide," *Journal of Applied Physics*, vol. 47, 1976, pp. 3203–3208.
17. E. H. Nicollian, C. N. Berglund, P. F. Schmidt, and J. M. Andrews, "Electrochemical charging of thermal SiO_2 Films by Injected Electron Current," *Journal of Applied Physics*, vol. 42, 1971, pp. 5654–5664.
18. H. Matsumoto, K. Sawada, S. Asai, M. Hirayama, and K. Nagasawa, "Effect of Long-Term Stress on IGFET Degradations Hot Electron Trapping," *IEEE Transactions on Electron Devices*, vol. ED-28, no. 8, 1981, pp. 923–928.
19. S. K. Ghandhi, *VLSI Fabrication Principles: Silicon and Galium Arsenide*, John Wiley & Sons, New York, N.Y., 1983, pp. 455–460.

PROBLEMS

2.1. A PMOS transistor has a substrate doping of $N_d = 10^{16}/cm^3$, and a gate doping of $N_d = 10^{20}/cm^3$. The oxide change density is $Q_{ox} = 4 \times 10^{10}q = 6.4$ nC/cm^2, and the thickness is $t_{ox} = 1000$ angstroms.

   (a) Calculate the threshold voltage with zero substrate bias, V_{TH0}.

   (b) Calculate the body-effect coefficient, γ.

   (c) Calculate the ion-implant doses required to change V_{TH0} to 1.0 V, and to change V_{TH0} to -3.0 V.

2.2. An NMOS transistor with $k = 20$ $\mu A/V^2$ and $V_{TH} = 1.5$ V is operated at $V_{GS} = 5$ V and $I_D = 100$ μA. Find V_{DS}. (*Hint:* Find I_{DS} and determine whether or not the transistor is in saturation first.)

2.3. An NMOS transistor has gate dimensions $L = 5$ μm and $W = 20$ μm, source and drain dimensions of 6 μm by 24 μm, source and drain doping of $10^{20}/cm^3$, and a body doping of $5 \times 10^{14}/cm^3$. The gate oxide thickness, t_{ox}, is 700 angstroms.

(a) Neglect the overlap capacitance and calculate the gate capacitance C_g.

(b) Neglect sidewall capacitance and calculate the source-to-substrate capacitance $C_{sb} = C_{db}$.

(c) How much is the gate capacitance increased if the gate overlaps the source and drain by 0.5 microns? By 1 micron?

(d) How much does the source-to-substrate capacitance increase if the sidewall capacitance is not neglected and if $x_j = 0.5$ microns? If $x_j = 1$ micron?

(e) Calculate the capacitance of a conducting line 0.5 cm long and 6 microns wide if the field-oxide thickness, t_{FOX}, is 5000 angstroms.

2.4. Repeat Prob. 2.3 for $L = 3$ microns, $W = 12$ microns, $t_{ox} = 400$ angstroms, $t_{FOX} = 4000$ angstroms, and $x_j = 0.4$ microns.

2.5. (a) Calculate the time required to charge the line of Prob. 2.3e, if the FET driving the line sources an average current of 200 μA, and the change in voltage is 5 V.

(b) Calculate the average current, I_{AV}, required to drive a 100 pF load through a voltage swing of 2 V in a time of 30 ns.

2.6. Find the threshold voltage of a device operating at a source-to-body voltage of 3.5 V, if $2\phi_f = -0.58$ V, $\gamma = 0.37$ $V^{1/2}$, and

(a) $V_{THO} = 1.0$ V

(b) $V_{THO} = -3.5$ V

(c) $V_{THO} = -4.0$ V and $V_{SB} = 5.0$ V

2.7. A device has an oxide capacitance of 69 nF/cm^2 and a threshold voltage of 0.64 V when $V_{GS} = 0$ V. Calculate the ion-implant dose necessary to change the threshold voltage, V_{THO}, of the device to (a) 1.0 V, and (b) -4.0 V. Assume 100 percent ionization of implanted impurities.

2.8. Equation (2.26) for the linear drain current of a FET was derived by treating V_{TH} as a constant, as in Eq. (2.17). Let $V_{SB} = 0$, and consider the voltage drop along the channel due to V_{DS}. Then the charge stored in the depletion region is obtained from Eq. (2.10) by adding V to $-2\phi_f$, where V is a function of distance y from the source toward the drain. The charge in the channel region is now given by $Q_B = -\sqrt{2q\epsilon_{si}N_a|-2\phi_f + V|}$

(a) Show that $V_{TH}(y) = V_{THO} + \gamma\left[\sqrt{|-2\phi_f + V|} - \sqrt{|-2\phi_f|}\right]$ where V_{THO} is given by Eq. (2.16), and γ is given by Eq. (2.15).

(b) Show that the drain current in the linear region is now:

$$I_D = I_D(\text{LIN}) - \frac{2k\gamma}{3}[(|-2\phi_f + V_{DS}|)^{3/2} - (|-2\phi_f|)^{3/2}]$$

$$+ k\gamma\sqrt{|-2\phi_f|}V_{DS}$$

where $I_D(\text{LIN})$ is given by Eq. (2.26).

(c) What is the effect of an ion implant dose, N_I, on the answer of part b?

2.9. (a) Write a program in BASIC, C, FORTRAN, or PASCAL, to calculate $I_D(\text{LIN})$ from Eq. (2.26) and I_D as given in Prob. 2.8b.

(b) Calculate and plot $I_D(\text{LIN})$ and I_D, as functions of V_{DS}, for $V_{GS} = 2.5$ V and 5.0 V, $k = 20\ \mu\text{A/V}^2$, $V_{THO} = 1.0$ V, $\phi_f = -0.36$ V, and $\gamma = 0.82\ \text{V}^{1/2}$. Increment V_{DS} in steps of 0.5 V.

2.10. From Eqs. (2.18) and (2.19), the threshold voltage with no back-gate bias, but corrected by an ion implant of density N_I is:

$$V_{THO} = V_{FB} - 2\phi_f - \frac{Q_{B0}}{C_{\text{ox}}} + \frac{qN_I}{C_{\text{ox}}}$$

If $t_{\text{ox}} = 400$ angstroms, $N_a = 10^{15}/\text{cm}^2$, $N_{ss} = 1.5 \times 10^{11}/\text{cm}^2$, $\phi_{GC} = -0.85$ V, and $N_I = 5 \times 10^{11}$ positive ions/cm^2, find V_{THO}.

2.11. Sketch the threshold voltage of the device in Prob. 2.10, for back-gate biases from 0 to 5 V.

DESIGN PROBLEM

2.12. Become familiar with Magic Tutorial 3: Advanced Painting (Wiring and Plowing).

CHAPTER
3

PROCESSING, SCALING, AND RELIABILITY

3.1 INTRODUCTION

The forces driving any technology are financial, rewarding improvements in performance and cost. The semiconductor industry has been reducing device and circuit size for over two decades, approximately doubling the number of devices on a single chip each year. This has become known as Moore's law (1).

Reducing the dimensions of a semiconductor technology requires new or improved techniques and creates problems in both physics and engineering. Some parameters and design aspects cannot be scaled for physical reasons, and others cannot be scaled without adversely affecting performance. In either case, a point is reached beyond which one can no longer utilize a specific design, and it must be redone.

One cannot scale leakage currents, intrinsic electron and hole densities, thermal voltages, and work-function differences, all of which are temperature-dependent. Bonding pads do not scale either, and as the individual transistors driving a pad are shrunk, the effective loading by the pad increases. Superbuffers compensate for this in the original design, but if the dimensions are shrunk by more than 50 percent, the design probably requires the addition of another superbuffer in each pad-driver stage.

The silicon-gate NMOS process is simpler than CMOS, and was historically the first to be scaled. It will be treated first, and the photolithographic steps required to design NMOS will be examined to obtain the background needed to create design rules. Once the feasibility of general design rules and NMOS scaling was proved, the Mead-Conway approach was applied to CMOS. CMOS design rules will also be derived. Two types of scaling, *full scaling* and *constant voltage scaling*, will be considered.

Threshold voltage (V_{TH}) is a measure of the voltage required to produce a specific drain current under conditions of constant drain voltage. FET *transconductance* (g_m) is a measure of the rate of change of drain current with gate bias when the drain voltage is fixed. These are important FET characteristics, and mechanisms which cause either the threshold voltage or the device transconductance to drift should be avoided.

Mobile and fixed ions in the gate oxide of a FET cause immediate, saturable effects, whereas silicon-silicon dioxide interfacial traps can cause both immediate and time-dependent effects. Dielectric breakdown is both time-dependent and saturable, while oxide charging by hot carriers can be time-dependent and nonsaturable. Immediate and saturable mechanisms are created at the time of wafer processing, whereas time-dependent and nonsaturable mechanisms are accelerated by the FET operating conditions.

Soft errors are random, nonrecurring failures caused by ionizing radiation present within the environment. All matter contains small amounts of radioactive material. Alpha particles emitted by an IC's packaging material can penetrate the enclosed circuit, and generate electron-hole pairs.

Error-correcting circuits can be designed into the system to increase its reliability, but this adds components to the system and increases its size. The system must now test and correct its data, which slows the system's performance.

3.2 ERROR CHECKING AND TESTING

The purpose of design rules is to make the performance of circuit components such as inverters, pass transistors, NAND gates, NOR gates, buffers, and combinations of these basic building blocks, as reliable as the behavior of discrete chips. The system architect is then relieved of circuit details and free to concentrate upon system design, which allows him/her to design large, complex integrated circuits with a minimal background in device physics and manufacturing process limitations.

The availability of a cell library of predesigned, debugged inverters, gates and more complex systems of basic cells, allows the system architect to sit at an interactive graphics terminal and design the layouts of a set of masks for a specific IC. If the design rules used to create the basic cell library are sufficiently general, the resulting design can be manufactured by any fabrication house which can read the computer tape on which the design information is stored. This allows a degree of flexibility in the choice of manufacturers, both as first and as second sources of IC chips.

Minimum line widths have been monotonically decreasing for over two decades, and a suitable choice of design rules is one that allows for shrinking line widths, so that successful circuit designs can be upgraded by simply specifying a parameter. To this end, the Mead-Conway design rules are specified in terms of a parameter called lambda, and all designs are done in multiples of lambda (2).

An obvious shortcoming of this approach is that the design rules must be sufficiently relaxed so that many, if not all, fabrication houses can construct the IC chip. This means that all design rules must be chosen to satisfy a worst-case scenario, and some rules will be more stringent than the requirements of any specific manufacturer would demand.

This penalty in size is offset by the flexibility and durability of the Mead-Conway design approach. Future design rules may be sufficiently flexible to allow tailored post-design rules to be implemented once a specific manufacturer has been chosen, or even to allow different design rules to be postspecified for two or more fabrication houses making the same IC chip.

The VLSI designer's task can be broken down into several steps which will be investigated prior to defining the design rules. These steps include inputting and outputting the design geometry in a machine-readable format, checking the layout for design-rule violations and logical errors, documenting the design, simulating the behavior of the complete circuit and testing the IC chip.

3.2.1 Inputting and Outputting the Design

An *interactive graphics editor* with a digitizing table and a mouse or a pointer is required in order to draw the desired layout by inputting the coordinates of vertices as the gate or circuit is being designed. For human visualization, a color graphics terminal is vastly superior to a black and white display.

A machine language is required that can specify elementary shapes such as rectangles, polygons, circles, and wires. An input program prompts for next entry and provides default values, warns of format errors, allows iteration of cells, provides reference points and relative coordinates specified in units of lambda, and manages generated files.

Once the layout is completed, a good input program fills out the features to default dimensions and compacts the geometric layout into a final mask specification. A library of cells specified by the user is a must, containing specific cells which can be recalled, rotated, translated, scaled, and mirrored about different axes.

Hard copy output is necessary for documentation and error checking, and for marking design changes and inserting comments. To do this, several mask levels must be displayed simultaneously and must be either color coded or stippled in some convenient manner.

A *technology-specification file* returns a cell with the proper line widths and registration tolerances for a specific technology. At a higher level, the equations for a block of boolean logic or the state diagram for a finite state machine could specify the desired design.

3.2.2 Error Checking

Humans possess tremendous pattern recognition capability, and each IC mask possesses a high level of structure and regularity, some of it intentionally introduced to further facilitate design rule checking. Many violations, such as open lines and lines too narrow or too close together, clearly stand out under visual inspection.

The mechanical nature of design rules facilitates computer checking. *Error-checking programs* incorporate the design rules for a given process, and examine computer files for violations. Design rules assign minimum distances to feature dimensions, spacing between features on the same mask layer, and spacing between features on different mask layers.

It can be quite difficult to display design-rule violations in a convenient way. An extra *error mask* which can be superimposed on the regular layout plot to locate violations may be both desirable and necessary.

There are catastrophic errors that do not show up as design-rule errors, and can be very difficult to catch. Some of the more common mistakes are: logic errors, such as interchanging true and complemented variables, initializing state machines erroneously, open connections that are separated by more than the minimum spacing, and incorrect connections on long or wide buses.

3.2.3 Testability

Simulation is required whenever it is too difficult to verify the correctness of a design by inspection. It allows the designer to test the circuit by modeling the components in detail, and computing interactions under various conditions. Simulation is useful at all levels from the system level down to the circuit level. The design of IC fabrication processes lends itself to simulation of process variations, and this is becoming more important as VLSI approaches the physical limits of device sizes (3).

Modern VLSI systems are very complex and must be designed with testing always in mind. To this end, a modular design can be a big asset. A system broken down into a number of blocks may be designed with each module a separate project, complete with input/output pads, so that each block can be tested separately before connecting the modules. The concept of modularity can be applied to testing specific cells in a repetitive design also. Testing small to moderately sized segments of a system gives results that are less dependent upon chip yield considerations.

Internal *test pads* allow for probing after the chip is manufactured, but this requires sophisticated probing equipment, and is risky because circuitry near the probe pad can be damaged if the probe slips. If standard pads are provided to monitor critical nodes in the system, and they are bonded in the usual manner, one has easy access to these nodes at no risk of damaging the circuitry.

A major disadvantage of using test pads is that they hang a large capacitance on the node under test. If the pads can be gated to disconnect them from the circuit after testing, the capacitive loading can be significantly reduced. A pad that is clocked could also be multiplexed to connect it to several nodes, thus increasing the testability of the circuit without increasing the pad count. This can be done by using a single output pad driven by a shift register that is parallel-loaded.

If the circuit doesn't work at all, test patterns consisting of simple transistors, capacitors, inverters, and ring oscillators can provide process quality control to determine the failure mechanism. If debugged support systems, such as clock circuitry, pad drivers, and I/O pads are available, they can be used to help test the rest of the circuitry.

3.3 THE SILICON-GATE NMOS PROCESS

The system design engineer must have sufficient knowledge of both the process and its limitations to understand the design rules, and to know what to expect if they are not followed. The engineer also needs to be familiar with the terminology employed by fabrication houses.

The silicon-gate *n*-channel process can be considered a "standard" fabrication process, and will be discussed in some detail. The advantages of silicon-gate NMOS technology over other processes are that it is conceptually and physically simpler than other modern processes because it requires less photolithographic steps. It has high functional density, good speed/power performance, and it has tremendous future potential due to its scalability.

The major drawbacks of the NMOS process are its high absolute power consumption and its electrical asymmetry. CMOS is replacing NMOS as the "standard" process because it minimizes both of the above disadvantages.

3.3.1 Silicon Patterning

Polysilicon refers to polycrystalline silicon, often abbreviated as polysi or just poly, and differs from bulk silicon which is monocrystalline in structure. Electrical conduction in polysilicon occurs along grain boundaries, and is very low. For this reason, polysilicon is often doped by either implanting or diffusing impurities into it that increase its conductivity.

Aluminum (Al) was the original metal gate material, but it has a very low melting pcint. Tungsten (W) or molybdenum (Mo) can be used for gate material, but refractory metals are difficult to work with. This leaves polysilicon as the best available compromise to date, and it has replaced metal in modern processes because the structure $Si\text{-}SiO_2\text{-}Polysi\text{-}SiO_2$ is easily manufactured. Also, since processing silicon and silicon dioxide requires very high temperatures, they are both very stable at room temperature.

Photolithography is used to pattern the layers of an integrated circuit. *Photoresist* (PR) is put on the wafer surface and the wafer is spun at high speed to leave a very thin coating of PR. PR is, as the name implies, a photosensitive chemical, used with a mask to define areas of the wafer surface by exposure to *ultraviolet* (UV) *light*. The mask consists of opaque and transparent materials patterned to define certain areas on the wafer surface. It is the pattern of each mask that the systems engineer must design.

With *negative photoresist*, the areas of the wafer exposed to UV light are hardened and retained, while with *positive photoresist*, the exposed areas of the wafer are softened and removed.

In *contact photolithography*, exposure takes place with the mask pressed against the wafer. This wears out masks, and is being replaced by *projection photolithography*, wherein the image is projected onto the wafer and no damage is done to the mask.

Development of the PR dissolves unexposed (negative) or exposed (positive) portions of the photoresist and a low-temperature bake hardens the remaining PR.

In *wet etching*, the wafer is immersed in a chemical bath to dissolve the exposed material. The etch is chosen to have no effect on silicon or silicon dioxide. *Silicon nitride* must be protected with a cover of silicon dioxide during wet etching.

Plasma etching, also called *ion etching* and *ion milling*, is a dry etch process using a stream of ions and electrons to blast material away. It is done by creating ions in a glow discharge, and then directing the ions to the target. Ions will typically penetrate about 800 angstroms of oxide or PR, and thick layers of either can be used to protect or mask some areas, while the exposed material is being sputtered away.

Ion etching is much more directional than wet chemical etching, and yields much better resolution. For this reason, it has replaced wet etching in most critical etch processes. Plasma etching can be too good in some cases, and the sidewalls of an etch can be too vertical for aluminum metallization to "step over" without a break in continuity. The solution to this problem is to deliberately cause the walls to slant when necessary.

The wafer is next etched in *hydrofluoric acid* (HF), which dissolves the exposed oxide down to the silicon surface. HF does not etch silicon in the absence of strong oxidizers such as nitric acid. After the wafer has been etched, the remaining PR is stripped off with a strong organic solvent, strong acids such as chromic acid, or exposure to atomic oxygen which oxidizes away the PR. The oxide that was previously protected by photoresist will act as a shield in the implantation or diffusion steps to come.

The photoresist cycle is a measure of process complexity, since a separate mask is required for each such cycle. A simple NMOS process requires about six of the above cycles, while a complicated bipolar technology may require over 20 PR cycles.

3.3.2 Mask Generation

In *optical generation* a master copy of the mask, which is called a *reticle*, is made at 10 times the actual final size. A pattern generator does the plotting by projecting the image of the master onto the reticle. Overexposed areas tend to grow slightly, and can be compensated for in advance.

Optically generated masks require special marking features which are used to identify, align, and orient the mask. These markings appear on the reticles outside the boundary of the pattern and are never on the finished plates. *Parity marks*, small arrows or triangles, are used to help the operator orient the mask, and *fiducials*, or small crosses on each layer, are used in *step-and-repeat* processes, and to register different masks.

Master plates are made from reticles in a step-and-repeat process that projects an image of the reticle, reduced 10 times, onto a photosensitized plate, producing a matrix of images of the reticle. Fiducials are used to control the separation between exposures and to align the reticle images relative to one another.

Electron-beam masters are faster, more flexible, and have less defects than optically generated masters. A defect on a reticle means that every chip has that defect, and the step-and-repeat process is a potential source of both alignment problems and defect propagation from dust specks. The electron-beam process eliminates both of these problems.

Electron-beam exposure systems are raster-oriented, with all geometric data converted into a *bitmap*, which is a rectangular array of 1's and 0's. Squares containing 1's are exposed and those containing 0's are not. Exposures are made by blanking and unblanking the beam according to the input stream of bits. The process of converting trapezoids and rectangles into a bitmap is called *corefill*.

Working plates are made from masters by contact printing, and are the actual contact-print masks used in wafer fabrication. Masters can be used directly for reduced turnaround time, but masters made for copying to working plates are compensated in advance for changes in copy dimensions. It is generally not possible to make working plates from a master intended for direct use.

Mask polarity is determined by the fabrication facility, and depends upon the process step and the type of photoresist used. The type of PR used is based partly upon the line widths desired. Whether the plates for a layer should be opaque field with clear features or clear field with opaque features must be specified when ordering plates.

A speck of dust on an otherwise clear area of a working plate will cause a pattern to be made in the photoresist. On a negative resist, the speck will make a hole in the resist that will enlarge slightly due to undercutting in the subsequent etch step; while positive resist will leave a small dot where the speck was, and etching may even remove it.

Plates can be made of inexpensive *green glass* or of more costly *low-expansion glass*, which provides more stable masks than green glass. Plates may be covered with *photographic emulsion*, which is cheap but easily damaged; or with *iron oxide* or *chromium*, both of which are more durable and give better line resolution, but are also more expensive.

Auxiliary patterns are not part of the circuit design, and consist of alignment markings, critical dimensions, test capacitors, test transistors, test inverters, and their probe pads. *Critical dimensions* (CDs) are simple lines or crosses of a fixed size on each layer, that are used to adjust exposure and developing times in order to obtain correct size.

Mask parity specifies up from down and left from right. which seems simple, but is actually quite confusing because some mask generators use left-handed coordinate systems, while others use right-handed systems. Initial data may be reversed (mirrored) a number of times, depending upon the process used, before arriving at the working plates. A string of text is the best way to specify mask parity, but instructions must accompany text to state how the text should appear on either the master plates or the working plates, and specify whether the text is to appear normal or reversed, and from which side of the mask the text is viewed, the chrome or the nonchrome side.

Blowbacks are color enlargements of each reticle, typically 100 to 130 times the actual chip size. Layers can be checked individually and in combination by superimposing the films on one another. Black and clear transparencies, usually 8.5 by 11, may also be made at the same time. Electron-beam mask blowbacks are generally not available.

3.4 PHOTOLITHOGRAPHIC STEPS IN THE NMOS PROCESS

The basic silicon-gate NMOS process consists of six photolithographic mask steps. Each mask step requires the creation of a mask, masking, photoresist, and etching; thus, the number of mask steps is a measure of the complexity of the process.

3.4.1 Active Area Definition

To define the active area of the wafer a thin thermal *silicon dioxide* (SiO_2) layer is grown, followed by a *chemical vapor deposition* (CVD) of *silicon nitride* (Si_3N_4). The thermal coefficients of expansion of silicon and silicon nitride do not match and thermally grown silicon dioxide is used to form a buffer zone to relieve mechanical stress. Silicon dioxide is also deposited by a CVD process to cover and mask the silicon nitride for protection.

PHOTOLITHOGRAPHIC STEP 1: GREEN MASK. The oxide is etched with hydrofluoric acid, where the PR has been removed. The nitride which is exposed by this step is etched next, while the CVD oxide protects the nitride which it covers.

A p^+ *channel-stop implant* is done to eliminate parasitic devices; after which a *field oxide* (FOX) approximately one-half micron thick is grown over the channel stop region. The field oxide and the channel stop implant are self-aligned with respect to the source and drain diffusion by the silicon nitride which acts as a mask against oxidation. Figure 3.1 is a cross section, showing the field oxide and protected nitride. The p^+ channel-stop is under the field oxide and the thin gate oxide is under the nitride. The channel-stop implant is to prevent the surface of the wafer from inverting and producing a *parasitic n-channel FET*. Where the

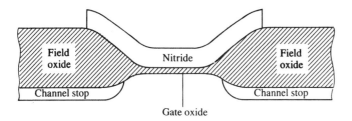

FIGURE 3.1
Cross section of wafer after the first mask step and field oxide growth.

thick field oxide (FOX) interfaces with a thin gate oxide (*thinox*) covered by a layer of nitride, the field oxide grows laterally under the nitride, giving rise to a structure called a *bird's beak*. The last step is to remove nitride.

3.4.2 Transistor Formation

PHOTOLITHOGRAPHIC STEP 2: YELLOW MASK. The entire wafer is processed with photoresist again, and the yellow mask is used to define ion-implant areas, by removing PR in the desired yellow regions. Ions are now implanted in the exposed areas to produce depletion-mode transistors by altering the device threshold voltage. This is followed by a very thin gate-oxide growth, typically 40 to 70 nm thick (400 to 700 angstroms).

PHOTOLITHOGRAPHIC STEP 3: BROWN MASK. A connection between the polysilicon and the source of the pull-up transistor is needed to short circuit the gate and source of the device. Part of the gate oxide must be etched from the contact area to expose the underlying silicon which is common to the *buried-contact* window and the active region. The field oxide exposed by the buried-contact window will be slightly etched during this process. Polysilicon is next deposited (CVD) to a thickness of about 400 or 500 nm, and a thin oxide layer is grown over the polysilicon to obtain good photoresist adherence. The polysilicon must be doped the same as the source to which it is connected, and a small *outdiffusion* of impurities from the poly into the source region will improve the reliability of the contact and reduce its contact resistance.

PHOTOLITHOGRAPHIC STEP 4: RED MASK. The oxide and polysilicon are removed in the nonred areas, followed by a diffusion or implant of phosphorus or arsenic to form n^+ source and drain regions. The polysilicon gate self-aligns the channel and the source/drain regions to minimize gate-drain and gate-source overlap capacitances. If a buried contact defines one end of the channel as shown in Fig. 4.16, this self-registration feature is lost. By placing the buried contact to one side as discussed in Sec. 4.7.2 and shown in Figs. 4.17 and 4.18, the self-alignment of the channel is preserved.

Impurities embed in the field oxide and in the polysilicon, and do not penetrate either one. Diffusion does proceed laterally under the gate to a distance about equal to the depth of the diffusion, x_j, while ion implanting has less lateral spreading.

Next, a thick layer of *phosphor glass* ($SiO_2 + P_2O_5$) is deposited over the wafer surface. Aluminum does not cling well to vertical edges, but phosphor glass plus aluminum is viscous at a relatively low temperature, and can be reflowed to smooth out ripples due to steps of elevation on the wafer surface. At this point both *depletion* and *enhancement* FETs are formed.

3.4.3   Contacts

PHOTOLITHOGRAPHIC STEP 5: BLACK MASK. *Ohmic contacts* connecting metal to polysilicon and/or diffusion are needed. These contacts are defined after the phosphor glass deposition and reflow. The phosphor glass is etched through wherever contacts must be made. The etching stops at either the polysilicon or the substrate. The result of this step is that all the contact areas are ready for metallization. Contacts should not be placed over active transistor areas.

3.4.4   Metallization

After the contact areas are defined, aluminum is evaporated over the entire wafer surface. To prevent *spike-through* (an aluminum short circuit to the substrate) in shallow source and drain junctions, either redope with n^+ material to form deeper junctions and/or higher surface concentrations of *n*-type impurities, or form a *palladium-silicide* barrier over the source and drain regions.

PHOTOLITHOGRAPHIC STEP 6: BLUE MASK. The aluminum is now etched in the nonblue areas, and the wafer is annealed for one hour at 450°C to remove radiation damage due to the electron beam that was used to heat the aluminum during the evaporation process. One now has a finished circuit.

The basic NMOS process described above has only one metal high-conductance layer. VLSI designs have reached a level of density which causes large-size and/or complex layouts to be limited by routing problems, producing a definite need for more than one metal layer.

The restriction to one metal layer can be removed by depositing another insulator after the metallization step of mask 6, cutting contact holes (*vias*) to lower levels where needed, and depositing a second metal layer. This will require two additional photolithographic steps to define metal layer 2 and via locations. When metal 2 is etched to the desired pattern one has a two-layer metal process. These steps can be repeated to obtain more than two levels of metallization.

Mask steps 6B to define vias connecting the two metal layers, and 6C defining the second metal layer must be added here if a second metallization layer is used.

Aluminum has a very low melting point compared to refractory materials, and if the first level metallization is aluminum, only lower melting-point metals can be used in subsequent steps, so as not to reflow the aluminum after the contact holes have been etched. If high-temperature steps are required after the first metallization, the process engineer must choose a first-level metal with a high melting point, such as tungsten or molybdenum, and new problems are now encountered with patterning and with electrochemistry. Polysilicon is a good compromise, and doping the polysilicon will enhance its conductivity.

3.4.5   Chip Packaging

The chip must be protected from chemical surface contamination, as well as from scratches during wire bonding and encapsulation. This protection is accomplished by depositing a thick layer of low-temperature glass over the entire surface of the wafer. This requires:

PHOTOGRAPHIC STEP 7: OVERGLASS MASK. The *overglass* (*passivation* or *glassification*) mask is required in order to define the bonding pad and to scribe line locations, where holes must be cut in the overglass to allow for wire-bonding and scribing.

After the overglass is etched, the individual circuits are tested at a *probe station*, where defective circuits are marked with a magnetic red ink. The circuits are either *scribed* with a diamond cutting tool and separated, or the chips are sawed apart with a diamond saw. The good chips are next mounted on headers with a conductive bonding epoxy, wire-bonded to the appropriate pinouts, encapsulated in an inert atmosphere, and hermetically sealed.

The chip is now completely packaged and ready for final testing. Once the chip is packaged, only the pins of the package are available for testing; any other testing must be done prior to encapsulation.

A cross-sectional drawing of a typical NMOS depletion-mode device is shown in Fig. 3.2. An enhancement-mode device is constructed in an identical manner except for omission of the ion-implant step.

3.4.6   Process Limitations

An assumption inherent in device scaling is that dimensional variations or tolerances can be scaled proportionately in fabricating smaller devices. Therefore, it is extremely important to keep dimensions under tight control during patterning and etching.

There are fundamental physical limitations to the amount of down-scaling that can be done, and the design engineer needs to be familiar with some of the more common limitations that will be encountered in determining the design rules.

The minimum wavelength of visible light is about 0.4 microns (blue), and objects much smaller than several wavelengths cannot be defined properly due to

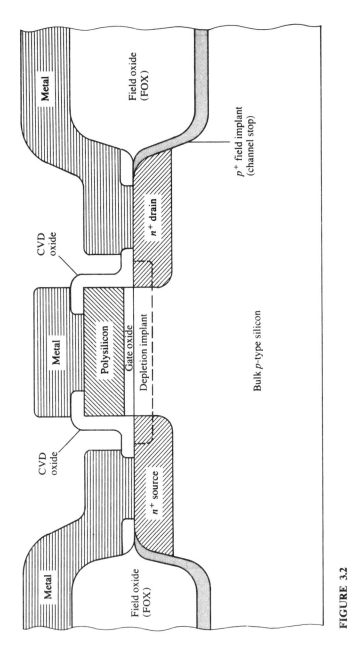

FIGURE 3.2
Cross-sectional view of a typical NMOS FET.

62

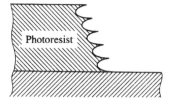

FIGURE 3.3
Layered zones in PR due to standing waves.

diffraction and interference patterning. Ultraviolet (UV) light can be used to extend the range to about 0.1 or 0.2 micron. X-rays and electron beams require new techniques and new photoresists. 10 to 100 keV electron beams and 10 angstrom x-rays are used for pattern definition.

Reflections can cause interference between the incident and the reflected light and produce layered zones of exposure due to standing waves, as shown in Fig. 3.3. Electron beams are back-scattered (reflected from the bottom surface) also, and produce standing-wave patterns. The layered effect can be minimized by combining three or more different wavelengths in an appropriate ratio.

Underetching and *overetching* cause errors in defining lines and windows in the oxide, as shown in Fig. 3.4. Plasma etching is more accurate than wet etching, and minimizes this problem. Outdiffusion of dopants occurs during succeeding high-temperature steps and causes interfaces to be offset from the designed locations. The offset can be calculated, and compensated for by the fabrication house.

In ion-implanting, the use of heavy atoms such as arsenic (As) implanted at low temperature will reduce outdiffusion problems. If possible, this implant should be done after diffusion and other high temperature steps are completed.

Due to the large resistance of polysilicon lines, positive and negative power lines must never be run for great distances in polysilicon. When short polysilicon lines are used it is desirable to calculate and compensate for the expected voltage drops along these lines. Diffusion and polysilicon are usually used only for tunneling under positive supply voltage (VDD) or ground (GND) lines, and should be as wide as possible, with multicontacts to the metal at both ends. Polysilicon crossunders are much better than diffused or implanted crossunders, and a two-metal process is the best way to cross two bus lines.

Beyond a certain maximum current flux through a metal conductor, metal atoms begin to drift slowly in the direction of the current. Current density

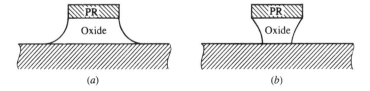

FIGURE 3.4
Errors caused by (*a*) underetching, and (*b*) overetching a protected oxide layer.

increases at a constriction in a conductor line, further increasing metal migration at that spot. Positive feedback occurs and eventually results in an open circuit.

The critical value of current density in aluminum is about $100 \, \text{kA/cm}^2$. This may sound high, but for a metal line of thickness 1 micron, the maximum current is 1 mA. Stated another way, 1 mA per micron of aluminum line width is the maximum safe steady state or average current an aluminum wire can handle. The width of metal lines is calculated by determining the maximum average current drawn by all the active devices connected to that line, as shown in Example 3.1. Transient pulses in excess of 1 mA per micron seem to cause no apparent damage.

Example 3.1. Determine the metal line width required to supply a fanout of 5 lines, each of which are driving 80 inverters with average current ratings of 0.07 mA. Assume $\lambda = 2$ microns.

Solution. Eighty inverters draw a total current of $80(0.07) = 5.6$ mA. This requires a line no less than 5.6 microns wide. The minimum metal line width in a 2-micron process is: $W = 3\lambda = 6$ microns. This will drive the specified 80 inverters. The metal line feeding five of these lines must be able to handle $5(5.6) = 28$ mA. This requires a line of minimum width 28 microns, or 14λ. 15λ would give a small safety factor.

The use of refractory metal silicides such as WSi_2 on top of polysilicon, re-duces the resistance of the poly line by a factor of from 10 to 20. Polycide tech-nology appears to be fully compatible with silicon-gate processing technology.

Implanting is a dirty process, embedding impurities along with the desired ions, and causing structural damage to the bulk silicon material. Implanting through a thin oxide layer tends to trap the impurities in the oxide and miniminize damage to the silicon crystal. Etching the SiO_2 removes most of the trapped impurities, and annealing can further reduce implant damage.

3.5 TYPES OF SCALING

VLSI is a rapidly advancing technology, and the goal is to design circuits that can be shrunk as the technology evolves to ever smaller designs in the future. Microcircuit design differs from previous digital design in the detailed attention that must be given to the physical design or layout of a system. Proper scaling allows one to shrink a design to meet new, smaller line-width capabilities.

There are two basic types of scaling to consider:

1. *Full scaling*, in which all device dimensions, both surface and vertical, and all voltages are reduced by the same amount, and
2. *Constant-voltage* (CV) *scaling*, wherein only device dimensions are scaled, while maintaining voltage levels which are compatible with supply voltages levels and TTL logic levels.

These two methods are compared in Table 3.1 below, with the scale factor specified by F. A compromise solution would be to use full scaling on all internal circuitry, maintaining TTL compatibility only at the package I/O pins.

TABLE 3.1

Parameter	Full scaling	CV scaling
Dimensions: W, L, t_{ox}	$1/F$	$1/F$
Voltages: V_{DD}, V_{TH}	$1/F$	1
Specific-oxide capacitances: C_{ox}, C_{sw}, C_{FOX}	F	F
Gate capacitance: $C_g = C_{ox}WL$	$1/F$	$1/F$
Process transconductance factor, k'	F	F
Current, I_D	$1/F$	F
DC power consumption, P	$1/F^2$	F
Propagation delay, t_p	$1/F$	$1/F^2$
Power-delay product, Pt_p	$1/F^3$	$1/F$

Example 3.2. Show that the gate specific capacitance, C_g, scales as $1/F$ for full scaling and constant-voltage scaling.

Solution. C_g is proportional to WL/t_{ox}. With either type scaling, W, L, and t_{ox} are each scaled by $1/F$, therefore WL/t_{ox} scales by $1/F$.

Example 3.3. Show that the process transconductance factor, k', scales as F for both types of scaling.

Solution. For both types of scaling, k' is proportional to the gate capacitance, C_{ox}, which is inversely proportional to the oxide thickness, t_{ox}. t_{ox} scales as $1/F$, therefore C_{ox} and k' both scale as F.

k' is also proportional to I/V^2, which scales as F in both cases.

3.6 DEVICE RELIABILITY

Very thick silicide films will consume excessive silicon during formation, which may cause degradation of device characteristics. Thickness control of thin metallic films is critical in order to avoid reliability problems such as metal migration and spiking.

Silicon-on-sapphire (SOS) technology has problems primarily due to inferior crystallinity of the silicon film near the sapphire interface and to high interface state density which contributes to back-channel leakage. Poor crystallinity results in low mobility and minority carrier lifetime, which reduces drain-field-dependent leakage currents as well as voltage swings in the substrate bias due to the floating substrate.

Instabilities result from fluctuations in the electric field across the gate oxide material. If an ion, an electron, or a hole is injected into the gate oxide, the relative repulsion of channel carriers is changed. Channel majority-carrier repulsion is increased by introducing charge of the same type as already on the gate, and it is decreased by introducing charge of the opposite type. The result is a change in threshold voltage of a FET, decreasing V_{TH} if repulsion is increased and increasing V_{TH} if repulsion is decreased. Positively charged alkali ions introduced into the gate dielectric as well as unannealed, radiation-induced positive charges in the gate oxide, lower FET threshold voltages, and complicate both device and process modeling. If not annealed, charged centers, and uncharged radiation-induced centers, act as permanent traps for *hot electrons* injected into the oxide during the operation of the device.

Electrons and holes that achieve sufficient energy can be injected from the channel into the gate oxide. These hot carriers are strongly attracted to the gate electrode by the electric field in the oxide. If $V_{GS} = V_{GD} = 5$ V, and $t_{ox} = 500$ angstroms, the field in the gate oxide is 1 MV/cm. Electron traps exist in any oxide due to crystal imperfections. Radiation-induced traps add to those already present in the oxide layer, increasing the probability that an injected electron becomes trapped while passing through the oxide.

Trapping of injected electrons in the gate oxide of a FET causes a shift in threshold voltage, degrades its performance, and eventually leads to an unacceptably low current output. Electrons must acquire more than 3.1 eV of energy to be injected into the gate oxide (4). This usually occurs near the drain, and a strong vertical field due to V_{GD} is required to pull these electrons to the gate electrode. Some electrons will be captured in traps in the oxide, causing an increase in NMOS threshold voltage. The hot-electron effect is more severe in very short channel devices, and higher operating temperatures mitigate the threshold-voltage shift by freeing trapped electrons more easily.

3.6.1 Soft Errors

A 25 fF capacitance charged to 4 V has a charge of $Q = CV = 100$ fC, or about 625,000 electrons on its negative plate. If the plate loses half a million electrons, the potential of the capacitance drops to about 0.8 V. This would be treated as a logical 0. Thus the difference between a logical 1 and a logical 0 is about one-half million electrons for a 25 fF capacitance. This *critical charge* is the minimum number of electrons that can change the data in a cell from 1 to 0 or 0 to 1. Any high-impedance node that is sensitive to about one-half million electrons may be affected. Since the cell will function correctly once new data is written into it, this type of failure is termed a *soft error*.

Alpha particles can penetrate about 10 microns into silicon, and the current produced by this impact may be sufficient to charge or discharge a storage node, causing a soft error. High storage capacitance also reduces soft errors. The number of stored charged electrons representing a logic-1 or a logic-0 is directly proportional to the storage capacitance. Higher storage capacitance requires more stored charge, which in turn increases the critical charge necessary to produce a soft error. Increasing the critical electronic charge beyond a million electrons significantly reduces the susceptibility to soft errors and may be necessary for operation in high radiation environments.

CMOS technology is less susceptible to soft errors than NMOS is. Devices built in a shallow *n*-well in a *p*-substrate, have a *pn* junction at the interface. If the

n-well is very shallow, the majority of electron-hole pairs are created in the p-substrate. Holes cannot traverse the reverse-biased pn junction, and it acts as a barrier to soft-error effects. Any electrons that do cross the junction are gathered at the V_{DD} node away from the storage cell. The probability that sufficient electron-hole pairs are generated within the n-well to produce a soft error is quite small. CMOS dynamic RAMs typically have soft error rates that are much lower than that of their NMOS counterparts.

3.6.2 Noise Margins

V_{oH} is defined as the minimum voltage that will appear at the output of a gate when the output is supposed to be at logic 1, and V_{oL} is defined as the maximum voltage that will appear at the output of a gate when the output is supposed to be at logic 0.

V_{iH} is the minimum input voltage that a gate will recognize as corresponding to a logic 1, and V_{iL} is the maximum input voltage that a gate will recognize as corresponding to a logic 0. The difference between V_{oH} and V_{iH} is defined as the noise margin for negative-going voltage excursions (NMH), while the difference between V_{iL} and V_{oL} is the noise margin for positive voltage spikes (NML). *Noise margins* are measures of a gate's susceptibility to spurious spikes. The larger the noise margin the more immune a gate is to extraneous voltage signals. In equation form:

$$\text{NMH} = V_{oH} - V_{iH} \quad \text{and} \quad \text{NML} = V_{iL} - V_{oL}$$

As physical size shrinks, the electrical separation of the power and ground rails, which is the maximum *logic swing*, must be reduced in order to keep electric fields to reasonable values. Small fluctuations in current and voltage (noise) set a lower limit to the minimum logic swing which can be reliably detected and transmitted.

Noise is related to the discrete nature of charge carriers and, in pn junctions, consists of thermal and shot noise. *Thermal noise* results from the random motion of electrons and holes in the bulk semiconductor regions, and *shot noise* results from the random injection of charge carriers across the depletion region. Thermal noise is proportional to the bulk resistance of the semiconductor material, and shot noise is inversely proportional to the injected current (5).

As VLSI device size shrinks and the density of devices on a chip continues to increase, wider and wider data buses are required. This results in an increase in the number of simultaneously switching driver circuits. Higher bus bandwidths also lead to current pulses of larger magnitude, which generate inductive power supply noise.

As noise margins shrink, the magnitude of the noise itself increases, and both exacerbate noise problems. Degraded signal levels lead to poor noise margins, and anything that reduces the voltage of a logic one or increases the voltage of a logic zero reduces noise margins.

Threshold voltage depends upon the substrate bias, as given in Eq. (2.17).

$$V_{TH} = V_{TH0} + \gamma \left[\sqrt{|-2\phi_f + V_{SB}|} - \sqrt{|-2\phi_f|} \right]$$

γ is proportional to the square root of the substrate doping. In order to make a well one must dope heavily. This increases γ, causing the transistor to have a high threshold voltage. This is a problem with the *p*-well process, where a pass-transistor might have a threshold voltage of 2 V rather than the 1 V designed, giving an output voltage of $V_{DD} - V_{TH} = 5 - 2 = 3$ V. If this signal is driving a CMOS inverter, the reduced value of V_{oH} reduces the value of NMH.

3.6.3   Lead Inductance

Eventually a point is reached where performance is limited by package inductances. Consider a clock that swings through 5 V in 1 ns, driving a capacitive load of 20 pF. The waveforms are shown in Fig. 3.5.

The clock transfers an average charge of $C\Delta V = (20 \text{ pF})(5 \text{ V}) = 100$ pC during this voltage excursion, and the average current is given by the time rate of change of the average charge, which is 100 mA. A triangular current pulse with this average value will have a peak current of 200 mA and a current rise rate, dI/dt, of 400 MA/s. Lead inductance must be kept very small to tolerate this current spike. For an inductance of 10 nH, the average induced voltage is $LdI/dt = (10 \times 10^{-9})(400 \times 10^6) = 4$ V, and the peak induced voltage is about twice this value. Improving the speed performance of the circuit by a factor of 2 will double the average induced voltage, making it greater than the supply voltage.

3.6.4   Gate Oxide Reliability

Electron beams are scattered in the forward direction as they pass through the resist, and backward when reflected from the silicon substrate. Some of the back-scattered electrons may collide with the walls of the vacuum chamber, giving rise to a very low level background radiation. Electron-beam radiation has been shown to introduce positive and neutral electron traps into SiO_2.

In most processing sequences, these traps can be removed by high-temperature anneals which have been intentionally introduced to eliminate them, or

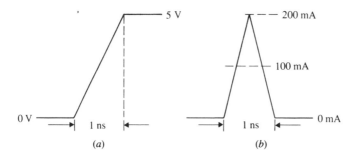

FIGURE 3.5
(*a*) Clock voltage swing, and (*b*) approximate current spike.

which automatically occur in the process. Because temperature limits may be imposed on post-metal anneals due to aluminum spiking, damage to the gate oxide caused by electron-beam lithography at the contact and interconnect metal level may still be present in the oxide following a low-temperature post-metal anneal.

Gate-oxide breakdown is one of the most important reliability problems in an MOS circuit due to its destructive nature. Gate-oxide breakdown voltage is a limiting factor in determining the minimum gate-oxide film thickness. To allow a safety factor, the maximum gate field applied across the oxide should be designed to be less than one-half the final oxide breakdown field, or

$$t_{\text{ox}} = \frac{BV_{\text{ox}}}{2E_{\text{MAX}}} = \frac{V_{DD}}{2E_{\text{MAX}}}$$

where E_{MAX} is the maximum electric field in the oxide material and BV_{ox} is the breakdown voltage of the gate oxide, which is assumed to be the maximum logic swing of V_{DD}. E_{MAX} is approximately 10^9 V/m or 1 kV/μm (6).

State-of-the-art oxide film thickness, t_{ox}, is between 200 and 700 angstroms (20 and 70 nm), giving a breakdown voltage between 20 and 70 V. Specifying a maximum allowable voltage of 10 V places no serious restriction on circuit behavior and gives a suitable safety margin for a 200-angstrom process. Input protection must be used to guarantee that this limit is not exceeded.

The input impedance of unprotected MOS devices is from 10^{14} to 10^{16} Ω, and may drop to about 10^{10} Ω when input protection is added. This is not of concern in most digital applications, and the protective circuit is designed to protect transistor gates from overvoltages (6).

3.6.5 Polysilicon Resistance

Polysilicon is the most common gate-electrode and interlayer connect material in use today in the manufacture of VLSI MOS devices. Polysilicon has many desirable properties including good etchability, good oxidation characteristics, mechanical stability at high temperatures, excellent step coverage, and adhesion. Its one major drawback is its relatively high resistance.

A typical heavily doped polysilicon layer 5000 angstroms thick will have a sheet resistance of 20 to 30 Ω/sq. For VSLI applications, polysilicon resistance is a major constraint in circuit design and performance. Large VLSI circuits require long lines and reduced geometries that require thinner lines, both of which cause unacceptably high RC time constants.

The need for a lower resistance material than polysilicon has resulted in the investigation of silicides and refractory metals for VLSI manufacturing. Refractory metals have lower bulk resistance, but poor oxidation characteristics and poor postanneal adhesion. These factors have limited their acceptance.

Silicides have higher bulk resistivities than refractory metals but have advantageous properties that are compatible with IC wafer processing. Silicides have demonstrated stability over the range of IC wafer processing temperatures,

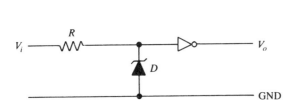

FIGURE 3.6
NMOS input overvoltage protection
circuitry.

good adhesion, good chemical resistance, and good dry etching characteristics. The major drawback has been the deposition technique, which causes processing difficulties (7).

Local oxidation, etching, and deposition processes create two-dimensional structures. Many two-dimensional properties, such as lateral diffusion, undercutting during etching and bird's beaks of local oxidation, do not scale proportionally with device size. Two-dimensional process simulation is increasingly important as device dimensions continue to shrink.

In addition to the well-known advantages of self-aligned silicon-gate MOSFET technology for achieving greater density and superior performance, the enhanced resistance to "wear-out" of an oxide layer further strengthens the case for employing silicon-gate technology to scaled-down devices.

3.6.6 Input Protection

FET transistors are required to interface with input pads, and *overvoltage protection* must be included whenever input signals are external to the chip. NMOS input-protection circuitry can be accomplished with a Zener diode that clamps positive input excursions to safe values and clamps negative excursions to one diode drop below ground. A current-limiting resistance is usually required to protect the diode from surges. The circuit is shown in Fig. 3.6.

For CMOS circuits, input protection is usually furnished by two diodes as shown in Fig. 3.7, which are inherent to the input buffer. One diode is taken from the pad-connect diffusion to the n-type substrate, which is connected to V_{DD}. The other diode is formed by the pad-connect diffusion to the p-well, which is connected to ground. The diodes limit voltage swings to within one diode drop of each power rail. As before, the input protection diodes are usually connected to the pad through a current-limiting resistor, R.

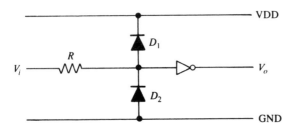

FIGURE 3.7
CMOS input overvoltage protection
circuitry.

Another common input protection structure consists of a length of n^+ active area terminated in the drain of an enhancement-mode device, with its source and gate connected to ground. The n^+ line has a current-limiting resistance of about 1 to 3 kΩ. The structure is a distributed RC transmission line, which acts as a low-pass filter to input spikes, while clamping the input to no lower than a diode drop below GND. An upper limit on the resistance size is set by the cutoff frequency of the filter, which must not adversely restrict the bandwidth of the input signal.

The enhancement-mode transistor clamps the internal voltage to no lower than a threshold voltage below GND, and also limits the positive voltage excursion to the avalanche breakdown voltage of the pn junction. The grounded gate of the FET reduces the breakdown voltage to a suitable value. Breakdown occurs near the surface of the wafer, and the transistor must be wide so it can dissipate the breakdown energy.

Some signals with large capacitance, such as clock lines, might require the protective resistance to be left out. When this happens, the enhancement-mode device must have a channel width of at least 200 microns.

Another input-protection strategy is to use two parasitic bipolar transistors for clamping the output of the pad. The structure is shown in Fig. 3.8, where it can be seen that the n^+ region in the epitaxial layer creates the emitter of a lateral

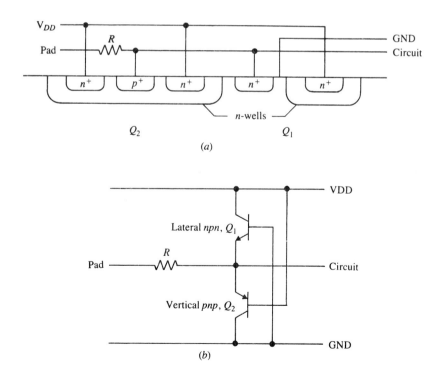

FIGURE 3.8
CMOS input protection with BJTs. (*a*) Cross-sectional view of BJTs; (*b*) equivalent circuit.

npn device, Q_1, while the p^+ diffusion in the *n*-well produces a vertical *pnp* transistor, Q_2. The base of Q_1 is the epitaxial or substrate layer, and the collector is the well-guard circuitry.

This protection circuitry reduces the input resistance to the neighborhood of 10^{10} Ω, which is not of concern in most digital applications. Output protection is usually provided by the pad drivers, which typically have channel widths of 500 microns or more.

3.7 SUBSTRATE PUMPING

Sometimes it is advantageous to have voltages lower than GND potential. A negative voltage, V_{BB}, reduces the sensitivity of threshold voltage to the back-gate bias. It reduces source and drain capacitances without decreasing the substrate doping, and decreases subthreshold leakage of clocked depletion transistors. It also protects the chip against forward-biasing of the substrate due to voltage undershoots at the inputs, which is a frequent problem when the input pads are driven by TTL gates.

The substrate forms a huge capacitance, and pumping electrons from the GND pad into the substrate lowers its voltage. The pump usually consists of an oscillating signal, amplified by a driving buffer, which drives a coupling capacitor that transfers energy to two diodes connected from the substrate to GND. The circuit is shown in Fig. 3.9. The diodes gate charge from the substrate to the ground connection.

When the pump voltage is near its positive peak diode D_1 is blocking, diode D_2 is forward biased, and charge is pumped into the GND pin. When the pump voltage is near its negative peak D_2 is blocking while D_1 conducts charge from the substrate to the coupling capacitor. A ring oscillator composed of 5 or 7 inverters, and having a frequency of about 10 MHz, can be used to drive the pump.

The theoretical minimum value of V_{BB} is determined by the peak-to-peak value of the pump voltage. During the positive half of the oscillator cycle, the pump voltage must be one diode drop above ground in order to pump charge. On the negative half cycle, the pump voltage must be one diode drop below V_{BB} to do work. If the peak-to-peak voltage of the pump is V_{DD}, then ideally, V_{BB} is equal to $-V_{DD}$ plus two diode drops. For $V_{DD} = 5$ V, V_{BB} is approximately -3.6 V. Since the substrate is a leaky capacitor, the actual value of V_{BB} is higher than -3.6 V. For a thorough discussion of *substrate pumping*, see Glasser and Dobberpuhl (8).

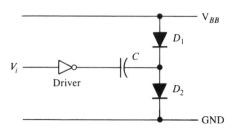

FIGURE 3.9
A simple substrate pump.

3.8 SUMMARY

The silicon NMOS process is examined in detail. Process limitations and design errors are investigated. Noise margins are defined, oxide reliability is investigated, soft errors are defined and discussed, and lead inductance is investigated. Input protection and substrate pumping are also discussed.

For a carrier to be injected into the gate dielectric, it must be energetic or "hot," since increased carrier energy results in a greater probability of surmounting the energy barrier at the silicon channel and tunneling into the dielectric. Once in the dielectric, the carrier will either travel to the gate electrode and contribute to a gate leakage current, or it will be trapped, depending upon the trapping efficiency of the oxide and the value of the gate bias.

The intensity of the electric field is greater for heavily doped substrates due to their narrower depletion-region widths. Some of the electrons heated by the high electric field generate electron-hole pairs by impact ionization. Most of the generated electrons move to the drain region, but a small fraction attain sufficient energy to surmount the energy barrier at the Si-SiO$_2$ interface, and are emitted into the gate oxide. Those electrons that are trapped in the gate oxide cause a shift in threshold voltage, whereas the generated holes are collected as substrate current and can forward-bias the source junction, causing drain-source breakdown.

When V_{GS} is less than V_{DS} the polarity of the electric field in the gate oxide near the drain junction is reversed and the emitted electrons tend to be returned to the silicon substrate, but when V_{GS} is larger than V_{DS} the electrons emitted into the oxide are attracted to the gate electrode and produce a gate current. The electron trapping occurs at the drain end of the oxide insulation and the threshold voltage shift is greatest at this end.

When $V_{GS} = V_{DS}$, the vertical electric field vanishes at the drain, and electron emission for a fixed drain voltage is maximum. Further increase in gate bias increases channel conductance, reduces the peak field in the channel, and reduces emission into the gate oxide.

Shottky barrier diodes are formed by the deposition of a metal such as TiW, which is alloyed with lightly doped silicon. This forms a silicide, and prevents aluminum spiking in shallow junctions. The same metal is also used for ohmic contacts to heavily doped regions. In this case too thin a film results in aluminum penetrating into the silicide and causing the diode characteristics to change, or aluminum spikes penetrating through shallow junctions and causing short circuits.

SOS devices have a speed advantage over bulk MOS devices due to reduced junction capacitance and elimination of interconnect-substrate capacitance. Guard rings, isolation-well diffusions, and well contacts are not needed either. The result is increased packing density, less masking steps, and increased layout design flexibility. Short channel length and narrow channel width effects are also less important in SOS. There is less hot-electron injection into the oxide layer, higher tolerance to transient ionizing radiation and cosmic rays, and freedom from latch-up. SOS is more expensive than bulk silicon, and electron and hole mobilities are less in SOS than in bulk silicon technology.

REFERENCES

1. G. E. Moore, "Are We Ready for VLSI?" Proc. CalTech Conference on VLSI, January, 1979, pp. 3–14.
2. C. A. Mead and L. A. Conway, *Introduction to VLSI Systems*, Addison-Wesley, Reading, Mass., 1980.
3. Stanford University Conference on "Computer-Aided Design of IC Fabrication Processes," Stanford, Calif., August, 1987.
4. T. H. Ning, P. W. Cook, R. H. Dennard, C. M. Osburn, S E. Schuster, and H. N. Yu, "1 μm MOSFET VLSI Technology: Part IV Hot-Electron Design Constraints," *IEEE Transactions on Electron Devices*, vol. ED-26, 1979, pp. 346–353.
5. A. Van der Ziel, *Noise in Measurements*, John Wiley & Sons, New York, N.Y., 1976.
6. J. Mavor, M. A. Jack, and P. B. Denyer, *Introduction to MOS LSI Design*, Addison-Wesley Publishing Company, London, 1983, pp. 159–160.
7. F. Mohammadi, "Silicide for Interconnecting Technology," *Solid State Technology*, vol. 24, no. 1, 1981, pp. 65–72.
8. L. A. Glasser and D. W. Dobberpuhl, *The Design and Analysis of VLSI Circuits*, Addison-Wesley Publishing Co., Reading, Mass., 1985, pp. 301–308.

PROBLEMS

The following inverting circuits are to be simulated with SPICE to obtain the voltage-transfer curves, from which to determine V_{oH}, V_{oL}, V_{iH}, V_{iL}, and the noise margins of the inverters. These terms are defined in Sec. 3.6.2. V_{inv} is the value of voltage for which $V_{in} = V_{out}$ and is also obtained from the voltage-transfer curve.

The input signal is a dc voltage which sweeps from 0 to 5 V, incrementing in steps of 0.1 V. The SPICE circuit is shown in Fig. 2.10, and the parameters needed are:

$k' = KP = 69$ μA/V^2 for NMOS devices and 34.5 μA/V^2 for PMOS devices. The source and drain regions are 6 μm by 6 μm, $t_{ox} = $ TOX $= 0.04$ μm, GAMMA $= 0.37$ V$^{1/2}$, $R_d = $ RD $= 1$ Ω, and $R_s = $ RS $= 1$ Ω. $C_{bd} = $ CBD $= 2$ fF, $C_{bs} = $ CBS $= 2$ fF, $C_j = $ CJ $= 200$ μF/m^2, $C_{gbo} = $ CGB0 $= 200$ pF/m, $C_{gso} = $ CGS0 $= 40$ pF/m, and $C_{gdo} = $ CGD0 $= 40$ pF/m. For NMOS enhancement-mode transistors, $V_{THE} = $ VT0 $= 1$ V, for NMOS depletion-mode devices, $V_{THD} = $ VT0 $= -3$ V, and for PMOS enhancement-mode devices, $V_{THP} = $ VT0 $= -1$ V.

3.1 The NMOS inverter consists of an NMOS enhancement-mode pull-up device, Q_1, with $L = 6$ μm and $W = 3$ μm, an NMOS enhancement-mode pull-down device, Q_2, with $L = 3$ μm and $W = 6$ μm as shown in Fig. P3.1.

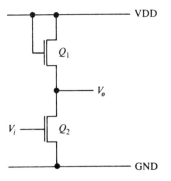

FIGURE P3.1
NMOS inverter with enhancement pull-up.

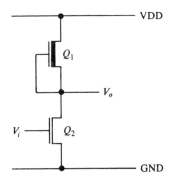

FIGURE P3.2
NMOS inverter with depletion pull-up.

3.2 The NMOS inverter consists of an NMOS depletion-mode pull-up device, Q_1, with $L = 6$ μm and $W = 3$ μm, an NMOS enhancement-mode pull-down device, Q_2, with $L = 3$ μm and $W = 6$ μm as shown in Fig. P3.2.

3.3 The conventional CMOS inverter consists of a PMOS enhancement-mode pull-up transistor, Q_1, with $L = W = 3$ μm, an NMOS enhancement-mode pull-down device, ϕ_2, with $L = W = 3$ μm as shown in Fig. P3.3.

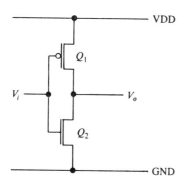 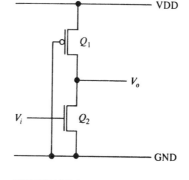

FIGURE P3.3
CMOS inverter.

FIGURE P3.4
A pseudo-NMOS inverter.

3.4 The pseudo-NMOS CMOS inverter consists of a PMOS enhancement-mode pull-up transistor, Q_1, with $L = 9$ μm, $W = 3$ μm, an NMOS enhancement-mode pull-down device, Q_2, with $L = W = 3$ μm as shown in Fig. P3.4.

DESIGN PROBLEM

3.5. Become familiar with Magic Tutorial 4: Cell Hierarchies.

CHAPTER
4

DESIGN
RULES
AND
LAYOUTS

4.1 INTRODUCTION

Following the Mead-Conway approach, minimum design rules which are pro-cess-independent and scalable will be derived. Due to the complexity of modern VLSI circuitry, designing for testability is mandatory. This requires designs which allow for controllability and testability of critical nodes.

Design rules need to be established when a new process is being created or when a process is upgraded from one generation to the next. The establishment of new design rules is normally a joint effort by circuit design engineers and process engineers. Circuit designers want smaller and tighter design rules which improve performance and decrease chip area, while process engineers want design rules that lead to controllable and reproducible fabrication. The result must be a compromise that yields a suitably competitive circuit designed and built for a reasonable cost.

In creating a new process, it is often desirable to simplify the design rules in order to reduce the time required to design a layout. Such simplification generally leads to inefficient use of chip area, and a satisfactory compromise between performance and cost must again be reached. A mature process has capabilities which the design engineer can rely on, whereas a new process will initially require more conservative design rules due to uncertainties in process capabilities and limitations.

Design rules are often dependent upon both process equipment and process design. For example, level-to-level registration can be smaller if a 10-to-1 wafer stepper is used instead of a 1-to-1 projection mask aligner. This is a process equipment decision, whereas field-oxide encroachment (bird's beak) is affected by the field oxide thickness, which is a process design parameter.

Design rules can never be met exactly at the wafer level because the physical nature of semiconductor processing causes statistical variations in all process parameters. The use of parameter limits that reflect all possible process variations would ensure proper device functioning under almost all conditions. Parameter limits that cover six standard deviations ($\pm 3\sigma$), ensure that 99.7 percent of the devices meet specifications, but device performance as well as chip area suffer from too conservative a design. On the other hand, parameters that cover only two standard deviations ($\pm 1\sigma$), result in a 68.3 percent satisfactory yield. This is a high yield loss, and may be unacceptable.

A range of four standard deviations ($\pm 2\sigma$) is probably a suitable compromise, and results in a 95.5 percent satisfactory yield with reasonable area utilization and device performance. The difficulty lies in determining what constitutes $\pm 2\sigma$ limits. One can tighten the design rules after the process becomes established, the design rules have been verified, and σ has been both determined and minimized to a reasonable extent.

Processes evolve and design rules must be chosen such that a transition from one generation of processing to the next is easily accomplished. Minimum geometries generally shrink from 20 to 40 percent in making a transition from one process generation to the next, and design rules should be determined in such a manner that they can adapt to a change of this size, while still providing a manufacturable device design.

4.2 THE PURPOSE OF DESIGN RULES

Design rules are supposed to prevent unworkable, unreliable, or hard-to-implement constructs. More specifically, layout rules are introduced to preserve the integrity of topological features on the chip: to prevent separate, isolated features from accidentally short circuiting, or thin features from opening, or contacts from slipping outside the area to be contacted.

The goal is to devise design rules which are simple, constant in time, applicable to many processes, standardized among many institutions, and which have a small number of exceptions for specific processes. To do this one must investigate the basic ideas behind design rules, the *meta design rules* which are the rules that generate design rules. There is one fundamental meta design rule that can be stated as follows:

> Under worst-case misalignment and maximum
> edge movement of any feature,
> no serious performance degradation should occur!

Unfortunately, this is too general a rule, and not much help unless one knows the process intimately. Therefore, the Mead-Conway approach is to characterize the process with a single scalable parameter called *lambda*, that is process-dependent and is defined as the maximum distance by which a geometrical feature on any one layer can stray from another feature, due to overetching, misalignment, distortion, over- or underexposure, etc., with a suitable safety factor included. Lambda is thus equal to the maximum misalignment of a feature from its intended position on the wafer, and two features on different mask layers can be misaligned by a maximum of 2 lambda on the wafer.

The purpose in defining lambda properly is to make the design itself independent of both process and fabrication house, and to allow the design to be rescaled at a future date when the fabrication tolerances are shrunk. Lyon (1) has specified the two meta design rules as follows:

> Two features on different mask layers can be misaligned by
> a maximum of two lambda on the wafer.
> If the overlap of these two different mask layers can be catastrophic
> to the design they must be separated by at least two lambda!
> If the overlap is just undesirable
> they must be separated by at least one lambda!

Among the many advantages of generalized design rules are:

1. Ease of learning because they are scalable, portable, and durable.
2. Longevity of designs that are simple, abstract, and have minimum clutter.
3. Increased designer efficiency due to fewer levels and fewer rules.
4. Design efficiency accomplished by compaction, layout-rule checking, electrical-rule checking, simulation, and verification.
5. Automatic translation to final layout.

The conceptual feature levels for all silicon-gate processes consist of the areas, *A*, labeled as in Table 4.1.

The generation of mask levels for an *n*-well CMOS process, where **M** means mask and **A** means area, consists of the set shown in Table 4.2.

Associated with any process is a *standard deviation*, defined in the usual manner as the square root of the sum of the squares of the deviations of the measured parameter divided by the number of measurements taken.

There is some standard deviation in line width, σ_w. Lines that are too small tend to disappear and lines too close together sometimes merge. There is also some standard deviation in interlayer registration, σ_i.

TABLE 4.1

ANWL, APWL	n-type or p-type well area in the bulk, or type of island doping in CMOS or SOS
ACAP	Capacitor bottom electrode areas
AND, APD	n^+ or p^+ source/drain areas
AIIN, AIIP	n-type or p-type ion implant areas
AII2, AII3, ...	Additional implant level areas
ASI, ASI2, ...	Polysilicon electrode implant areas
AME, AME2, ...	Metal interconnect areas
ACC	Contact-cut areas
ABC	Buried-contact areas
AOC	Overglass cut areas

TABLE 4.2

	Mask	Area	
MNWL	Well definition	ANWL	Shrunk for outdiffusion
MPCA	p^+ capacitor plates	ACAP	
MAAN	NMOS active areas	AND $\cup$ ANWL	
MAAP	PMOS active areas	APD $\cup$ APWL	
MSIN	NMOS polysi gates	ASI $\cup$ (ANWL $\cap$ AN$\overline{\text{D}}$)	
MSIP	PMOS polysi gates	ASI $\cup$ (APWL $\cap$ AP$\overline{\text{D}}$)	
MCC	Contact cuts	ACC	
MME	Metallization	AME	
MBC	Buried-contact mask	ABC	
MOC	Overglass cuts	AOC	

The above two deviations are typically of the same order of magnitude. It is not economically useful to make one much smaller than the other, and they are being shrunk together as geometries get smaller.

Normally there is a minimum line width and line separation for a given fabrication line. This is an empirical value, and if one goes below it, failure rates go up. Define lambda as the halfwidth of the minimum lines. One can think of lambda as either some multiple of the standard deviation of the process or as the resolution of the process.

4.3 NMOS DESIGN RULES

Following are the Mead-Conway Scalable NMOS Process Rules as specified by MOSIS in November 1984. The rules are given in units of lambda. For further clarification and color diagrams illustrating the design rules, the reader is referred to the MOSIS User's Manual (2,3). For a two-metal NMOS process, see the design rules for metal 1, metal 2, and vias listed in the CMOS design rules.

The MOSIS NMOS design rules

N$^+$ diffusion mask

Diffusion width 2λ (due to the standard deviation of the line widths, σ_w).

Diffusion spacing 3λ (to keep depletion regions from short circuiting. 2λ if channel stop is used).

Implant mask

Implant gate overlap 1.5λ (to avoid an enhancement FET around the depletion FET.) MOSIS recommends using 2λ.

Implant to enhancement gate spacing 1.5λ (to avoid short circuiting gates).

Buried contact mask

Buried contact to active device 2λ (to avoid short circuits).

Overlap in diffusion direction 2λ (to ensure contact).

Overlap in poly or field direction 1λ (to ensure contact).

Buried contact to unrelated poly or diffusion spacing 2λ (to avoid short circuits due to fluctuations in spacing).

Buried-contact poly to unrelated poly spacing 2λ (to avoid short circuits due to fluctuations in spacing).

Poly mask

Poly width 2λ (due to the standard deviation of the line width, σ_w).

Poly spacing 2λ (to avoid short circuiting due to fluctuations in line widths).

Poly-diffusion spacing 1λ (to avoid overlap capacitance).

Poly gate extension beyond diffusion 2λ (to avoid shorting the source and drain around the gate).

Diffusion to poly edge 2λ (to ensure source and drain regions on the appropriate sides of the channel).

Contact mask

Contact size $2\lambda \times 2\lambda$ (to ensure good contact).

Contact-diffusion overlap 1λ (to ensure good contact).

Contact-poly overlap 1λ (to ensure good contact).

Contact to contact space 2λ (to avoid short circuiting contacts).

Contact to FET channel 2λ (to avoid short circuiting gates).

Contact-metal overlap 1λ (to ensure good contact).

Metal mask

Metal width 3λ (metal runs over roughest terrain).

Metal spacing 3λ (metal runs over roughest terrain).

Maximum current density 1 mA/μm (to avoid metal migration).

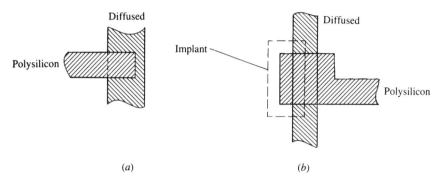

FIGURE 4.1
Fatal errors. (*a*) Short-circuited channel; (*b*) EMD in parallel with a DMD.

Design rules must protect against fatal errors such as a short circuited channel due to misregistration of poly and diffusion, or the formation of an enhancement-mode FET in parallel with a depletion-mode device, due to misregistration of the ion-implant area and the source/drain diffusion as shown in Fig. 4.1.

Errors can be noncatastrophic also. Two examples of nonfatal registration errors are shown in Fig. 4.2. Contact resistance will be increased at both contact sites, but the circuit can still function.

Photoresist is applied to a wafer following metal deposition, and the wafer is spun to obtain a thin resist film. The photoresist will be thicker over contact cuts, since they are depressions on the wafer surface. This causes the PR to be underetched at the contact, and the protected metal area to be larger than anticipated, as shown in Fig. 4.3.

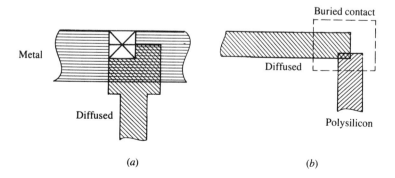

FIGURE 4.2
Nonfatal misregistration errors. (*a*) Metal/diffused/contact-cut; (*b*) poly/diffused buried contact.

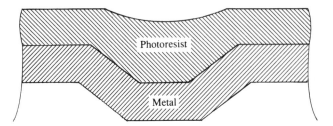

FIGURE 4.3
PR is thicker at contact cuts.

Scribe lines and bonding pads do not scale down with improved processing. Reasonable rules for pads and scribe lines are given below.

Bonding pad size 100 μm × 100 μm (a large wire must be bonded to it).

Probe pad size 75 μm × 75 μm (to avoid probe damage to adjacent circuitry).

Overglass mask

Bonding pad overglass cut 90 μm × 90 μm (to protect pad edges).

Probe pad overglass cut 65 μm × 65 μm (to protect pad edges).

Scribe line width 100 μm (a diamond stylus must score it).

Feature distance from scribe line 50 μm (to avoid circuit damage when scribing).

Feature distance from bonding pad 40 μm (to avoid damage when bonding).

Bonding pad separation 80 μm (to avoid short circuiting adjacent bonding wires).

Bonding pad pitch 180 μm (determined by size and separation).

4.4 CMOS DESIGN RULES

It is desirable to postpone the decision to fabricate in an *n*-well, *p*-well or twin-tub process, and design rules should assist the designer in this respect. One can design a single-well layout without regard to which type device is built in a well, but the well cannot then be used as an electrical node, since it is not known at the time of design whether any particular region is an isolated well or a common substrate. The use of a well as an electrical node is important in input protection. See Sec. 3.6.6.

One approach is to work with two abstract transistor types, those in a well and those in the substrate. Then the drawn features represent real mask levels, and the design can be converted from one process to the other by reversing the polarities of all external power supplies and interface signals. Chips made by both processes will not be plug compatible due to the polarity difference, but this is seldom an issue in prototype design.

Portable design rules have been introduced for bulk CMOS, but the extension of the Mead-Conway NMOS dimensionless design rules to bulk

CMOS is not a simple matter of adding several more masks. The problem is exacerbated by the varieties of CMOS technologies, and the various parasitic effects associated with them (4,5).

Design rules that are dependent upon electrical performance may not scale uniformly, and may not scale with lambda at all. Those rules that do scale are often incompatible with lithographic rules. In bulk CMOS design, the spacing between the p^+ regions and the p-wells should be a function of latchup susceptibility, which is strongly nonlinear, regardless of what CMOS technology is chosen. (Latchup is discussed in Sec. 7.3.) Scaling the above spacing by a linear reduction factor, lambda, will not guarantee a design free of latchup.

A p-transistor's channel must be surrounded by 2λ of p^+ implantation, similar to the ion implantation for depletion NMOS. An n-channel transistor, within a p-well, must maintain at least 2λ between its gate and a neighboring p^+ region.

There must be a minimum spacing between p^+ and p-well regions also. This rule has no electrical significance and is due to the fact that no photoresist should be allowed to have less than 2λ width on the wafer or it will register as a lithographic error.

The MOSIS Scalable CMOS Design Rules for two metal layers and either n-well, p-well, or twin-tub, will be used in this text for design layouts, and will be discussed in more detail below (6). Instructions are included with the MOSIS rules, and must be understood before doing a CMOS layout. As with the NMOS design rules, the CMOS rules are given in multiples of lambda.

The MOSIS portable CMOS design rules

n-well and p-well mask
n-well or p-well width 6λ (p- and n-wells must not overlap but they may be coincident).
n-well or p-well space 6λ if they are at the same potential. 9λ if they are at different potentials.

n^+ or p^+ active (diffusion or implant) mask
Active width 3λ
Active to active spacing 3λ
Source/drain active to well edge 6λ
Substrate/well contact, active to well edge 3λ

Poly mask
Poly width 2λ
Poly spacing 2λ
Gate overlap of active 2λ
Active overlap of gate 2λ
Field poly to active 1λ

(Continued)

The MOSIS portable CMOS design rules (*continued*)

---

p-select, *n*-select mask

(If both *p*-select and *n*-select are submitted, they may touch, but must not overlap.)

Select-space (overlap) to (of) channel 3λ

Select-space (overlap) to (of) active 2λ

Select-space (overlap) to (of) contact to well or substrate 1λ

Simpler contact to poly mask

Contact size $2\lambda \times 2\lambda$

Active overlap of contact 2λ

Contact-to-contact spacing 2λ

Contact-to-gate spacing 2λ

Denser contact to poly mask

Contact size $2\lambda \times 2\lambda$ (associating contacts with poly or active allows MOSIS to independently bloat the layer and the layer overlap of the contact).

Poly overlap of contact 1λ

Contact spacing on same poly 2λ

Contact spacing on different poly 5λ

Contact to noncontact poly 4λ

Space to active short run 2λ

Space to active long run 3λ

Simpler contact to active mask

Contact size $2\lambda \times 2\lambda$

Active overlap of contact 2λ

Contact/contact spacing 2λ

Contact/gate spacing 2λ

Denser contact to active mask

Contact size $2\lambda \times 2\lambda$

Active overlap of contact 1λ

Contact/contact spacing on same active 2λ

Contact/contact spacing to different active 6λ

Contact to different active 5λ

Contact to gate spacing 2λ

Contact to field poly, short run 2λ

Contact to field poly, long run 3λ

Metal 1 mask

Width 3λ

Metal 1 to metal 1 3λ

Overlap of contact to poly 1λ

Overlap of contact to active 1λ (*Continued*)

The MOSIS portable CMOS design rules (*continued*)

Via mask

Size $2\lambda \times 2\lambda$ (via must be on a flat surface and not stacked over a contact).
Via-to-via separation 2λ
Metal 1/via overlap 1λ
Space to poly or active edge 2λ
Via to contact spacing 2λ

Metal 2 mask

Width 3λ
Metal 2/Metal 2 spacing 4λ
Metal overlap of via 1λ

Overglass mask

Bonding pad 100 μm $\times$ 100 μm (there must be metal 2 under a glass cut).
Probe pad 75 μm $\times$ 75 μm
Pad to glass edge 6 μm

When designing, one can assume that both *n*-wells and *p*-wells exist. To ensure correct electrical connections and to minimize latchup, the minimum number of plugs needed is 1 in each well containing active transistors, and 1 per every 10 minimum geometry transistors. (40 λ^2 of area.) 1 in each 2 by 1 rectangle that contains 10 minimum size transistors. (40 λ^2 of area.)

4.5   MOS INVERTERS

MOS inverters all use an enhancement-mode device (EMD) as a switching transistor to pull the output low, because it can be switched off when the input signal to its gate is low. In the off mode it draws negligible current from supply.

The pull-up can be a simple resistor, an EMD operating as a current source with its gate connected to the positive supply, a depletion-mode device (DMD) operating as a current source with its gate short circuited to its source, or a PMOS EMD acting as a pull-up switch. Switching-circuit equivalents of the three MOS inverter types are shown in Fig. 4.4, and are discussed in detail below.

4.5.1   The Passive-Load NMOS Inverter

The simple NMOS inverter consists of an inverting FET and a pull-up resistor, as shown in Fig. 4.5. The physical layout of an NMOS inverter with a minimum-geometry pull-down FET and a resistive pull-up is shown in Fig. 4.6. A *minimum-geometry* FET has the smallest gate area possible, consistent with the available technology, $2\lambda \times 2\lambda$.

The major problem with this inverter is the physically large pull-up resistor

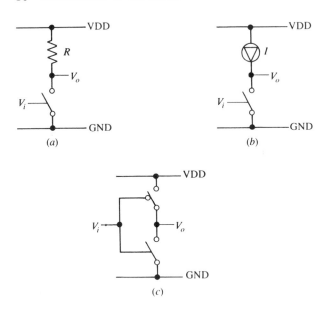

FIGURE 4.4
Switching-circuit equivalents of MOS inverters, with (a) a resistive load, (b) a saturated EMD or DMD load, and (c) a PMOS active-low pull-up switch.

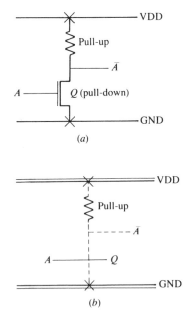

FIGURE 4.5
The passive-load NMOS inverter. (a) Circuit diagram; (b) stick drawing.

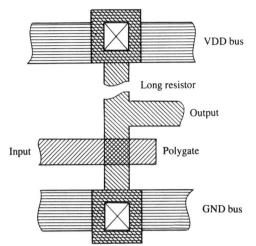

VDD bus

Long resistor

Output

Input   Polygate

GND bus   **FIGURE 4.6**
Layout of NMOS inverter with passive pull up.

required. For a typical process, the on resistance of the FET (the resistance from the source to the drain of the FET when the gate voltage is high) might be in the neighborhood of 10 kΩ, and the *sheet resistance* (resistance of a square area) of the diffusion layer might be about 20 Ω/sq.

The load or pull-up resistance must be much larger than the on resistance or pull-down resistance of the FET in order for the output voltage to go low when the pull-down transistor is conducting. If the pull-up resistor is to be at least ten times larger than the on resistance of the pull-down FET, then the value of the load resistance must be 100 kΩ, which requires a diffused pull-up resistor of 5000 squares length. This is unacceptably large.

The width of the pull-down transistor can be increased to give an *aspect ratio* (length-to-width ratio of the gate) of $L/W = 0.1$ for the gate of the pull-down. This device would require a pull-up resistor only 500 squares in size, but the overall gate area is still unacceptably large.

The aspect ratio is specified by the symbol Z and is often shown with the transistor symbol in stick drawings, although sometimes the reciprocal of the aspect ratio, $1/Z$, is given. It is usually clear from the numbers specified whether Z or $1/Z$ is implied. If the design can be done with all devices of the same length, only the width need be specified on the drawing.

4.5.2 The Active-Load NMOS Inverter

A much smaller inverter can be designed with a FET used as the active load. The load can be an enhancement-mode device or a depletion-mode device. An *enhancement-mode FET* has no channel with zero gate-to-source voltage, and must have either a separate gate bias voltage or have its gate connected to its drain in order to be used as an active load.

A *depletion-mode device* has a conducting channel with zero gate bias, and will not turn off until sufficient reverse bias is applied to its gate. To be used as a load device, the gate is connected to the source. The earliest MOS inverters consisted of *p*-channel FETs (PMOS devices) with aluminum metal gates and used an enhancement-mode pull-up configuration with negative logic, as shown in Fig. 4.7. Hence the acronym MOS, short for Metal-Oxide-Semiconductor.

The metal gate has since been replaced by polycrystalline silicon for better process control of small devices and for better control of threshold voltage. The acronym MOS is really a residual anachronism, modern devices being more accurately described as *polysilicon-oxide-substrate* or *POS* devices.

Once feasible NMOS devices became available, they quickly replaced PMOS devices. Depletion-mode pull-ups have replaced enhancement-mode pull-ups due to their superior switching speed, as well as the fact that the threshold-voltage drop from gate to source required for enhancement-mode devices can only pull the output up to within a threshold voltage of the positive rail.

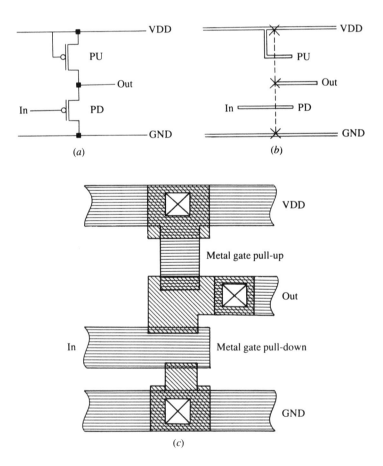

FIGURE 4.7
PMOS metal-gate inverter. (*a*) Circuit diagram; (*b*) stick drawing; (*c*) physical layout.

Enhancement-mode devices can be made to pull up to the positive rail, but this requires a separate gate bias which is greater than V_{DD} by at least one threshold voltage.

The major disadvantage of an NMOS load device is the fact that it never turns off and the inverter dissipates power whenever the pull-down device is on, just as the passive resistance inverter does. This is one of the major reasons for the popularity of CMOS design when power dissipation is a major concern.

The first type of active load investigated was the enhancement-mode pull-up shown in Figs. 4.7 and 4.8, with the gate tied to the positive rail to keep the device on until the output voltage reaches one threshold voltage below positive supply, at which point the pull-up switches off.

NMOS inverters today usually have depletion-mode load devices as shown in Fig. 4.9 due to their better speed and pull-up characteristics. This will be taken as the standard NMOS inverter, and NAND and NOR gates will be designed based upon this inverter. The depletion-mode inverter requires a separate ion-implant step to change the threshold voltage of the pull-up FET from enhancement to depletion type. This implant step is shown by a box around the pull-up device in the stick drawing and by dotted lines to outline the implant area on the layout drawing. On color drawings, yellow is the color of the implant region.

4.5.3 NMOS NAND and NOR Gates

The basic NMOS NAND gate with depletion-mode pull-up is shown in Fig. 4.10. The *inverter ratio*, R, is defined as the pull-up aspect ratio, Z_{pu}, divided by the pull-down aspect ratio, Z_{pd}. Inverter ratios determine the voltage-transfer curve of a gate, and will be discussed quantitatively in Chap. 5.

Assume for now that an inverter ratio of 4 to 1 is desired. For a 2-input NMOS NAND gate, there are two pull-down devices in series, and if they each have an aspect ratio of 1/2, the pull-up must have an aspect ratio of 4/1 in order to maintain an inverter ratio of 4/1, and the pull-up FET has to have an aspect ratio eight times that of either pull-down. In Fig. 4.10c, the pull-up ratio is taken to be 4/1, and each pull-down device has an aspect ratio of 1/2. A major disadvantage of NMOS NAND gates is that either the length of the load FET or the width of each pull-down device is proportional to the fan-in of the gate.

The basic NMOS NOR gate with depletion-mode pull-up is shown in Fig. 4.11. The NOR pull-up FET does not have to be increased in length as the fan-in is increased. In fact, if the aspect ratios of the load and pull-down devices are as shown in Fig. 4.11, the NOR gate works quite well for any fan-in, although the width of the NOR gate is proportional to the number of inputs. The worst-case inverter ratio occurs when only one input is high.

The power dissipation of the NMOS NAND gate is determined by the aspect ratio of the pull-up device. The maximum power dissipation of the NOR gate occurs when all the inputs are high and determines the minimum pull-up resistance. Speed also is a critical factor, and the rise time of the output voltage

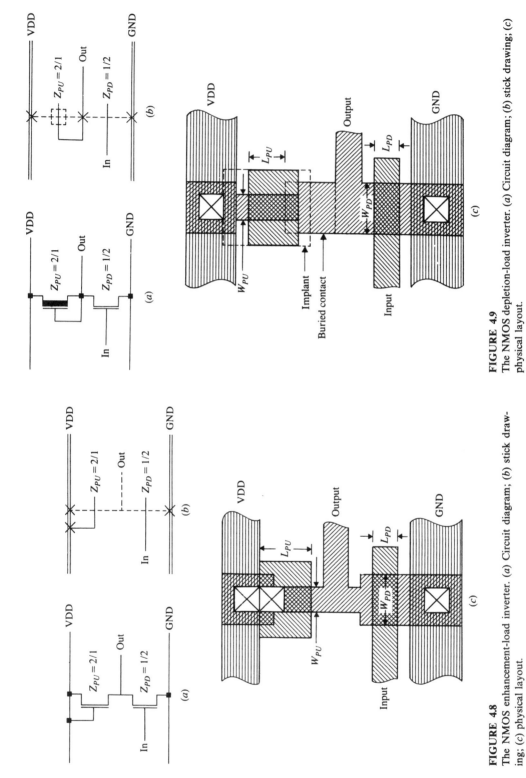

FIGURE 4.9

The NMOS depletion-load inverter. (a) Circuit diagram; (b) stick drawing; (c) physical layout.

FIGURE 4.8

The NMOS enhancement-load inverter. (a) Circuit diagram; (b) stick drawing; (c) physical layout.

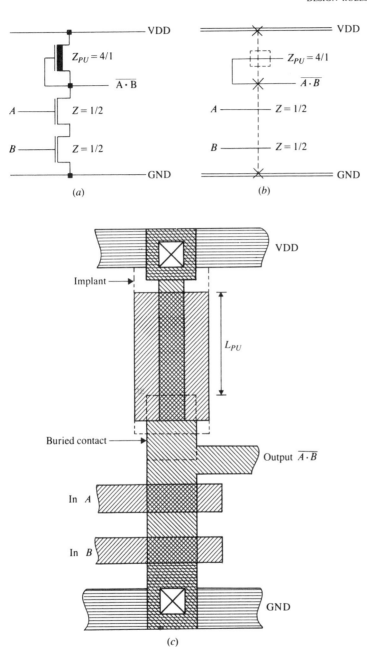

FIGURE 4.10
The NMOS 2-input NAND gate. (*a*) Circuit diagram; (*b*) stick drawing; (*c*) physical layout.

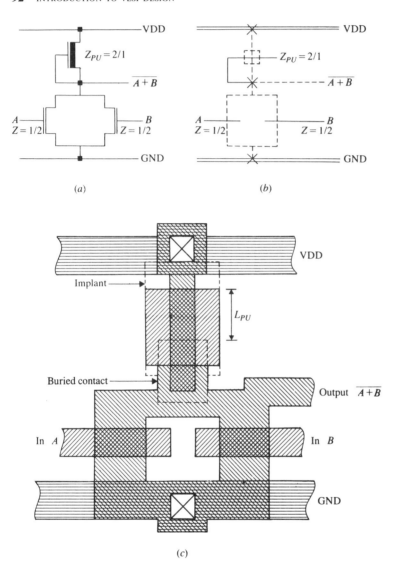

(a)

(b)

(c)

FIGURE 4.11
The NMOS 2-input NOR gate. (a) Circuit diagram; (b) stick drawing; (c) physical layout.

increases as the NAND gate pull-up aspect ratio increases. If the pull-down aspect ratios are fixed, the pull-up aspect ratio and the rise time of the NAND gate are proportional to the fan-in, whereas the NOR gate has both a fixed pull-up aspect ratio and a constant rise time. In general, NMOS NAND gates are much slower than NMOS NOR gates having the same fan-in and power dissipation.

4.6 THE CMOS PROCESS

PMOS transistors require an n-type substrate, while NMOS transistors require a p-type substrate. To be compatible with NMOS technology, which also requires a p-type substrate, one must diffuse or implant an n-type well (also called a *tub* or an *island*) in the original p-type substrate. This is referred to as an *n-well CMOS process*.

The p-channel devices are placed in the n-well, which is connected to the positive rail to keep the pn isolation junction reverse-biased at all times. The substrate is connected to the negative rail to keep its pn junction reverse-biased also. Reverse bias is required to maintain electrical isolation between NMOS and PMOS devices.

The *p-well CMOS process* starts with an n-type substrate for the PMOS devices, with NMOS devices placed in a p-type well. In this case, the substrate must be connected to the most positive potential and the well connected to the most negative potential to maintain isolation.

The *twin-tub CMOS process* incorporates both an n-well and a p-well diffused into a lightly doped substrate. The typical CMOS process requires, in addition to the basic NMOS steps, a masking and diffusion step or ion implant to do a deep n-type or p-type well diffusion, or both. Separate masks are also required for either source/drain diffusions or source/drain ion implants to create the n-channel and the p-channel devices.

4.6.1 The CMOS Inverter

The basic CMOS inverter, with its p-channel device in an n-type well and its n-channel device in the p-type substrate, is shown in Fig. 4.12, wells and well contacts omitted for clarity. See Plates 1 and 2 also. The CMOS inverter always has one transistor OFF, and since the OFF transistor has an extremely high impedance, the output voltage can swing from the positive to the negative voltage rail.

Statically speaking, the CMOS inverter has one transistor off when the other is conducting, and both the pull-up and the pull-down can have a minimum channel length and width as shown in Fig. 4.12. For dynamic reasons it may be desirable to increase the PMOS channel width to obtain equal rise and fall times. This will be discussed quantitatively in Sec. 5.5.1. A minimum size FET gate is 2λ wide by 2λ long.

4.6.2 CMOS NAND and NOR Gates

The CMOS NAND gate is shown in Fig. 4.13 and Plate 3a, and the CMOS NOR gate is shown in Fig. 4.14 and Plate 3b. Because the pull-down device does not oppose the pull-up device, the long pull-up necessary for NMOS NAND gates is not required, and a CMOS NAND gate is no larger than an equivalent CMOS NOR gate.

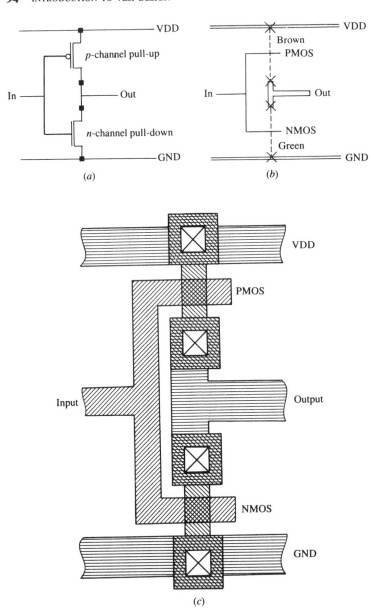

FIGURE 4.12
The CMOS inverter. (*a*) Circuit diagram; (*b*) stick drawing; (*c*) physical layout.

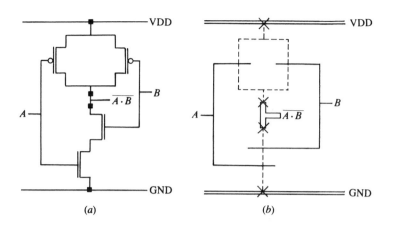

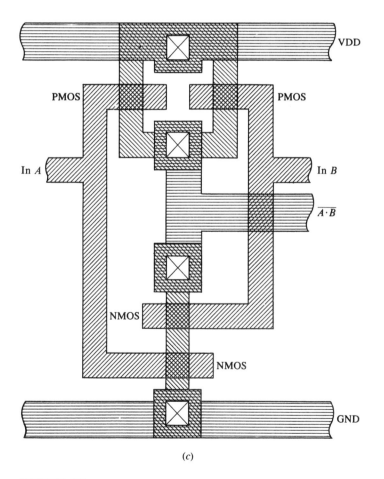

FIGURE 4.13
The CMOS 2-input NAND gate. (a) Circuit diagram; (b) stick drawing; (c) typical layout.

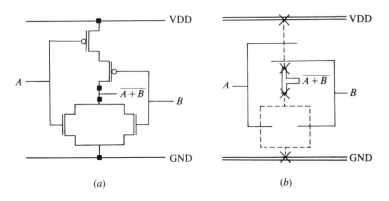

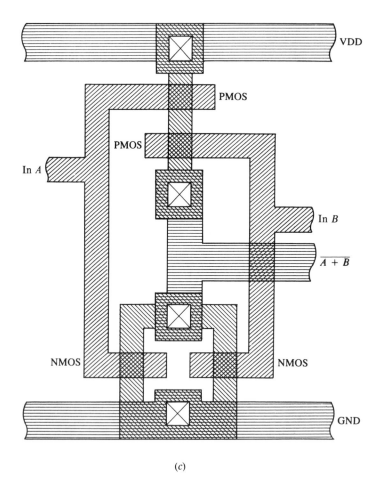

FIGURE 4.14
The CMOS 2-input NOR gate. (a) Circuit diagram; (b) stick drawing; (c) typical layout.

4.7 INTERLAYER CONTACTS

4.7.1 Conventional Contacts

Layers of metal, polysilicon, and diffused material are normally isolated by silicon dioxide. After the masks for a layout are designed a scheme for interconnecting appropriate layers is required, and masks are needed to define areas where the oxide is to be etched to produce the desired contacts.

Metal is normally connected to either polysilicon or diffusion by a contact cut. The minimum sized contact cut is 2λ by 2λ. A metal overlap of λ around all four sides of the oxide cut will ensure a good low-resistance contact.

Cuts called vias are used to make contact between two metal layers, and are typically 2λ by 2λ also. First-level metal is usually used to make contact to polysilicon or diffusion, and connections between second-level metal and poly or diffusion areas is normally done by connecting the second metal to the first layer, which in turn connects to the diffusion or polysilicon.

Process control is usually optimized for $2\lambda \times 2\lambda$ cuts and vias, and etching much larger areas is not feasible. Sometimes it is necessary to make low-resistance contacts. One should use several standard-sized contacts for this purpose instead of making one large contact. If large currents are involved, multiple contacts will result in a more uniform distribution of current also.

4.7.2 Butting and Buried Contacts

CMOS technology only requires standard metal-polysilicon or metal-diffusion contacts, and most CMOS processes only support metal contacts. In NMOS design it is sometimes advantageous to connect polysilicon to diffusion, and the two basic contacts used for this are referred to as the *butting contact* and the *buried contact*.

The butting contact is shown in Fig. 4.15. This is a simple contact to make, when connecting diffusion to polysilicon, but suffers from reliability problems, as it can easily short circuit the contacts to the substrate. It is smaller than two separate contacts and involves no extra masking steps, but it requires a metal cap.

Metallization is required only over the butting contact holes which are $2\lambda \times 4\lambda$ in size. A border of width λ around all four sides is added to allow for misregistration, and to ensure a proper contact, bringing the metallization size to $4\lambda \times 6\lambda$.

The buried contact is shown in Fig. 4.16. This contact is more reliable than the butting contact, and has the added advantage that no metal cap is needed. Thus, metal can cross over a buried contact, which can ease routing requirements considerably. The major disadvantages are that self-registration may be lost, and that an extra mask level is required.

It is simple enough to maintain self-registration with a buried contact with a slight penalty in extra area required. One does have the choice of outputting from the buried contact on either polysilicon or on diffusion, as shown in Figs. 4.17 and 4.18. The trick is simply to ensure that the buried contact occurs where

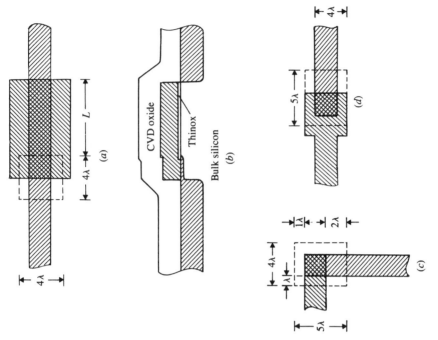

FIGURE 4.16

The buried contact. (a) Top view of the contact from gate to source; (b) cross-sectional view of the contact from gate to source; (c) a self-registered buried contact; (d) a non-self-registered buried contact.

FIGURE 4.15

The butting contact, showing a top view projected over a cross-sectional view.

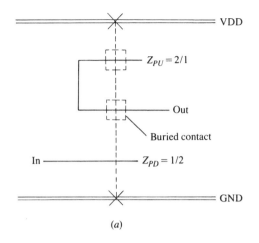

(a)

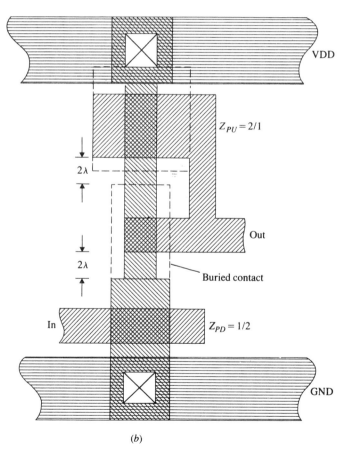

(b)

FIGURE 4.17
Self-registered buried contact with output on polysilicon. (a) Stick drawing; (b) layout.

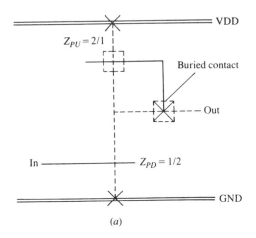

(a)

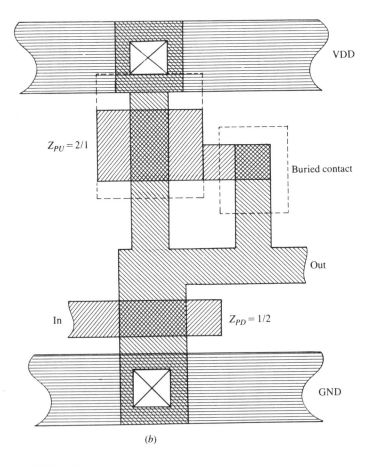

(b)

FIGURE 4.18
Self-registered buried contact with output on diffusion. (a) Stick drawing; (b) layout.

diffusion and polysilicon meet at right angles, with no edge defining a channel length (9).

4.8 SUMMARY

The purpose of design rules is to allow an engineer to lay out a VLSI circuit with reasonable assurance that it will work. The complexity of modern circuits forces one to design with testing in mind, otherwise adequate testing may be difficult, if not impossible, to accomplish.

The theory behind VLSI layout design rules is examined and a scale parameter, lambda, is defined as the half-width of a minimum-width line, or as a multiple of the standard deviation of a process. Designing layouts in terms of lambda allows for future scaling and makes the layout portable.

The Mead-Conway NMOS design rules, as updated by MOSIS, are examined and explained. The MOSIS portable CMOS design rules are given. These rules are applicable for lambdas of 3 microns down to 0.6 microns.

The complexity of modern VLSI design requires development of the necessary tools to communicate with computers at a much higher level than was previously necessary or even possible. Customized IC design can greatly enhance system functionality and significantly reduce the chip count for a given system. Effective design tools and proper techniques can ensure accomplishing the primary goal of obtaining a working chip in the shortest possible time.

Basic NMOS and PMOS transistor structures are discussed, and their physical layouts are given. A brief introduction to passive-load and both enhancement-mode and depletion-mode active-load NMOS inverters is given. Stick drawings and their relationship to physical layouts of NMOS inverters, NAND, and NOR gates are given.

The CMOS process and a brief comparison to NMOS design and mask requirements are covered. The CMOS inverter, NAND gate, and NOR gate are discussed, and example stick drawings and physical layouts are given.

General contacts of metal to either diffusion or polysilicon layers are discussed, as are butting contacts and buried contacts. Methods of maintaining registration lengths of FET channels when using buried contacts are given, along with layouts to implement them.

REFERENCES

1. R. F. Lyon. "Simplified Design Rules for VLSI Layouts," *Lambda*, 1st Quarter, 1981.
2. C. A. Mead and L. A. Conway, *Introduction to VLSI Systems*, Addison-Wesley, Reading, Mass., 1980.
3. "MOSIS Scalable NMOS Process, Version 1.0," USC Information Sciences Institute, USC, November, 1984.
4. T. W. Griswold, "Portable Design Rules for Bulk CMOS," *VLSI Design*, September/October 1982.
5. J. Y. Chen, "Scaling CMOS to Submicron Design Rules for VLSI," *VLSI Design*, July 1984, pp. 78–83.
6. "MOSIS Scalable & Generic CMOS Design Rules, Revision 6," USC Information Sciences Institute, USC, February 1988.

7. I. Sutherland and C. Mead, "Microelectronics and Computer Science," *Scientific American,*
September 1977.
8. B. Lattin, "VLSI Design Methodology, the Problem of the 80's for Microprocessor Design,"
Proceedings of the Caltech Conference on VLSI, Caltech, January, 1979, pp. 247–252.
9. J. Mavor, M. A. Jack, and P. B. Denyer, *Introduction to MOS LSI Design,* Addison-Wesley,
London, 1983. pp. 74–75.

PROBLEMS

4.1. Gate capacitance is defined as $C_g = WL\epsilon_{ox}/t_{ox}$. Assume W, L, ϵ_{ox}, and t_{ox} are
statistically independent.
  (a) Obtain an expression for the standard deviation of the capacitance value, σ_c.
  (b) Calculate σ_C for $\Delta W = \Delta L = 0.30$ μm, $W = L = 5$ μm, $\Delta \epsilon_{ox} = 0.01$ pF/cm, $\epsilon_{ox} = $
  0.345 pF/cm, $\Delta t_{ox} = 15$ angstroms, and $t_{ox} = 500$ angstroms.
  (c) Repeat part b for $W = L = 25$ μm, $\Delta t_{ox} = 25$ angstroms, and $\Delta \epsilon = 0.015$ pF/cm,
  the other parameters remaining the same.
  (d) What terms are more important for physically large capacitors? For small-size
  capacitors?
  (e) What can be done to minimize capacitance errors?

4.2. Resistance is defined as $R = \rho_\square L/W$. Assume W, L, and $\rho_\square$ are statistically independent.
  (a) Obtain an expression for the standard deviation of the resistance value σ_R.
  (b) Calculate σ_R for $\Delta W = \Delta L = 0.30$ μm, $W = 3$ μm, $L = 55$ μm, $\Delta \rho_\square = 2$ Ω/sq,
  $\rho_\square = 50$ Ω/sq.
  (c) Repeat part b for $W = 5$ μm and $L = 500$ μm, the other parameters remaining
  unchanged.
  (d) Would $\Delta \rho_\square$ be larger in bulk silicon or polysilicon, and why?
  (e) What terms are more important for long resistors? For short resistors?

4.3. All n-channel current is summed into the ground line and flows toward the ground
pin. How can voltage drops due to this current be minimized?

4.4. Specify what rules must be observed foī wire bonding.

4.5. Why should thin oxide not cross well boundaries?

4.6. (a) Make a stick drawing of a 2-input, NMOS NAND gate with an enhancement-
  mode pull-up with an aspect ratio of 2/1. Use a self-registered buried contact and
  take the output on polysilicon.
  (b) Repeat part a for a depletion-mode pull-up device.

4.7. Repeat Prob. 4.6 for a 2-input, NMOS NOR gate with $Z_{pu} = 2/1$. Calculate the
rectangular areas required by both gates. Which occupies less chip area?

4.8. Make a stick drawing of a 2-input CMOS NAND gate with an n-type well and a p-
type substrate. Show the well contact. The well can be contacted on the supply rail.
Do not use the pull-up contact for the n-well contact, because the pull-up contact
connects metal to a p^+ region and the well contact connects metal to n^+ material.

4.9. Repeat Prob. 4.8 for a 2-input CMOS NOR gate. Calculate the rectangular areas
required by both gates. Which occupies less chip area?

DESIGN PROBLEMS

4.10. (*a*) Use the Mead-Conway NMOS Design Rules to design a 2-input NAND gate with an inverter ratio of 4, and a depletion-mode pull-up device. Include VDD and GND bus lines, use a buried contact, and take the output on polysilicon.

(*b*) What is the minimum rectangular area needed by this gate in units of λ^2? If the VDD and GND buses can be shared with other gates, how should they be counted?

4.11. Repeat Prob. 4.10 for a 2-input NMOS NOR gate. Compare the NMOS NOR gate to the NMOS NAND gate. Which requires a larger rectangular area?

4.12. Use the MOSIS CMOS Design Rules to design a 2-input, CMOS NAND gate of minimum rectangular area, with an *n*-type well and a *p*-type substrate. Include VDD and GND bus lines, and show connections for the substrate and well.

4.13. Repeat Prob. 4.12 for a 2-input CMOS NOR gate. Compare the CMOS NOR gate to the CMOS NAND gate. Which requires a larger rectangular area?

CHAPTER
5

MOS
INVERTERS

5.1 INTRODUCTION

When a FET is operating at low-voltage drain-to-source, it acts as a resistance which is controlled by the gate bias. The n-channel *enhancement-mode FET* can be switched from very high resistance when the gate voltage is less than the threshold value, to low resistance when V_{GS} exceeds the threshold voltage V_{TH}. The enhancement NMOS FET thus makes an excellent electronic switch, and is used as a pull-down device in both NMOS and CMOS circuits.

An enhancement-mode NMOS FET can be used as a pull-up device also, in which case it usually is operated with the gate connected to the drain. One now has an inverter with an active load. The drain-to-source voltage of the pull-up device is equal to the gate-to-source voltage, the FET is always in the saturation mode and behaves as a current source. When it is used as an active load the NMOS enhancement FET can supply current to the capacitive load, causing the output to rise rapidly until it reaches a maximum value of $V_{DD} - V_{THE}$. At this point the pull-up FET pinches off and the output voltage cannot rise higher.

An NMOS *depletion-mode FET* can also be used as an active pull-up, and it is normally operated with the gate connected to the source. Since a negative gate-to-source voltage is required to turn off the depletion FET, it draws current whenever the power is on. It can charge a load capacitance faster than an equivalent enhancement-mode device can, and will pull the output voltage up to the plus rail, making it a better pull-up than an equivalent enhancement-mode NMOS FET. The depletion-mode FET never turns off though, and when the pull-down device is on, the inverter sinks a relatively large current, and dissipates large standby power.

One solution to the dilemma is to use a PMOS enhancement device as a pull-up, with an NMOS enhancement pull-down FET. The threshold voltage of a PMOS enhancement FET is negative, thus the CMOS inverter operates as two electronic switches in series, with only one of them on at a time. The CMOS inverter has a much lower power consumption at low frequencies than an equivalent NMOS inverter with either type active pull-up.

Aspect ratios, inverter ratios, and methods of estimating both will be discussed first, after which the two NMOS inverters will be investigated, followed by the CMOS inverter. Noise margins, V_{oL} values, and switching speed will then be calculated and compared for the various inverters.

5.2 MOSFET ASPECT AND INVERTER RATIOS

The length-to-width ratio of the channel of an MOS device, Z, is referred to as the *aspect ratio* of the device, and is specified as the number of squares of the channel region, which is proportional to the channel resistance. The voltage-transfer characteristics of an NMOS inverter depend upon the aspect ratios of the pull-up and pull-down devices Z_{pu} and Z_{pd}, respectively. The *inverter ratio*, R_{inv}, is defined as the ratio of the pull-up aspect ratio to the pull-down aspect ratio, Z_{pu}/Z_{pd}, and determines the output voltage, V_{oL}, of the inverter when the input is high. To a first approximation, $V_{oL} = V_{DD}/(1 + R_{inv})$.

For rectangular device geometry there is no current crowding, and the current density is uniform over the cross-sectional area of the channel. In this case there is no problem in computing the effective resistance of the pull-up and/or pull-down devices. Two possible rectangular aspect ratios are shown in Fig. 5.1. If these two devices are used to form an inverter, with the larger resistance used as a pull-up device, the inverter ratio would be 4 to 1, or $R_{inv} = 4$.

Sometimes it is necessary to deviate from rectangular gate geometry in the interest of saving space. When irregular geometries are involved, the calculations required to obtain precise answers become much more difficult. There are several possible methods of obtaining a reasonable estimate of the effective aspect ratio associated with the simpler geometric shapes.

An L-shaped gate area is shown in Fig. 5.2. The channel area is seen to consist of four squares, and this is the effective area for computing gate-to-channel capacitance. Due to current crowding, the effective length-to-width ratio

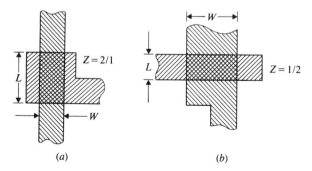

FIGURE 5.1
MOSFET devices with aspect ratios of (a) 2 to 1, and (b) 1 to 2.

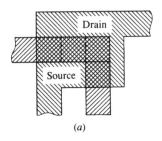

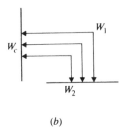

(a)   (b)

FIGURE 5.2
An L-shaped FET gate. (a) Layout; (b) three width estimates.

is not 1 to 4. However, 1 to 4 is a first approximation to the aspect ratio of this device, the width of the channel, W_c, being four times the length when measuring across the center-line of the channel as shown in Fig. 5.2b.

A lower bound and an upper bound on the aspect ratio can be obtained by considering the width as measured along the longest and the shortest dimensions, labeled W_1 and W_2, respectively, in Fig. 5.2b. If a minimum line width of two lambda is assumed and the dimensions of L and W given in multiples of lambda, one can conclude that the aspect ratio lies between $Z_1 = L/W_1 = 2/10 = 0.20$ and $Z_2 = L/W_2 = 2/6 = 0.33$, with the median value being $Z_c = L/W_c = 2/8 = 0.25$.

Another common method of estimating the aspect ratio is to consider the corner square to be a triangle of effective area one-half square, to account for the current crowding at the inside corner of this square. This yields an effective width of 7λ and an aspect ratio of $2/7 = 0.286$. One can conclude from the above discussion that the aspect ratio is between 0.25 and 0.29 and that $Z = 0.27$ is reasonably accurate.

A frequently occurring channel geometry is shown in Fig. 5.3. In this case, current flairs out at the lower end of the gate. Proceeding as before, one can estimate a maximum aspect ratio of 2.50 squares with no current spreading.

If the current spreading is approximated as in Fig. 5.3b, the channel looks like two squares in series with a parallel combination of $0.5 + 1 + 1 + 0.5 = 3$ squares, and the aspect ratio is 2.33. If the current could spread uniformly over squares A, B, C and D of Fig. 5.3c, the channel would appear to be two squares in series with a parallel combination of four squares, and the aspect ratio would be 2.25. The aspect ratio is between 2.25 and 2.50 squares, and the estimate of 2.33 squares is probably quite good. If this device is to be used as a pull-up FET, a conservative estimate that guarantees proper switching would be obtained by using the lower value pull-up aspect ratio while, if this device is to be used as a pull-down, the larger value of 2.5 would be a more conservative guess. In both cases, the voltage division of the inverter with the pull-down on will be as good as, or better than, the conservative estimate, and the output voltage with the inverter input high will be lower than the estimated value.

Horowitz and Dutton have done a study of the effective resistance of several irregular geometries, some of which are shown in Fig. 5.4 (1). The shape in Fig. 5.4a has an aspect ratio of L/W. The geometry shown in Fig. 5.4b consists of two squares and a rectangle. If the current spreads at 45 degrees, when the ratio W_1/W_2 is unity, the corner square looks like a half-square and $Z = 2.5$. As W_1 is increased with respect to W_2, the corner becomes a rectangle and the aspect ratio

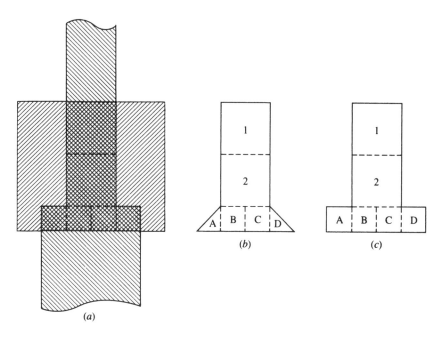

FIGURE 5.3
Channel widening at one end. (a) Layout; (b) and (c) approximate geometries.

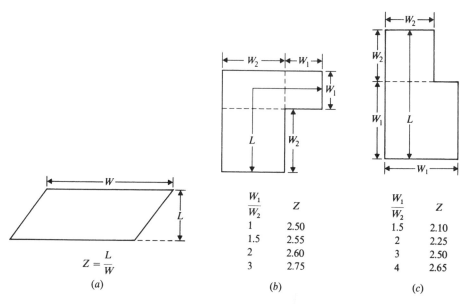

$$Z = \frac{L}{W}$$

(a)

$\dfrac{W_1}{W_2}$	Z
1	2.50
1.5	2.55
2	2.60
3	2.75

(b)

$\dfrac{W_1}{W_2}$	Z
1.5	2.10
2	2.25
3	2.50
4	2.65

(c)

FIGURE 5.4
Resistive values of three irregular shapes (1).

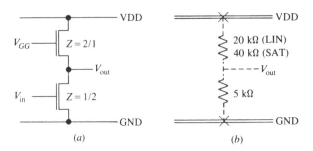

FIGURE 5.5
An NMOS inverter. (*a*) Circuit diagram; (*b*) equivalent dc circuit.

will increase from 2.5. Thus, for $W_1/W_2 = 1$, 1.5, 2, and 3, the aspect ratio increases from 2.50 to 2.55, 2.60, and 2.75, respectively.

Similar reasoning applied to Fig. 5.4*c*, indicates that as W_1/W_2 increases from unity, the aspect ratio increases from two squares; and for W_1/W_2 ratios of 1.5, 2, 3, and 4, the aspect ratios are 2.10, 2.25, 2.50, and 2.65, respectively.

5.3 NMOS INVERTER RATIOS

An inverter with a ratio of 4 to 1 is shown in Fig. 5.5, with two values of resistance for the pull-up, depending upon its mode of operation. If the pull-up and the pull-down are both biased by the same amount, the inverter ratio gives the ratio of the pull-up channel resistance to the pull-down channel resistance.

The inverter ratio gives an upper limit on the value of V_{oL}, which is larger than the actual value, since the two devices are not biased by the same amount when the input to the inverter is high. Actually when the input signal is V_{DD} and the output voltage is V_{oL}, the pull-down device is in the linear region of operation while the pull-up is saturated. For the resistances given in Fig. 5.5, $V_{oL} = V_{DD}/5$ if the pull-up is in the linear mode, and $V_{oL} = V_{DD}/9$ if the pull-up is saturated. Correct values of V_{oL} will be calculated in the next section.

5.4 ENHANCEMENT VS. DEPLETION PULL-UPS

The active pull-up of a MOSFET inverter can be operated in either the depletion mode or in the enhancement mode. Normally, the depletion-mode device has its gate connected to its source, while the enhancement-mode device has its gate connected to its drain. When the output goes high, an enhancement-mode device turns off as soon as V_{out} rises to within a threshold value of the positive rail, whereas a depletion-mode device remains on when the output voltage goes high.

The *voltage-transfer curve* of an inverter of ratio 4 to 1 is shown in Fig. 5.6. The voltage-transfer curve becomes steeper (more gain for the inverter), and V_{oL} becomes smaller as R_{inv} increases. The inverter threshold is defined as the point on the transfer curve for which $V_{in} = V_{out}$, and can be measured by simply connecting the input to the output of the inverter. V_{iL} and V_{iH} are defined as the points on the transfer curve where the slope is minus one, as shown in Fig. 5.6. At V_{iL}, the NMOS pull-down is in saturation and the PMOS pull-up is still in the

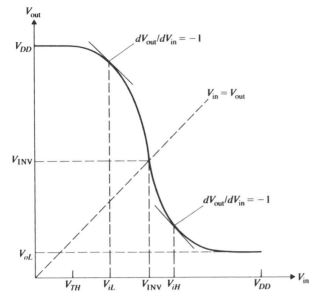

FIGURE 5.6
Voltage-transfer curve for a depletion-load inverter with a ratio of 4 to 1.

linear region of operation. At V_{iH} the NMOS pull-down is in the linear region while the PMOS pull-up is saturated.

5.4.1 Rise time of the EMD Pull-Up Inverter

Consider an inverter driving a capacitive load C_L. Typically C_L is the input capacitance of one or more identical inverters. When the input voltage to the inverter is low the pull-down device is off and acts as a very high resistance, while the enhancement-mode active pull-up charges the capacitive load, C_L. The output current-voltage relationship of the enhancement-mode pull-up with its gate connected to its drain is shown by the heavy line in Fig. 5.7a. The pull-up remains in the saturation region the entire time that the FET is on. The load line seen by the inverting pull-down device is given by mirroring this line about the voltage axis and shifting the axis by V_{DD} volts, as shown in Fig. 5.7b.

The gate-to-source voltage and the drain-to-source voltage of the enhancement-mode pull-up are the same, since the gate is connected to the drain.† The threshold voltage, V_{THE}, of the enhancement-mode device is typically 1 V at zero back-gate bias, and rises to about 1.5 V when the output goes high and the back-gate bias is about 3.5 V. Using an output-high threshold voltage of 1.5 V, the condition for saturation is that $V_{DS} > V_{GS} - V_{THE} = V_{DS} - 1.5$ V, and $V_{GS} > 1.5$ V.

---

† An enhancement-mode device can be made to pull the output up to the positive rail by biasing its gate to at least one threshold voltage above the positive rail. This requires routing a third power bus throughout the chip, or using a bootstrap technique to pull the gate high enough. These solutions are normally considered unacceptable.

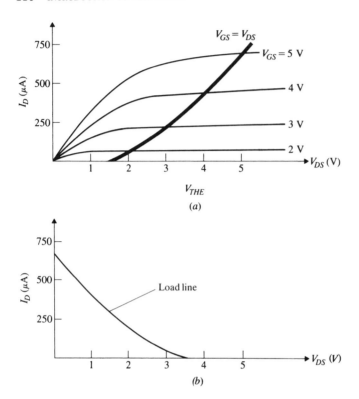

FIGURE 5.7
(a) Output characteristic of an enhancement FET with $V_{GS} = V_{DS}$; (b) the load line of the EMD.

Thus, the pull-up is in saturation for V_{GS} above the threshold of 1.5 V. This occurs when $V_o < V_{DD} - V_{THE} = 3.5$ V. As V_o approaches $V_{DD} - V_{THE} = 3.5$ V, the device pinches off. While the FET is in saturation, the drain current is given by Eq. (2.27), repeated below.

$$I_D(\text{SAT}) = \frac{k_{pu}}{2} [V_{GS} - V_{THE}]^2 = \frac{k_{pu}}{2} [V_{DD} - V_o - V_{THE}]^2$$

$$= \frac{k_{pu}}{2} [(V_{DD} - V_{THE}) - V(t)]^2 = C_L \frac{dV(t)}{dt} \tag{5.1}$$

where $V(t)$ is the varying output voltage of the inverter, and at time t, $V(t) = V_o$. k_{pu} and V_{THE} are the transconductance gain and threshold voltage of the pull-up device. Separate the variables, treat V_{THE} as a constant, and integrate both sides of Eq. (5.1) to obtain

$$\int_{V_{oL}}^{V_o} \frac{dV}{[(V_{DD} - V_{THE}) - V]^2} = \int_0^t \frac{k_{pu}\, dt'}{2C_L}$$

$$\frac{1}{[V_{DD} - V_{THE} - V]} \bigg|_{V_{oL}}^{V_o} = \frac{k_{pu}t}{2C_L}$$

$$\frac{1}{[V_{DD} - V_{THE} - V_o]} - \frac{1}{[V_{DD} - V_{THE} - V_{oL}]} = \frac{k_{pu}t}{2C_L}$$

Solve for the output voltage V_o as a function of time, and

$$V_o = V_{DD} - V_{THE} - \frac{2C_L}{k_{pu}t + 2C_L/(V_{DD} - V_{THE} - V_{oL})} \tag{5.2a}$$

Typically, $V_{DD} = 5$ V, $V_{THE} = 1.5$ V at $V_o = V_{oH}$, and $V_{oL} = 0.4$ V. Using these values, V_o as a function of time is

$$V_o = 3.5 - \frac{2C_L}{k_{pu}t + C_L/1.55} \tag{5.2b}$$

For a load of 31 fF, a transconductance factor of 34.5 μA/V^2, and t in nanoseconds, Eq. (5.2b) becomes

$$V_o = 3.5 - \frac{1.8}{0.58 + t}$$

This is plotted in Fig. 5.11 as the curve labeled EMD.

5.4.2 V_{oL} of the EMD Pull-Up Inverter

When the input voltage is $V_{DD} = 5$ V, the output voltage is V_{oL}, the pull-up is in saturation, and the pull-down is in the linear region of operation. The drain currents of the two devices are the same once the capacitive fan-out load has been charged or discharged, and the fan-out devices have been switched off.

Equations (2.26) and (2.27) can be used to calculate V_{oL} for an inverter of ratio R_{inv}, composed of an enhancement-mode pull-up device and an enhancement-mode pull-down device, both having a nominal threshold voltage of 1 V. When $V_o = V_{oL}$, the back-gate bias of the pull-up transistor is typically less than one-half volt, and $V_{TH} \approx V_{THO}$. For the pull-up, $V_{GS} = V_{DD} - V_{oL} = 5 - V_{oL}$, and the drain current is

$$I_D(\text{SAT}) = \frac{k_{pu}}{2} [V_{GS} - V_{TH}]^2 = \frac{k_{pu}}{2} [4 - V_{oL}]^2 \tag{5.3}$$

while, for the pull-down device, $V_{GS} = 5$ V, $V_{DS} = V_{oL}$, and the drain current is

$$I_D(\text{LIN}) = \frac{k_{pd}}{2} [2(V_{GS} - V_{TH})V_{DS} - V_{DS}^2]$$

$$= \frac{k_{pd}}{2} [8V_{oL} - V_{oL}^2] \tag{5.4}$$

To determine the value of V_{oL} for an arbitrary inverter ratio, R_{inv}, note that once the capacitive load has been discharged the fan-out devices are turned off and the pull-up and pull-down device drain currents are equal. Equate the two drain currents given by Eqs. (5.3) and (5.4), to obtain

$$\frac{k_{pu}}{2}[4 - V_{oL}]^2 = \frac{k_{pd}}{2}[8V_{oL} - V_{oL}^2]$$

Now

$$R_{\text{inv}} = \frac{Z_{pu}}{Z_{pd}} = \frac{k_{pd}}{k_{pu}}$$

therefore:

$$[4 - V_{oL}]^2 = R_{\text{inv}}[8V_{oL} - V_{oL}^2]$$

$$V_{oL}^2 - 8V_{oL} + \frac{16}{R_{\text{inv}} + 1} = 0$$

$$V_{oL} = 4 - 4\sqrt{1 - \frac{1}{R_{\text{inv}} + 1}} \qquad V \qquad (5.5)$$

The actual value of V_{oL} for an inverter with an enhancement-mode pull-up is about 0.42 V for an inverter ratio of 4 and about 0.23 V for an inverter ratio of 8.

For a reasonably large inverter ratio, the second term in V_{oL} can be expanded in a Taylor series and truncated to give

$$V_{oL} \approx 4 - 4\left[1 - \frac{1}{2(R_{\text{inv}} + 1)}\right] = \frac{2}{R_{\text{inv}} + 1} \qquad V \qquad (5.6)$$

The truncated series gives values of $V_{oL} = 0.40$ V for $R_{\text{inv}} = 4$, and $V_{oL} = 0.22$ V for $R_{\text{inv}} = 8$. The value given by Eq. (5.6) are too low; a safer approximation, which is reasonably accurate, would be

$$V_{oL} \approx \frac{2}{R_{\text{inv}}} \qquad V \qquad (5.7)$$

Equation (5.7) gives a quick estimate of $V_{oL} = 0.5$ V for an inverter ratio of 4, and $V_{oL} = 0.25$ V for an inverter of ratio 8. For most purposes these estimates are quite satisfactory.

5.4.3 Rise Time of the DMD Pull-Up Inverter

The output current-voltage relationship of the depletion-mode pull-up with its gate connected to its source is shown by the heavy line in Fig. 5.8a. The pull-up is in the saturation region until the output voltage exceeds 2 V, and the drain-to-source bias becomes too small. Neglecting back-gate and short-channel effects, the load line seen by the inverting pull-down device is again given by mirroring this line about the voltage axis, and shifting the axis by V_{DD} volts. This is shown in Fig. 5.8b, where line 1 is the load line neglecting back-gate bias.

It appears that the saturated pull-up device approximates a good current source over about half the operating range. However, back-gate bias causes the

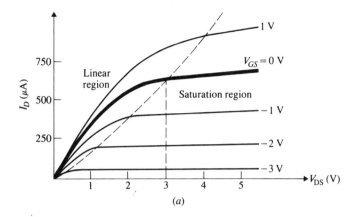

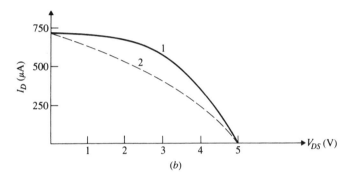

FIGURE 5.8
(a) Output characteristics of a depletion-mode FET with $V_{GS} = 0$; (b) the load line of the DMD.

threshold voltage of the load V_{THD} to change from -3.5 V at no back-gate bias to about -3.0 V when the output approaches the positive rail. Shortening of the channel length due to the Early effect causes the DMD to deviate from an ideal current source also. The combined result of these two effects is that the load line of the DMD more closely resembles a linear resistance than a constant current source. This is shown by line 2 in Fig. 5.8b.

The criterion for linear operation of a depletion-mode FET is that $0 \leq V_{DS} \leq V_{GS} - V_{THD} = 3$ V. Thus, the pull-up will be in the resistive or linear region for the final stages of a rising transient and a capacitive load, C_L, will be charging through the pull-up resistance R_{pu}. The drain current of the pull-up operating in the linear region is given by Eq. (2.26)

$$I_D(\text{LIN}) = \frac{k_{pu}}{2} [2(V_{GS} - V_{THD})V_{DS} - V_{DS}^2]$$

$$= \frac{k_{pu}}{2} [2(-V_{THD})V_{DS} - V_{DS}^2] \tag{5.8}$$

The effective pull-up resistance of the FET for $V_{DS} \ll V_{THD}$ can be approximated by estimating the average drain current and voltage for the pull-up from Eq. (5.8). To compare the rise times of the depletion-mode FET and the enhancement-mode FET let $V_{THD} = -3$ V, $C_L = 31$ fF, and $k_{pu} = 34.5$ μA/V^2. Then

$$R_{pu} = \frac{V_{DS}(\text{AV})}{I_D(\text{AV})} = \frac{V_{DS}(\text{AV})}{17.25[6V_{DS}(\text{AV}) - V_{DS}^2(\text{AV})]} \tag{5.9}$$

For $V_o < 2$ V the pull-up FET is in the saturation region, $I_D = I_D(\text{SAT})$ is constant, and V_o is ramping up. When V_o reaches 2 V, the pull-up enters the linear region of operation, the load capacitance is now charging through a constant resistance, and the output rises exponentially. Actually, as seen in Fig. 5.8a, the drain current of the pull-up becomes linear with V_{DD} when V_o is almost 3 V. During the time interval from $V_o = 3$ V to 5 V, the average value of the drain to source voltage is 1 V, and the pull-up resistance can be estimated by substituting $V_{DS} = 1$ V into Eq. (5.9)

$$R_{pu} = \frac{1}{17.25(6 - 1)} = 11.6 \ k\Omega \tag{5.10}$$

This gives a time constant of $R_{pu}C_L = 11.6 \times 10^3(31 \times 10^{-15}) = 0.36$ ns, and a rise time of $2.2(0.36) = 0.79$ ns.

An exponential waveform does not differ appreciably from a ramp for times that are small compared to a time constant, and the output voltage is given, approximately, by

$$V_o(t) = V_{oL} + (V_{DD} - V_{oL})[1 - e^{-t/R_{pu}C_L}]$$

$$= V_{DD} + (V_{oL} - V_{DD})e^{-t/R_{pu}C_L} \quad \text{for} \quad V_o > 1 \text{ V} \tag{5.11}$$

Equation (5.11) is plotted in Fig. 5.11 also, labeled DMD.

5.4.4 V_{oL} of the DMD Pull-Up Inverter

To calculate V_{oL} consider an inverter with a ratio of R_{inv}, a depletion-mode pull-up with a threshold voltage of -3 V, and an enhancement-mode pull-down device with a threshold voltage of 1 V. When the input voltage is $V_{DD} = 5$ V, the output voltage is V_{oL}, the pull-up is in saturation and the pull-down is in the linear region of operation. The currents through the two devices are the same once the capacitive fan-out load has been discharged and the fan-out devices have been switched off.

The equations for the drain currents in linear and saturation mode are again given by Eqs. (2.26) and (2.27), respectively. For a depletion-mode pull-up, V_{oL} can be calculated as follows:

The pull-up device is in saturation with $V_{GS} = 0$, and $V_{THD} = -3$ V.

$$I_D(\text{SAT}) = \frac{k_{pu}}{2}[V_{GS} - V_{THD}]^2 = \frac{9k_{pu}}{2} \tag{5.12}$$

For the pull-down device, $V_{GS} = 5$ V, V_{DS} is much less than 4 V, and the device is in the linear region with $V_{THE} = 1$ V, and

$$I_D(\text{LIN}) = \frac{k_{pd}}{2}[2(V_{GS} - V_{THE})V_{DS} - V_{DS}^2]$$

$$= \frac{k_{pd}}{2}[2(5 - 1)V_{oL} - V_{oL}^2] \qquad (5.13)$$

Equate the two drain currents given by Eq. (5.12) and (5.13), and

$$9\left(\frac{k_{pu}}{k_{pd}}\right) = 8V_{oL} - V_{oL}^2$$

$$V_{oL}^2 - 8V_{oL} + \frac{9}{R_{\text{inv}}} = 0$$

$$V_{oL} = 4 - 4\sqrt{1 - \frac{9}{16R_{\text{inv}}}} \qquad (5.14)$$

For $R_{\text{inv}} = 4$, $V_{oL} = 0.29$ V, and for $R_{\text{inv}} = 8$, $V_{oL} = 0.14$ V.

For a reasonably large inverter ratio, the second term can again be expanded in a series and truncated to give

$$V_{oL} \approx 4 - 4\left[1 - \frac{9}{32R_{\text{inv}}}\right] = \frac{9}{8R_{\text{inv}}} \qquad (5.15)$$

This gives approximate values of $V_{oL} = 0.28$ V for $R_{\text{inv}} = 4$ and $V_{oL} = 0.14$ V for $R_{\text{inv}} = 8$. As before, these values of V_{oL} are slightly too low. A safety factor can be included by letting $V_{oL} = 1.25/R_{\text{inv}}$.

Circuit diagrams and stick drawings of both inverters with enhancement-mode pull-up and with depletion-mode pull-up are shown in Fig. 5.9. The voltage

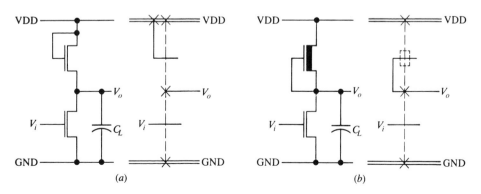

(a)   (b)

FIGURE 5.9
Circuit diagrams and stick drawings of an NMOS inverter with (a) an enhancement-mode pull-up, and (b) a depletion-mode pull-up.

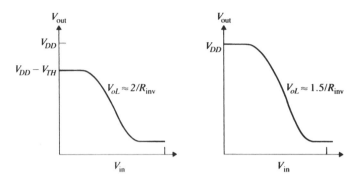

FIGURE 5.10
The voltage-transfer characteristics of an inverter with (a) an enhancement-mode pull-up, and (b) a depletion-mode pull-up.

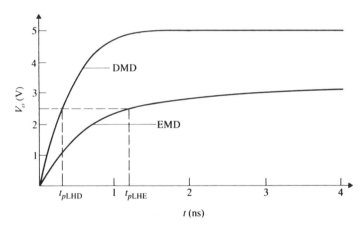

FIGURE 5.11
Output waveforms versus time for enhancement-mode and depletion-mode pull-ups.

transfer characteristics of both types of inverters are shown in Fig. 5.10, and the output rising waveforms versus time are shown in Fig. 5.11.

5.5 THE STANDARD CMOS INVERTER

The standard CMOS inverter with well and well-contact omitted is shown in Fig. 5.12. The CMOS inverter is ratioless in the steady state since one device is always off and has a very high impedance. The output voltage can swing essentially from rail to rail, and the noise margins of the CMOS circuit are larger than those of an NMOS gate operating between the same supply rails.

The *channel mobility* of electrons is approximately twice that of holes, giving

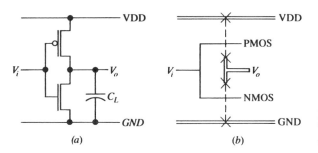

FIGURE 5.12
The CMOS inverter. (*a*) Circuit
diagram; (*b*) stick drawing.

NMOS devices twice the conductivity of identical PMOS devices. Because of this, CMOS inverters with identical pull-up and pull-down aspect ratios have high-to-low output transitions that are twice as fast as low-to-high transitions. For this reason many designers have doubled the channel width of the PMOS pull-up to compensate for the lower hole mobility, and balance the switching speeds. This requires more surface area for the inverter, increases the pull-up capacitance, yields a higher power dissipation, and it may be neither necessary nor advisable. To determine the best channel ratio, consider the following arguments by Seitz (2).

5.5.1 Transient Characteristics of CMOS

The ac performance of a CMOS inverter is given by its switching speed. For a CMOS inverter driving a capacitive load C_L, the *propagation-delay high-to-low* is determined by the load capacitance and the pull-down resistance of the inverter, whereas the *propagation delay low-to-high* is determined by C_L and the pull-up resistance.

Consider a CMOS inverter with a specific channel capacitance of $C_\square$ F/sq, and an NMOS channel specific resistance of $R_\square$ Ω/sq. Also, let the pull-up consist of N squares in parallel, and the pull-down be a minimum geometry FET. Then, for a mobility ratio of 2 to 1, the pull-up resistance is $2R_\square/N$, and the pull-down resistance is $R_\square$; the pull-up capacitance is $NC_\square$, and the pull-down capacitance is $C_\square$. When driving an identical inverter, the load capacitance C_L is $C_{pu} + C_{pd} = (N + 1)C_\square$, and the pull-up and pull-down time constants are

$$R_{pu}C_L = \left(\frac{2R_\square}{N}\right)(N + 1)C_\square = \left[\frac{2(N + 1)}{N}\right]R_\square C_\square \tag{5.15a}$$

$$R_{pd}C_L = R_\square(N + 1)C_\square \tag{5.15b}$$

The *inverter pair delay* is defined as the propagation delay, low-to-high, plus the propagation delay, high-to-low, and the average propagation delay t_p is one-half the pair delay. The pair delay is proportional to the pull-up plus the pull-down time constants. In fact, for a step input, the time required for the output to fall from V_{DD} to $0.5V_{DD}$ is $0.7R_{pd}C_L$, while the time to rise from 0 V to $0.5V_{DD}$ is $0.7R_{pu}C_L$, since $1 - e^{-0.7} = 0.5$. For the CMOS inverter, the pair delay P is

$$P = 2t_p = 0.7(R_{pu} + R_{pd})C_L$$

$$= 0.7\left(1 + \frac{2}{N}\right)(N + 1)R_\square C_\square$$

$$= 0.7\left(N + 3 + \frac{2}{N}\right)R_\square C_\square \tag{5.15c}$$

To determine the width of the pull-up channel that minimizes the inverter pair delay, differentiate P with respect to N.

$$\frac{dP}{dN} = 0.7R_\square C_\square\left(1 - \frac{2}{N^2}\right) \tag{5.16}$$

The minimum average switching speed occurs for $N = 2^{1/2}$. The pair delay and average delay are given in Table 5.1 for several values of N. If R and C in Table 5.1 refer to the resistance and capacitance of 1 square, these can be considered as normalized delays.

The optimum value of pull-up to pull-down ratio in this case is 1.4, but the gain in ac performance is probably not worth the added real estate needed to increase the width of the pull-up device, since the main effect of this is to increase the switching power dissipation. The average propagation delay of an inverter with a minimum-geometry pull-up is the same as that of an inverter with a pull-up of twice the minimum width, and uses less drive energy. Also, it seems logical not to increase the capacitive load of the p-channel devices without sufficient reason. And lastly, making the pull-up and the pull-down the same size gives a more symmetrical layout. In Sec. 5.10.3, propagation delays are calculated for $N = 1$, 1.414, and 2.

5.5.2 DC Characteristics of CMOS

The logic-threshold voltage, V_{INV}, is the value of the input voltage when the input and the output are at the same potential, as shown in Fig. 5.6. To determine the best channel ratio for noise margins, consider the CMOS inverter with V_i near V_{INV}. Both the pull-up and the pull-down are in saturation, and for the pull-up,

TABLE 5.1
Delay vs. R_{inv}

$N = 1/R_{inv}$	Pair delay	t_p
1.0	4.16RC	2.08RC
1.4	4.02RC	2.01RC
2.0	4.16RC	2.08RC
3.0	4.64RC	2.32RC

the gate bias V_{GSP} is given by (2)

$$V_{GSP} = V_i - V_{DD} = V_{INV} - V_{DD}$$

$$I_{DS}(PU) = \frac{k_{pu}}{2} [V_{INV} - V_{DD} - V_{THP}]^2 \tag{5.17}$$

while for the pull-down device, the gate bias V_{GSN} is

$$V_{GSN} = V_i = V_{INV}$$

$$I_{DS}(PD) = \frac{k_{pd}}{2} [V_{INV} - V_{THN}]^2 \tag{5.18}$$

Define R_{inv} the same as for the NMOS inverter, and

$$R_{inv} = \frac{Z_{pu}}{Z_{pd}} = \frac{(L/W)_{pu}}{(L/W)_{pd}}$$

$$k_{pu} = \mu_p C_{ox} \left(\frac{W}{L} \right)_{pu}$$

$$k_{pd} = \mu_n C_{ox} \left(\frac{W}{L} \right)_{pd} \tag{5.19}$$

The inverter ratio and the mobility ratio are related by

$$\frac{k_{pd}}{k_{pu}} = \left(\frac{\mu_n}{\mu_p} \right) \left(\frac{Z_{pu}}{Z_{pd}} \right) = \left(\frac{\mu_n}{\mu_p} \right) R_{inv} \tag{5.20}$$

The drains of the two FETs are tied together at the output, and the drain currents of the two devices are equal in magnitude, but opposite in direction, requiring the negative square root below.

$$\frac{k_{pu}}{2} [V_{INV} - V_{DD} - V_{THP}]^2 = \frac{k_{pd}}{2} [V_{INV} - V_{THN}]^2 \tag{5.21}$$

Let

$$X = \sqrt{\left(\frac{\mu_n}{\mu_p} \right) R_{inv}} = \sqrt{\frac{k_{pd}}{k_{pu}}}$$

and

$$V_{INV} - V_{DD} - V_{THP} = -X(V_{INV} - V_{THN})$$

$$V_{INV}(1 + X) = V_{DD} + V_{THP} + X V_{THN}$$

$$V_{INV} = \frac{V_{DD} + V_{THP} + X V_{THN}}{1 + X} \tag{5.22}$$

For $V_{DD} = 5$ V and $V_{THN} = -V_{THP} = 1$ V, the inverter voltage is

$$V_{INV} = \frac{4 + X}{1 + X} \tag{5.23}$$

TABLE 5.2

V_{INV} vs. R_{inv}

$1/R_{inv}$	V_{INV}, V
1.0	2.24
1.4	2.37
2.0	2.50
3.0	2.65

For silicon the electron-to-hole mobility ratio is 2 and $X = (2R_{inv})^{1/2}$. For a PMOS channel which is wider by a factor of $1/R_{inv}$ than an NMOS channel of the same length, the results are given in Table 5.2. Similar results can be calculated for other mobility ratios.

As the inverter ratio varies from 1 to 1/3, the inverter voltage varies from 2.24 to 2.65 V. The inverter voltage is seen to be relatively insensitive to R_{inv} over this range. V_{oL} and V_{oH} are independent of the inverter ratio, and are approximately ground and V_{DD} respectively, hence the noise margins are not greatly affected by varying the pull-up channel width.

Near V_{INV}, both the pull-up and the pull-down are in saturation, and look like two current sources in series. V_o is unstable, and a small change in the input voltage will switch the output. The voltage-transfer curve has a vertical slope at V_{INV} and, since the saturation drain currents vary slightly with drain-to-source voltages, the gain is very high but finite near V_{INV}.

5.6 THE PSEUDO-NMOS CMOS INVERTER RATIO

A PMOS transistor with a grounded gate can be used for the pull-up device, as shown in Fig. 5.13. It remains on all the time, and is roughly equivalent to a depletion-mode NMOS pull-up. It achieves a high output, but the inverter will draw standby current since the pull-up is never switched off. On the plus side, the load capacitance is just due to the pull-down gate capacitances of the fan-out, and for large fan-outs this gives a considerable reduction in switching speed. For more complex CMOS gates a large saving in real estate is also accomplished by pseudo-NMOS CMOS designs.

For the PMOS pull-up

$$V_{GS} = -V_{DD} \quad \text{and} \quad V_{DS} = V_o - V_{DD} \tag{5.24}$$

Refer to Eqs. (2.26) and (2.27) for the NMOS device. To extend these equations to include PMOS devices, put absolute value signs on the inequalities so that the PMOS is linear for

$$|V_{GS}| \geq |V_{THP}| \quad \text{and} \quad |V_{DS}| \leq |V_{GS} - V_{THP}| \tag{5.25}$$

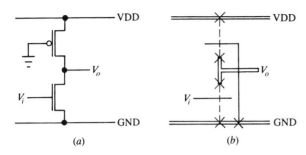

FIGURE 5.13
A pseudo-NMOS CMOS inverter. (a) Circuit diagram; (b) stick drawing.

while the PMOS is in saturation for

$$|V_{GS}| \geq |V_{THP}| \quad \text{and} \quad |V_{DS}| \geq |V_{GS} - V_{THP}| \tag{5.26}$$

Thus, for the above pull-up, with $V_{GS} = -V_{DD}$, $V_{DS} = V_o - V_{DD}$, and $V_{THP} = -1$ V; $V_{GS} > V_{THP}$ always, and the transistor never turns off. Also

$$|V_{DS}| = |V_{DD} - V_o| \quad \text{and} \quad |V_{GS} - V_{THP}| = 4 \text{ V}$$

Therefore

$$|V_{DS}| > |V_{GS} - V_{THP}| \quad \text{for} \quad |V_o - 5| > 4 \quad \text{or} \quad V_o < 1 \text{ V}$$

The pull-up is saturated for $V_o \leq 1$ V, and linear for $V > 1$ V. In particular, when $V_i = V_{INV} = V_{DD}/2$, the pull-up is in the linear region, and the drain current is given by

$$I_D(\text{PU}) = \frac{k_{pu}}{2} [2(-V_{DD} - V_{THP})V_{DSP} - V_{DSP}^2] \tag{5.27}$$

The pull-down is in saturation, and its drain current is

$$I_D(\text{PD}) = \frac{k_{pd}}{2} [V_{GS} - V_{THN}]^2 \tag{5.28}$$

Again, the pull-up drain current is the negative of the pull-down drain current, and:

$$\frac{k_{pu}}{2} [2(-V_{DD} - V_{THP})V_{DSP} - V_{DSP}^2] = \frac{k_{pd}}{2} [V_{INV} - V_{THN}]^2 \tag{5.29}$$

Equation (5.29) can be solved for the inverter voltage

$$V_{INV} = V_{THN} + \sqrt{\frac{k_{pu}}{k_{pd}}} \sqrt{2(-V_{DD} - V_{THP})(V_{DSP} - V_{DSP}^2)} \tag{5.30}$$

Equation (5.29) can also be solved for the ratio of k_{pd} to k_{pu}

$$\frac{k_{pd}}{k_{pu}} = \frac{2(-V_{DD} - V_{THP})V_{DSP} - V_{DSP}^2}{(V_{INV} - V_{THN})^2} \tag{5.31}$$

Let $V_{DD} = 5$ V, $V_{INV} = 2.5$ V, $V_{THN} = 1$ V, $V_{THP} = -1$ V, and $V_{DSP} = -2.5$ V. Then

$$\frac{k_{pd}}{k_{pu}} = \frac{2(-5 + 1)(-2.5) - (2.5)^2}{(2.5 - 1)^2} = 6.11$$

The conductivity ratio is again given by Eq. (5.20), $k_{pd}/k_{pu} = (\mu_n/\mu_p)R_{inv} = 2R_{inv}$. For a conductance ratio of approximately 6, the inverter ratio is about 3.

For $V_{INV} = 2.24$ V, as for the standard CMOS gate with an inverter ratio of unity, $V_i = 2.24$ V, $V_{DSP} = 2.24 - 5 = -2.76$ V, and the conductance ratio is

$$\frac{k_{pd}}{k_{pu}} = \frac{2(-5 + 1)(-2.76) - (2.76)^2}{(2.24 - 1)^2} = 9.4 \tag{5.32}$$

Again

$$\frac{k_{pd}}{k_{pu}} = 2R_{inv} \quad \text{or} \quad R_{inv} = \frac{9.4}{2} = 4.7 \approx 5 \tag{5.33}$$

For $R_{inv} = 4$, $V_{INV} = 2.32$ V is close to 2.24 V. An inverter ratio of 3, 4, or 5 will give reasonable noise margins for this inverter. Inverters of this type are typical in CMOS VLSI.

5.6.1 The Pseudo-NMOS CMOS Inverter V_{oL}

V_{oL} can be obtained for the pseudo-NMOS inverter in the same manner as for the NMOS inverters discussed earlier. Thus, for $V_i = V_{DD}$ and $V_o = V_{oL}$; the pull-up device is in saturation with $V_{GS} = -V_{DD}$ and $V_{DS} = V_{oL} - V_{DD}$, and the pull-down device is in the linear region of operation, with $V_{GS} = V_i = V_{DD}$ and $V_{DS} = V_{oL} = 0$ V. Again, the two drain currents are equal in magnitude, and

$$I_D(\text{PU}) = \frac{k_{pu}}{2}[V_{GSP} - V_{THP}]^2$$

$$I_D(\text{PD}) = \frac{k_{pd}}{2}[2(V_{GSN} - V_{THN})V_{DSN} - V_{DSN}^2]$$

$$k_{pu}[V_{GSP} - V_{THP}]^2 = k_{pd}[2(V_{GSN} - V_{THN})V_{DSN} - V_{DSN}^2] \tag{5.34}$$

$$[-5 + 1]^2 = \frac{k_{pd}}{k_{pu}}[2(5 - 1)V_{oL} - V_{oL}^2]$$

$$V_{oL}^2 - 8V_{oL} + 16\left(\frac{k_{pu}}{k_{pd}}\right) = 0 \tag{5.35}$$

Solve the quadratic to obtain

$$V_{oL} = 4\left[1 - \sqrt{1 - \frac{k_{pu}}{k_{pd}}}\right] = 4\left[1 - \sqrt{1 - \frac{1}{2R_{inv}}}\right] \tag{5.36}$$

For $R_{inv} = 3$, 4, and 5

$$\frac{k_{pd}}{k_{pu}} = 2R_{inv} = 6, 8, \text{ and } 10 \text{ respectively}$$

and the corresponding values of V_{oL} are 0.35 V, 0.26 V, and 0.21 V. All of these values are satisfactory.

5.7 NMOS THRESHOLD VOLTAGE AND INVERTER RATIOS

To calculate the value of V_{INV} for an NMOS depletion-load inverter, let us assume the pull-up and the pull-down devices are both in saturation. Actually, the pull-up is not quite in saturation but it is close to it, and the current is almost equal to the saturation value.

In saturation, the drain current is given by Eq. (2.27).

$$I_D = \frac{k}{2}[V_{GS} - V_{TH}]^2 \tag{5.37}$$

where $k = k'W/L$ and $k' = \mu_n C_{ox}$ is the same for the pull-up and pull-down devices. The gate-to-source voltage of the pull-down device is the inverter voltage V_{INV}, and its threshold voltage is V_{THE}. The gate-to-source voltage of the pull-up device is 0, and its threshold voltage is V_{THD}. Thus

$$\frac{W_{pd}}{L_{pd}}(V_{INV} - V_{THE})^2 = \frac{W_{pu}}{L_{pu}}(-V_{THD})^2 \tag{5.38}$$

$$\frac{1}{Z_{pd}}(V_{INV} - V_{THE})^2 = \frac{1}{Z_{pu}}(-V_{THD})^2 \tag{5.39}$$

Solve for the inverter voltage, and

$$V_{INV} = V_{THE} - \frac{V_{THD}}{\sqrt{Z_{pu}/Z_{pd}}} \tag{5.40}$$

To increase the current drive capability of the pull-down one must maximize $V_{GS} - V_{THE}$. This can be done by minimizing V_{THE}, but if V_{THE} is too low V_{oL} may not be less than V_{THE}, and the pull-down may not turn off. As a compromise choose $V_{THE} = 0.2V_{DD}$.

To maximize the current drive capability of the pull-up device set $V_{THD} \ll$ 0 V. Decreasing V_{THD} for a given V_{INV} and V_{THE} means making Z_{pu} large. As a fabrication compromise, tie the gate to the source and set V_{THD} to turn the device on about as strongly as an enhancement FET would be turned on with V_{DD} connected to its gate and its source grounded. In other words, design such that depletion FETs and enhancement FETs of equal dimensions would have equal saturation drain currents, given by the expression

$$I_D = \frac{k'}{2}\left(\frac{W_E}{L_E}\right)(V_{DD} - V_{THE})^2 = \frac{k'}{2}\left(\frac{W_D}{L_D}\right)(-V_{THD})^2$$

$$-V_{THD} = V_{DD} - V_{THE} = V_{DD} - 0.2V_{DD} = 0.8V_{DD} \tag{5.41}$$

Thus, a maximum value of the pull-up threshold voltage is

$$V_{THD} = -0.8V_{DD} \tag{5.42}$$

To reduce the pull-up length, let the minimum value of the threshold voltage be

$$V_{THD} = -0.6V_{DD}. \tag{5.43}$$

Design for $V_{THO} = -3.5$ V, and $V_{THD} = -3$ V when the back-gate bias is 3.5 V. The magnitude of V_{THD} will then be in the range of $0.6V_{DD}$ to $0.8V_{DD}$.

If V_{INV} is less than $0.5V_{DD}$ the noise-margin-high (NMH), is small, while if V_{INV} is greater than $0.5V_{DD}$ the noise-margin-low (NML), is small. This is shown in Fig. 5.14. For optimum noise margins choose $V_{INV} = 0.5V_{DD}$. The inverter ratio is then found from

$$0.2V_{DD} + \frac{0.6V_{DD}}{\sqrt{R_{inv}}} \leq 0.5V_{DD} \leq 0.2V_{DD} + \frac{0.8V_{DD}}{\sqrt{R_{inv}}} \tag{5.44}$$

The range of inverter ratios that satisfies Eq. (5.44) is

$$4 \leq R_{inv} \leq 7 \tag{5.45}$$

NMOS inverters will normally be designed with a 4-to-1 ratio in order to save space and minimize the rise time of the inverter output voltage. If the high input to the inverter is much lower than V_{DD}, which occurs when the input is taken from a pass-transistor, then an inverter ratio of 8 to 1 will be used. These two values will be sufficient for almost all inverters, AND gates, and OR gates.

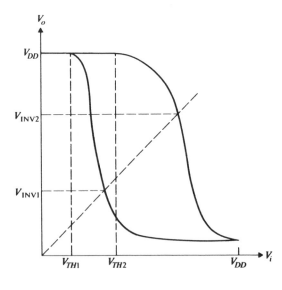

FIGURE 5.14
NMOS inverter voltage-transfer curves for low and high inverter ratios.

5.8 NMOS NAND AND NOR GATES

A two-input NAND gate is shown in Fig. 5.15. The inverter voltage is still given by Eq. (5.40), which is repeated here for convenience.

$$V_{\text{INV}} = V_{THE} - \frac{V_{THD}}{\sqrt{Z_{pu}/Z_{pd}}} \tag{5.46}$$

For the 2-input NAND gate, Z_{pd} must be replaced by

$$Z_{pdA} + Z_{pdB} = \frac{L_{pdA}}{W_{pdA}} + \frac{L_{pdB}}{W_{pdB}}$$

It is assumed for the present that the aspect ratios of pull-down A and pull-down B are both the same. In order to maintain an inverter ratio of 4 to 1, either the length of the pull-up device or the width of each pull-down device must be doubled. In Fig. 5.15 the pull-down aspect ratios have been halved, and the inverter logic threshold of the NAND gate is

$$V_{\text{INV}} = V_{TH}(\text{NAND}) = \frac{V_{DD}}{2} \tag{5.47}$$

The total pull-down aspect ratio for N identical geometry pull-down devices is N times the value of the ith pull-down, or

$$Z_{pd} = NZ_{pdi} \tag{5.48}$$

To maintain an inverter logic threshold of $V_{DD}/2$ one must either keep increasing Z_{pu} by increasing the channel length as more inputs are added, or else lower Z_{pd} by widening the pull-down devices as more inputs are added. If the length of the pull-up device is increased as inputs are added, then the resistance of the pull-up increases in proportion to N. On the other hand, if the pull-down devices are widened as inputs are added, the gate capacitance of an identical load is increased by N. A simple rule of thumb would be to multiply the width of each pull-down by the number of inputs to a NAND gate. This neglects back-gate bias effects on the stack of pull-down devices.

In either case the switching time constant, τ, is increased by N, with the result that for N identical inputs $\tau(\text{NAND}) = N\tau(\text{INV})$ and both the rising and falling transitions of the NAND gate increase by the fan-in N.

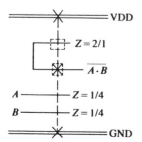

FIGURE 5.15
2-input NMOS NAND gate with identical pull-down devices and an inverter ratio of 4 to 1.

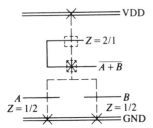

FIGURE 5.16
2-input NMOS NOR gate with identical pull-downs.

A conservative estimate of the total load capacitance of a NAND gate is obtained by lumping all the pull-down capacitances together at the output node of the NAND gate.

A 2-input NOR gate is shown in Fig. 5.16, again with identical pull-down device geometries. The pull-up aspect ratio is 2 and the pull-down aspect ratio is 1/2. If one input is held low, the voltage-transfer curve is the same as for an inverter with a ratio of 4 to 1. When both inputs are pulled low the effective width of the pull-down is doubled and the NOR gate looks like an 8-to-1 inverter. The capacitances of the pull-down devices are in parallel for the NOR gate.

The logic threshold voltage of a NOR gate decreases as a function of the number of inputs that are switching high together. If the pull-downs are all the same size then the inverter ratio of an N-input NOR gate is $4M$, where M is the number of pull-down devices that are driven on.

Except for the extra capacitance of the added inputs the propagation delay of a NOR gate with one active input is the same as that of an inverter, and the delay time for falling transitions decreases as more inputs become active.

> NAND gates have very poor area and delay characteristics,
> and should be used carefully in digital design.
> Use NOR gates in lieu of NAND gates whenever possible!
> For more than two inputs, NAND logic is not economically
> attractive in NMOS, and NOR logic is preferred!

5.9 LOADING AND FAN-OUT OF NMOS INVERTERS

In general the *gate capacitance* consists of three terms, the capacitance gate-to-source, the capacitance gate-to-drain, and the capacitance gate-to-body, or $C_g = C_{gs} + C_{gd} + C_{gb}$. The gate-to-source capacitance and the gate-to-drain capacitance are due to overlap of the gate material with the source and drain regions respectively, $C_{ox}x_jW$, while the gate-to-body capacitance is $C_{ox}LW$.

An NMOS inverter driving an identical load inverter is shown in Fig. 5.17. The gate-to-drain capacitance is the Miller feedback capacitance output to input, designated as C_M. To calculate the Miller capacitance, consider that, when the

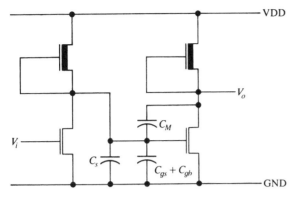

FIGURE 5.17
Capacitance loading the output of
an inverter driving another identical
inverter.

inverter input switches from 0 to 5 V the output must switch from 5 to 0 V (neglecting V_{oL}). The Miller capacitance must switch 10 V as shown in Fig. 5.18, and the gain of the inverter is -1. Thus, $C_M = 2C_{gd}$.

The stray capacitance associated with the output node is labeled C_s and is primarily due to parasitic wiring capacitance. The field oxide thickness is typically about 10 times the gate oxide thickness, hence the specific wiring capacitance is typically 10 times less than the specific gate capacitance. One can estimate C_s from a layout by counting the area of wiring and dividing by 10 times the gate area.

The total capacitive load of the inverter is thus

$$C_L = C_g + C_s = C_{gs} + C_{gb} + C_M + C_s$$
$$= C_{gs} + C_{gb} + 2C_{gd} + C_s \qquad (5.49)$$

To estimate the load capacitance of an inverter prior to layout, a rule of thumb would be to consider that typically, the wiring load has about 10 times the surface area of the gate. Since the specific capacitance of the wiring is about one-tenth that of the gate, the stray capacitance is about equal to one gate capacitance. The total load capacitance can then be approximated by

$$C_L \approx 2C_g \approx 2(C_{gs} + C_{gd} + C_{gb}) = 2C_{ox}LW \qquad (5.50)$$

In other words, if one calculates the gate-to-channel capacitance plus the gate-to-source capacitance plus the gate-to-drain capacitance, the load capacitance is twice this value, or the effective fan-out is 2.

A fan-out of N identical inverters means N times the load capacitance of the driver, increasing the rise time, fall time, and inverter pair delay by the factor N.

0 V ————| |———— +5 V
C_M

$$Q_g = C_g[5 - 0]$$
$$Q_s = C_s[5 - 0]$$
$$Q_M = C_M[5 + 5]$$

+5 V ————| |———— 0 V
C_M

FIGURE 5.18
The Miller capacitance switches 10 V in going from (*a*) input low to (*b*) input high.

5.10 TRANSIT AND SWITCHING TIMES

5.10.1 Transit Time of an Inverter

The time required for an electron or hole to travel from the source to the drain of a FET is defined as the *transit time*, T, for that carrier. T is a figure of merit that gives an estimate of how fast a given technology is. It is easy to estimate the transit time of majority carriers crossing the channel from source to drain when V_{DS} is small and the electric field in the channel is primarily due to the drain-to-source voltage. In this case

$$T = \frac{L}{\langle \text{velocity} \rangle} = \frac{L}{\mu \langle E \rangle} = \frac{L^2}{\mu \langle V_{DS} \rangle} \tag{5.51}$$

where L is the channel length, μ is the carrier mobility, E is the electric field in the channel, and V_{DS} is the voltage across the channel. The brackets "$\langle$" and "$\rangle$" signify the average value of the quantity enclosed.

Electron and hole velocities saturate at high values of electric field. The room-temperature saturation velocity of electrons in bulk silicon is about 10^7 cm/s while that of holes in bulk silicon is about 5×10^6 cm/s. Both occur at a critical field of about 500 kV/cm (3). In the channel region of a FET both *surface scattering* and *bulk scattering* occur. Due to the large surface-to-volume ratio in an MOS channel region, both effects must be considered. It is reasonable to assume that the two scattering mechanisms are independent, in which case the effective mobility of channel carriers is given by the expression (4)

$$\frac{1}{\mu_{\text{eff}}} = \frac{1}{\mu_{\text{bulk}}} + \frac{1}{\mu_{\text{surface}}}$$

When surface scattering is as effective as bulk scattering, μ_{bulk} and μ_{surface} will be of the same order of magnitude. Assuming this is true at high electric field values, one would expect the saturation velocity in the channel to be about one-half the bulk value, or about 5×10^6 cm/s for electrons, and about half that value for holes in silicon (5):

Near the saturation value, the velocity of carriers as a function of electric field, E in kV/cm, can be approximated as (3)

$$v_n = \frac{5 \times 10^6}{\sqrt{1 + (7/E)^2}}$$

$$v_p = \frac{2.5 \times 10^6}{1 + 20/E} \tag{5.52}$$

Example 5.1. Calculate the time for electrons to cross a channel of length 3 microns, if $V_{DD} = 5$ V.

Solution. The average voltage from drain to source is $V_{DD}/2 = 2.5$ V. Assuming

$\mu = 800 \text{ cm}^2/\text{V} \cdot \text{s}$, the electron transit time is

$$T_n = \frac{2L^2}{\mu V_{DD}} = \frac{2(3 \times 10^{-4})^2}{800(5)} = 0.045 \text{ ns}$$

The average velocity in this case is calculated to be

$$\langle v \rangle = \frac{L}{T_n} = \frac{3 \times 10^{-4}}{0.045 \times 10^{-9}} = 6.67 \times 10^6 \text{ cm/s}$$

which is greater than the saturation value.

The electric field along the channel is $E = V_{DD}/L = 5/(3 \times 10^{-4}) = 16.7 \text{ kV/cm}$, and from Eq. (5.52) $v_{n(MAX)} = 5 \times 10^6/\sqrt{1 + (7/16.7)^2} = 0.92v_{\text{sat}} = 4.6 \times 10^6 \text{ cm/s}$, and the average velocity of channel electrons is one-half this value, or $2.3 \times 10^6 \text{ cm/s}$. This yields a transit time of

$$T_n = \frac{3 \times 10^{-4}}{2.3 \times 10^6} = 0.13 \text{ ns}$$

The field is sufficient to produce electron velocity saturation, and the correct answer is 0.13 ns.

As device geometries get smaller, supply voltages must also be scaled down to avoid destructive electric fields. For a 1-micron channel, an oxide thickness of 400 angstroms, and a supply voltage of 5 V, the maximum field in the channel is 50 kV/cm and the maximum field in the oxide is 1.25 MV/cm. A supply voltage of 2.5 V would halve both field values.

5.10.2 NMOS Switching Speed

Rise time and fall time are determined by the current capabilities of the pull-up and pull-down devices, and the capacitive load being switched. The current will be calculated under the assumption that the input changes abruptly.

Rise times and fall times will be estimated in several ways by simple hand calculations. They can be calculated more accurately with a good SPICE model, once the design is laid out.

A gate driving a capacitive load, C_L, exhibits a rise time and a fall time determined by the resistance through which C_L is charging or discharging. For an inverter driving another identical inverter, the capacitive load is the gate-to-source capacitance of the driven inverter, the charging resistance is the drain-to-source resistance of the pull-up device, and the discharging resistance is the drain-to-source resistance of the pull-down device.

Figure 5.19 shows an NMOS inverter with a depletion-mode pull-up driving another identical inverter. The input signal and the rising and falling transitions of the first inverter are shown in Fig. 5.20. The ratio of the charging resistance to the discharging resistance of the inverter is approximately the inverter ratio, R_{inv}, and the ratio of rise time to fall time of the inverter is

$$\frac{t_{\text{rise}}}{t_{\text{fall}}} \approx \frac{R_{pu}C_L}{R_{pd}C_L} = \frac{Z_{pu}}{Z_{pd}} = R_{\text{inv}} \tag{5.53}$$

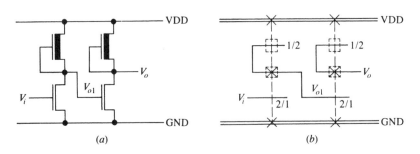

FIGURE 5.19
An NMOS inverter driving a second inverter. (*a*) circuit diagram; (*b*) stick drawing.

Let the gate oxide specific capacitance be 0.86 fF per square micron. Then the capacitance of a gate with an aspect ratio of 1/2, and area 3 microns by 6 microns, is 15.5 fF. This is the gate-to-body capacitance and must be augmented by the gate-to-source, gate-to-drain, and stray capacitances. Assuming these capacitances double the above capacitance, one obtains a load capacitance of about 15.5(2) = 31 fF. Since junction capacitances vary with the voltage across them, this is assumed to be an average value of C_L. The pull-up and pull-down resistances are obtained as follows:

$$R_{pu} = \frac{V_{DS}}{I_{pu}} = \frac{V_{DD} - V_o}{I_{pu}} \quad \text{and} \quad R_{pd} = \frac{V_o}{I_{pd}} \quad (5.54)$$

To obtain the average resistance as the output rises from 0 to 5 V, or drops from 5 to 0 V, use $I_D(\text{SAT})$ for the pull-up and/or pull-down current. The average voltage is 2.5 V, and the transconductance factors are

$$k_{pu} = \frac{\mu_n C_{ox}}{Z_{pu}} = 34.5 \mu\text{A/V}^2 \quad \text{and} \quad k_{pd} = 4k_{pu} = 138 \ \mu\text{A/V}^2$$

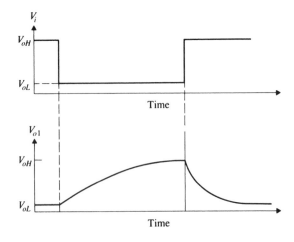

FIGURE 5.20
(*a*) Input-signal waveform, and (*b*) output-signal waveform of an NMOS inverter driving another identical inverter.

The saturation sourcing and sinking currents are given by Eq. (2.27) as $I_D = (k/2)(V_{GS} - V_{TH})^2$. This gives currents of $I_{pu} = (34.5/2)(-3)^2 = 155\ \mu A$, and $I_{pd} = (138/2)(5 - 1)^2 = 1104\ \mu A$. The net pull-down current is

$$I_{net} = I_{pd} - I_{pu} = 1104 - 155 = 949\ \mu A$$

and the average resistances are

$$R_{pu} = \frac{V_{AV}}{I_{pu}} = \frac{2.5}{0.155} = 16.13\ k\Omega$$
$$R_{pd} = \frac{V_{AV}}{I_{net}} = \frac{2.5}{0.949} = 2.63\ k\Omega$$

(5.55)

For the given load capacitance and calculated resistances, the time constants are

$$\tau_{rise} = R_{pu}C_L = 16.13(31) = 0.500\ ns$$
$$\tau_{fall} = R_{pd}C_L = 2.63(31) = 0.082\ ns$$

(5.56)

Define the *rise time* to be the time for the load capacitance to charge from 10 to 90 percent, and the *fall-time* to be the time for the load capacitance to discharge from 90 to 10 percent. The rise time and the fall time are 2.2 respective time constants, and for the above example are found to be

$$t_{rise} = 2.2\tau_{rise} = 2.2(0.500) = 1.10\ ns$$
$$t_{fall} = 2.2\tau_{fall} = 2.2(0.082) = 0.18\ ns$$

(5.57)

The minimum time interval required for the output voltage of an inverter to stabilize is the rise time or fall time of the inverter. To make a transition from V_{oL} to V_{oH} and back again requires a minimum time interval of $t_{rise} + t_{fall}$, and the maximum frequency at which the circuit can switch reliably is:

$$f_{max} = \frac{1}{t_{rise} + t_{fall}}$$

(5.58)

Propagation delay is the time interval between a signal transition at the input of a gate and the switching transition at the output of the gate. It is usually measured from the time the input voltage passes through the inverter voltage, V_{INV}, to the time the output voltage passes through the same inverter voltage.

Propagation delay for a high-to-low transition, t_{pHL}, is defined as the time required for the output to drop from V_{oH} to V_{INV} following a step input transition from low to high; and the propagation delay for a low-to-high transition, t_{pLH}, is defined as the time for the output to rise from V_{oL} to V_{INV} following a step input transition from high to low. If the input voltage switches very fast the propagation delay is the time for the output to charge to $0.7\tau_{rise}$ or discharge to $0.7\tau_{fall}$.

In the above case the propagation delays are

$$t_{pLH} = 0.7\tau_{rise} = 0.7(0.500) = 0.35\ ns$$
$$t_{pHL} = 0.7\tau_{fall} = 0.7(0.082) = 0.06\ ns$$

(5.59)

These time delays were computed assuming the input signal rise and fall times were negligible and the devices were in saturation and supplying or sinking the maximum possible current. The actual current is less when the device is operating in the linear mode, and the time intervals are larger than calculated above. It will be shown that these answers are about 30 percent too small, but for a rough estimate of propagation delays or to obtain relative estimates of performance, the above calculations are quick and easy.

For more accurate estimates of timing delays consider the following. If a load capacitance, C_L, is charged by a fixed voltage supply

$$I = C_L \frac{dV}{dt} \approx C_L \frac{\Delta V}{\Delta t}$$

and

$$\Delta t \approx C_L \frac{\Delta V}{I_{av}} \tag{5.60}$$

the propagation delays can be computed directly from the defining equations, viz,

$$t_{pLH} = C_L \frac{V_{INV} - V_{oL}}{I_{LH}(AV)}$$

$$t_{pHL} = C_L \frac{V_{oH} - V_{INV}}{I_{HL}(AV)} \tag{5.61}$$

The average propagation delay, t_p, and inverter pair delay, P, are defined as

$$P = 2t_p = t_{pLH} + t_{pHL} \tag{5.62}$$

One can measure propagation delay with a ring oscillator. A ring oscillator consists of a string of cascaded identical inverter stages with the output of the last inverter fed back to the input of the first inverter. For an odd number of stages the feedback is out of phase with the input signal, causing oscillation at a frequency determined by the average propagation delay, t_p, or the pair delay, P. To a first approximation the inverter pair delay is $(1 + R_{inv})t_{pHL}$.

For a good inverter V_{oH} is approximately V_{DD}, V_{oL} is close to 0 V, and V_{INV}, taken as the average value between V_{oH} and V_{oL}, is about $0.5V_{DD}$. Assuming these values the propagation delays simplify to

$$t_{pLH} = \frac{0.5V_{DD}C_L}{I_{LH}(AV)}$$

$$t_{pHL} = \frac{0.5V_{DD}C_L}{I_{HL}(AV)} \tag{5.63}$$

For a conservative calculation of the rise or fall time, take the output voltage swing as the difference between V_{oL} and V_{oH}. Using the rail values of V_o will give a more conservative estimate of the time than computing the time to switch from $0.9V_{DD}$ to $0.1V_{DD}$ or vice versa. From Eq. (5.60)

$$t_{\text{rise}} = C_L \frac{V_{oH} - V_{oL}}{I_{\text{rise}}} = C_L \frac{V_{DD}}{I_{\text{rise}}}$$

$$t_{\text{fall}} = C_L \frac{V_{oH} - V_{oL}}{I_{\text{fall}}} = C_L \frac{V_{DD}}{I_{\text{fall}}}$$

(5.64)

In the above expressions it is assumed that the average charging and discharging currents will give a best estimate of the rise and fall times. The simplest way to estimate the average charging and discharging currents is to calculate the current values at the beginning and end of the transition, and average them.

Let I_{LO} be the current when $V_o = V_{oL} = 0$ V, I_{INV} be the current when $V_o = V_{\text{INV}} = 0.5V_{DD}$, and I_{HI} be the current when $V_o = V_{oH} = V_{DD}$. During the low-to-high output transition the pull-down device is off and $I_{pd} = 0$. Thus

$$t_{pLH} = \frac{2.5C_L}{(I_{\text{LO}} + I_{\text{INV}})/2} = \frac{5C_L}{I_{\text{LO}} + I_{\text{INV}}}$$

(5.65)

During a high-to-low transition the pull-up of an NMOS inverter fights the pull-down and

$$t_{pHL} = \frac{2.5C_L}{(I_{\text{HI}} + I_{\text{INV}})/2} = \frac{5C_L}{I_{\text{HI}} + I_{\text{INV}}}$$

(5.66)

where I_{HI} and I_{INV} are the differences between the pull-down currents and the pull-up currents at the two voltage extremes, V_{oH} and V_{INV}.

Example 5.2. Estimate the propagation delays and pair delay of an NMOS inverter with a depletion-mode pull-up, with $C_L = 31$ fF, $C_{ox} = 0.86$ fF/micron², $\mu_n = 800$ cm²/V·s $= 8 \times 10^{10}$ microns²/V·s, $Z_{pu} = 2$, and $Z_{pd} = 0.5$.

Solution.

$$k_{pu} = \frac{\mu_n C_{ox}}{Z_{pu}} = 34.5 \ \mu\text{A/V}^2$$

$$k_{pd} = 4k_{pu} = 138 \ \mu\text{A/V}^2$$

When $V_o = V_{oL}$ the pull-up is saturated with $V_{DS} = V_{DD} = 5$ V (point *a* in Fig. 5.21*a*) and

$$I_{\text{LO}} = \frac{k_{pu}(-V_{THD})^2}{2} = \frac{34.5(9)}{2} = 155.25 \ \mu\text{A}$$

When $V_o = V_{\text{INV}}$ the pull-up is just entering the linear region (point *b* in Fig.

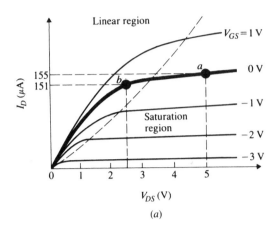

(a)

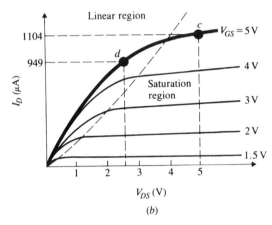

(b)

FIGURE 5.21
(a) Depletion-mode pull-up, and (b) enhancement-mode pull-down of Examples 5.2 and 5.3.

5.21a) and

$$I_{INV} = \frac{k_{pu}[2(-V_{THD})V_{DS} - V_{DS}^2]}{2} = \frac{34.5[15 - 6.25]}{2} = 150.9 \ \mu A$$

$$I_{AV} = \frac{155.25 + 150.9}{2} = 153.1 \ \mu A$$

$$t_{pLH} = \frac{2.5(31)}{153.1} = 0.51 \ ns$$

When $V_o = V_{oH}$ the pull-up is off and the pull-down is saturated with $V_{DS} = V_{DD} = 5$ V (point c in Fig. 5.21b), and

$$I_{HI} = I_{pd} = \frac{k_{pd}(5 - 1)^2}{2} = \frac{138(16)}{2} = 1104 \ \mu A$$

When $V_o = V_{INV}$ the pull-up and the pull-down are both in the linear region of operation (point b in Fig. 5.21a and point d in Fig. 5.21b), and

$$I_{pu} = \frac{34.5[2(3)2.5 - (2.5)^2]}{2} = 150.9 \ \mu A$$

$$I_{pd} = \frac{138[2(5-1)2.5 - (2.5)^2]}{2} = 948.8 \ \mu A$$

$$I_{INV} = I_{pd} - I_{pu} = 948.8 - 150.9 = 797.8 \ \mu A$$

$$I_{AV} = \frac{1104 + 797.8}{2} = 950.9 \ \mu A$$

$$t_{pHL} = \frac{2.5(31)}{951} = 0.081 \ ns$$

The pair delay is $0.51 + 0.08 = 0.59$ ns and the ratio of the propagation delays $= 0.51/0.081 = 6.30$. The estimated pull-up/pull-down ratio of 4 to 1 is in reasonable agreement with these calculations.

If the pull-up current had been neglected during the high-to-low transition the average pull-down current would have been 1026 μA, and the propagation delay would be 0.076 ns, which differs from the above 0.081 ns by 6 percent.

A more accurate evaluation of charging and discharging times can be obtained by computing the average currents as follows (6):

$$I_{AV} = \frac{\int I(V) \, dV}{\int dV} = \frac{\int I(V) \, dV}{\Delta V} \tag{5.67}$$

To compute propagation delays from Eq. (5.67) the integration is from 0 to $0.5V_{DD}$, or from $0.5V_{DD}$ to V_{DD}, and the denominator is $0.5V_{DD}$. To compute rise and fall times, the limits of integration are 0 and V_{DD} and the denominator is V_{DD}. Whether the transistor is in the linear or saturation region, the constant term in the numerator is

$$\frac{k}{2} = \frac{\mu_n C_{ox}}{2Z} \tag{5.68}$$

This term can be removed from the integral sign. Define I' as the drain current divided by $k/2$ and the average propagation-delay currents are

$$I_{pu}(\text{AV}) = \frac{k_{pu}}{V_{DD}} \int_0^{0.5V_{DD}} I'_{pu}(V) \, dV$$

$$I_{pd}(\text{AV}) = \frac{k_{pd}}{V_{DD}} \int_{0.5V_{DD}}^{V_{DD}} I'_{pd}(V) \, dV - \frac{k_{pu}}{V_{DD}} \int_{0.5V_{DD}}^{V_{DD}} I'_{pu}(V) \, dV \tag{5.69}$$

Example 5.3. Calculate the pair delay of the inverter of Example 5.2, using Eq. (5.69).

Solution. The depletion-mode pull-up is in saturation for $V_{DS} > 3$ V and linear for $V_{DS} < 3$ V as shown in Fig. 5.21a, while the pull-down is off. The input voltage is a step, $V_{DD} = 5$ V, $V_{THD} = -3$ V, and $k_{pu} = 34.5$ μA/V^2.

To calculate the rising transition $I_{pu}(\text{SAT}) = 17.25(9)$ μA, and $I_{pu}(\text{LIN}) = 17.25[6V_{DS} - V_{DS}^2]$.

Let V_{DS} be the variable of integration, V. Then

$$I_{pu}(\text{AV}) = \frac{17.25}{2.5}\left[\int_{2.5}^{3}(6V - V^2)\,dV + \int_{3}^{5}9\,dV\right]$$

$$= 6.9\left[\left(3V^2 - \frac{V^3}{3}\right)\Big|_{2.5}^{3} + 9V\Big|_{3}^{5}\right] = 155\ \mu\text{A}$$

$$t_{pLH} = \frac{2.5C_LV_{DD}}{I_{pu}(\text{AV})} = \frac{2.5(31)}{155} = 0.50\ \text{ns}$$

To calculate the falling transition, the pull-down is in saturation for $V > 4$ V and linear for $V < 4$ V as shown in Fig. 5.21b, while the pull-up is linear over the range of 2.5 to 5 V. For the pull-down, $V_o = V_{DS}$. Let $V_o = V$ for the pull-down FET, and

$$I_{pd}(\text{LIN}) = \frac{138}{2}[8V - V^2] = 69[8V - V^2]$$

and

$$I_{pd}(\text{SAT}) = 69(16) = 1104\ \mu\text{A}$$

$$I_{pd}(\text{AV}) = \frac{69}{2.5}\left[\int_{2.5}^{4}(8V - V^2)\,dV + \int_{4}^{5}16\,dV\right]$$

$$= 27.6\left[\left(4V^2 - \frac{V^3}{3}\right)\Big|_{2.5}^{4} + 16\,V\Big|_{4}^{5}\right] = 1073\ \mu\text{A}$$

Let V be the drain-to-source voltage of the pull-up again, and

$$I_{pu}(\text{AV}) = \frac{17.25}{2.5}\int_{0}^{2.5}(6V - V^2)\,dV$$

$$= 6.9\left[3V^2 - \frac{V^3}{3}\right]\Big|_{0}^{2.5} = 93.44\ \mu\text{A}$$

The net average pull-down current is

$$I(\text{NET}) = I_{pd}(\text{AV}) - I_{pu}(\text{AV}) = 1073 - 93.44 = 979.56\ \mu\text{A}$$

and

$$t_{pHL} = \frac{2.5C_L}{I(\text{NET})} = \frac{2.5(31)}{979.56} = 0.079\ \text{ns}$$

$P = 0.50 + 0.08 = 0.58$ ns, and the ratio of rising to falling delay is

$$\frac{0.50}{0.079} = 6.33$$

Reinhard (7) uses Eq. (5.67) to obtain the following expressions for the rise time from 0 to V_{DD} (see Prob. 5.10) and the pull-down time from V_{DD} to 0 V, neglecting the current from the pull-up load (see Prob. 5.11).

$$t_{\text{rise}} = \frac{6C_L Z_{pu} V_{DD}^2}{\mu_n C_{ox}(-V_{THD})^2(3V_{DD} + V_{THD})} \tag{5.70}$$

$$t_{\text{fall}} = \frac{6C_L Z_{pd} V_{DD}^2}{\mu_n C_{ox}(V_{DD} - V_{THE})^2(2V_{DD} + V_{THE})} \tag{5.71}$$

Evaluation of Eqs. (5.70) and (5.71) for the device parameters assumed in the above two examples yields

$$t_{\text{rise}} = 1.25 \text{ ns} \qquad \text{and} \qquad t_{\text{fall}} = 0.19 \text{ ns}$$

$$t_{pLH} = 0.7\tau \qquad \text{and} \qquad t_{\text{rise}} = 2.2\tau$$

$$t_{pLH} = \frac{0.7}{2.2} t_{\text{rise}} = 0.318 t_{\text{rise}}$$

This gives propagation delays $t_{pLH} = 0.318(1.25) = 0.40$ ns and $t_{pHL} = 0.318(0.19) = 0.06$ ns. These answers are somewhat lower than those in Examples 5.1 and 5.2 but all four performance estimates are in reasonable agreement. SPICE will give more accurate answers and should be used before a chip is fabricated, but any of the above methods gives a good estimate of the switching speed of the inverter.

5.10.3 CMOS Switching Speed

CMOS time constants, rise times, and propagation delays can be calculated using the above techniques. This will be left for an exercise. Using Reinhard's approach (7) for CMOS devices, one obtains (see Prob. 5.12)

$$t_{\text{rise}} = t_{\text{fall}} = \frac{6C_L Z V_{DD}^2}{\mu C_{ox}(V_{DD} - |V_{TH}|)^2(2V_{DD} + |V_{TH}|)} \tag{5.72}$$

The threshold voltage, V_{TH}, equals 1 V for the NMOS device and -1 V for the PMOS FET. In calculating t_{rise} the values of Z and V_{TH} are those of the pull-up device, and μ is the hole mobility. For t_{fall}, the values are those of the pull-down device, and μ is the electron mobility.

For CMOS inverters whose pull-up and pull-down devices are of minimum geometry and for which the input voltage changes abruptly, the rise time and fall time can be calculated in the same manner as for the NMOS inverters. Again, the simplest calculation is to use saturation currents as a first estimate.

For minimum-size pull-up and pull-down devices $C_L = 31$ fF, since the inverter must drive both the pull-up and pull-down capacitances.

$$k_{pu} = \frac{\mu_p C_{ox}}{Z_{pu}} = \frac{400(0.86)}{1} = 34.5 \ \mu\text{A/V}^2$$

$$k_{pd} = \frac{\mu_n C_{ox}}{Z_{pd}} = \frac{800(0.86)}{1} = 69.0 \ \mu\text{A/V}^2$$

For a low-to-high transition the NMOS is off. The PMOS is in saturation for $V_o = 0$ V, and is in the linear mode for $V_o = V_{INV}$. Define I_{INV} as above and I_{LO} as the current when $V_o = 0$ V.

$$I_{LO} = \frac{k_{pu}}{2}[V_{GS} - |V_{THP}|]^2 = \frac{34.5}{2}(5-1)^2 = 276 \ \mu A$$

$$I_{INV} = \frac{k_{pu}}{2}[2(V_{GS} - |V_{THP}|)V_{DS} - V_{DS}^2]$$

$$= \frac{34.5}{2}[2(5-1)2.5 - (2.5)^2] = 237 \ \mu A$$

The average pull-up current is

$$\frac{I_{LO} + I_{INV}}{2} = 256.5 \ \mu A,$$

and the delay is

$$t_{pLH} = \frac{C_L(V_{DD}/2)}{I_{AV}} = \frac{31(2.5)}{256.5} = 0.302 \ ns \tag{5.73}$$

During a high-to-low transition the PMOS is off, the NMOS is in saturation for $V_o = V_{DD} = V_{HI}$, and the NMOS is in the linear region for $V_o = 0.5V_{DD} = V_{INV}$. Define I_{HI} as the pull-down current when $V_o = V_{DD}$ and I_{INV} as the pull-down current when $V_o = V_{INV}$.

$$I_{HI} = \frac{k_{pd}}{2}[V_{GS} - V_{THN}]^2 = \frac{69}{2}(5-1)^2 = 552 \ \mu A$$

$$I_{INV} = \frac{k_{pd}}{2}[2(5-1)2.5 - (2.5)^2] = 474 \ \mu A$$

The average pull-down current is

$$\frac{I_{HI} + I_{INV}}{2} = 513 \ \mu A$$

which is twice the average pull-up current, and

$$t_{pHL} = \frac{C_L(V_{DD}/2)}{I_{AV}} = \frac{31(2.5)}{513} = 0.151 \ ns \tag{5.74}$$

$t_{pLH}/t_{pHL} = 2$, and the pair delay is 0.453 ns.

If the pull-up resistance is set equal to the pull-down resistance the pull-up width must be doubled for an electron-to-hole mobility ratio of 2. C_{pu} is now twice the value of C_{pd} and the load capacitance of the previous inverter is now

$$C_L = (2+1)C_{pd} = 3(15.5) = 46.5 \ fF$$

With $k_{pu} = k_{pd} = 69 \ \mu A/V^2$, $I_{pu} = I_{pd} = 513 \ \mu A$, and

$$t_{pHL} = t_{pLH} = \frac{46.5(2.5)}{513} = 0.227 \ ns \tag{5.75}$$

The pair delay is now 0.453 ns. This is identical to the value calculated when the pull-up was a minimum-geometry device as predicted in Sec. 5.5.1.

Let the pull-up be wider than the pull-down by the square root of two and $C_L = (1.414 + 1)C_{pd} = 2.414(15.5) = 37.4$ fF.

$$k_{pu} = \frac{k_{pd}}{1.414} = \frac{69}{1.414} = 48.8 \ \mu A/V^2 \quad \text{and} \quad I_{pu} = 390 \ \mu A$$

$$k_{pd} = 69 \ \mu A/V^2 \quad \text{and} \quad I_{pd} = 474 \ \mu A$$

$$t_{pLH} = \frac{37.4(2.5)}{474} = 0.197 \ \text{ns} \tag{5.76}$$

$$t_{pHL} = \frac{37.4(2.5)}{390} = 0.240 \ \text{ns} \tag{5.77}$$

The pair delay is now 0.437 ns, and is the minimum value, as shown in Sec. 5.5.1.

If the input to the inverter is not a step function, which is usually the case when the inverter is being driven by a pass transistor or another inverter, calculations of rise time and fall time become more complicated. Mukherjee (8) discusses more sophisticated methods of calculating rise times and fall times of MOS circuits, especially when the input signal is not a step function.

5.11 SUMMARY

The aspect ratio of a FET is defined as the ratio of the length to the width of the channel. Several of the more common geometries are discussed, and methods of estimating the corresponding aspect ratios are given. The inverter ratio is defined as the .pull-up aspect ratio divided by the pull-down aspect ratio. The inverter ratio affects rise time, V_{oL} and the inverter voltage, V_{INV}, which is the voltage at which the inverter input and output voltage are the same. V_{INV} in turn affects the noise margins and propagation delays of the inverting gate.

NMOS inverters with enhancement pull-ups and depletion pull-ups are compared for transfer characteristics such as V_{iH}, V_{iL}, V_{oH}, V_{oL}, speed, and noise margins. The saturated enhancement-mode pull-up exhibits a large rise time compared to a depletion-mode pull-up, and only rises to within a threshold voltage of the positive rail. For both these reasons NMOS design is usually done with depletion-mode pull-up devices.

CMOS inverters are also investigated and compared to NMOS inverters. CMOS inverters are ratioless because one device is always off, and thus they have more symmetrical rise and fall times. CMOS output voltages can swing from the positive rail to the negative rail, giving CMOS inverters optimum noise margins. In silicon, electron channel mobilities are about twice the value of hole channel mobilities. This leads to geometric considerations for determining the optimum size of CMOS inverters. Minimum pair delay occurs for an inverter ratio of

$$\frac{1}{\sqrt{2}}$$

NMOS NAND and NOR gates are examined. NOR gates are generally found to be better than NAND gates and, for anything but the simplest circuits, are the preferred way to design. Conventional CMOS NAND and NOR gates can have pull-up and pull-down devices of the same size, and the distinction is not so clear cut.

Methods of calculating transit times of carriers across channels, propagation times, and rise and fall times of NMOS and CMOS inverters are given. Because of the importance of these time intervals, several methods of calculating them are discussed. Hand calculations are essential in order to obtain·a feeling for the limitations of a design, especially before the layout is finalized.

All of the propagation delay and rise-time/fall-time calculations are based upon the assumptions that threshold voltages are constant, and that the input voltage makes a step transition. The answers could be made more accurate by using an appropriately averaged value for the threshold voltage. For NMOS, V_{oL} is typically about 0.3 V. For equal noise margins, the inverter voltage would be $(5 + 0.3)/2 = 2.65$ V. In this case, the propagation delays are more accurately calculated from 0.3 to 2.65 V and 2.65 to 5.0 V.

SPICE can be used when the design has been laid out, and more accurate performance data are needed. When the circuit is implemented in silicon, a ring oscillator consisting of an odd number of inverters, typically from 5 to 25 inverters, can be used to measure propagation delays and obtain experimental values.

REFERENCES

1. M. Horowitz and R. W. Dutton, "Resistance Extraction from Mask Layout Data," *IEEE Transactions on Computer-Aided Design*, vol. CAD-2, no. 3, July 1983, pp. 145–150.
2. C. L. Seitz, "The MOSIS System CMOS/SOS Design Rules," MOSIS User's Manual, USC Information Sciences Institute.
3. S. M. Sze, *Semiconductor Devices, Physics and Technology*, John Wiley & Sons, New York, N.Y., 1985, p. 62.
4. T. E. Dillinger, *VLSI Engineering*, Prentice-Hall, Englewood Cliffs, N.J., 1988, pp. 262–264.
5. A. S. Grove, *Physics and Technology of Semiconductor Devices*, John Wiley & Sons, New York, N.Y., 1967, pp. 108–110 and pp. 346–347.
6. *MOS Integrated Circuits, Theory, Fabrication, Design, and Systems Applications of MOS LSI*, W. M. Penney and L. Lau, (eds.), Van Nostrand Reinhold Company, New York, N.Y., 1972, pp. 215–232.
7. D. K. Reinhard, *Introduction to Integrated Circuit Engineering*, Houghton Mifflin Company, Boston, Mass., 1987, pp. 141–144.
8. A. Mukherjee, *Introduction to nMOS & CMOS VLSI Systems Design*, Prentice-Hall, Englewood Cliffs, N.J., 1986, pp. 182–196.

PROBLEMS

5.1. An NMOS inverter with a butting-contact to the pull-up gate/source is shown in Fig. P5.1. If the current spreading can be ignored the aspect ratio of the pull-up is seen to be 3.5.

    (*a*) Find the aspect ratio of this pull-up if the current spreading is approximated as shown in Fig. P5.1, parts *b* and *c*.

    (*b*) Estimate the inverter ratio of this circuit.

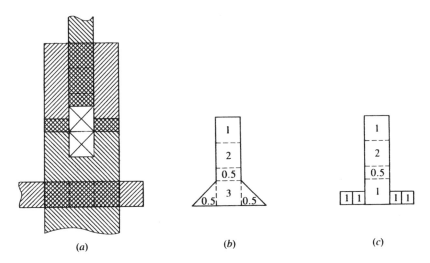

(a)   *(b)*   *(c)*

FIGURE P5.1
An inverter with a butting contact. (*a*) Lay-out; (*b*) and (*c*) approximate geometries of the channel.

5.2. (*a*) Show that Eq. (5.2) of the text is correct.

    (*b*) Plot Eqs. (5.2) and (5.11) from $t = 0$ to 5 ns, for an inverter with $V_{DD} = 5$ V, $V_{THE} = 1$ V, $V_{THD} = -3$ V, $V_{oL} = 0.4$ V, $C_L = 10$ fF, and $k = 20 \ \mu A/V^2$.

5.3. For the standard CMOS inverter discussed in Sec. 5.5, calculate the output voltage as a function of input voltage when the PMOS device is saturated and the NMOS device is in the linear region of operation. Let $C_{oxn} = C_{oxp}$, and $\mu_n = 2\mu_p$.

For Probs. 5.4 through 5.8

An NMOS inverter with a depletion-mode pull-up and enhancement-mode pull-down is shown in Fig. P5.4. It has polysilicon gates, and drains and sources formed by n^+ diffusions. The following data apply:

Junction depth = lateral diffusion distance, $x_j = 1$ micron.

Pull-up device dimensions:

Gate width	$W_{pu} = 3.0$ microns	Transconductance	$k' = 41.4 \ \mu A/V^2$
Gate length	$L_{pu} = 7.5$ microns	Body factor	$\gamma = 1.02 \ V^{1/2}$
Threshold voltage	$V_{THD} = -3.0$ V	Body doping	$N_a = 1.5 \times 10^{16}/cm^3$
		Source, drain doping	$N_d = 10^{18}/cm^3$
		Gate oxide thickness	$t_{ox} = 0.05$ microns
Pull-down device dimensions:		CVD oxide thickness	$t_{CVD} = 0.12$ microns
Gate width	$W_{pd} = 6.0$ microns	Field oxide thickness	$t_{FOX} = 1.00$ micron
Gate length	$L_{pd} = 3.0$ microns	Polysilicon thickness	$t_{PS} = 0.12$ microns
Threshold voltage	$V_{THE} = +1.0$ V	Aluminum thickness	$t_{Al} = 0.50$ microns

5.4. Draw a cross section of Fig. P5.4 from top to bottom (*A* to *B*). Take a scale of $\lambda = 1$ cm for the horizontal distance, and magnify the vertical dimensions by 10.

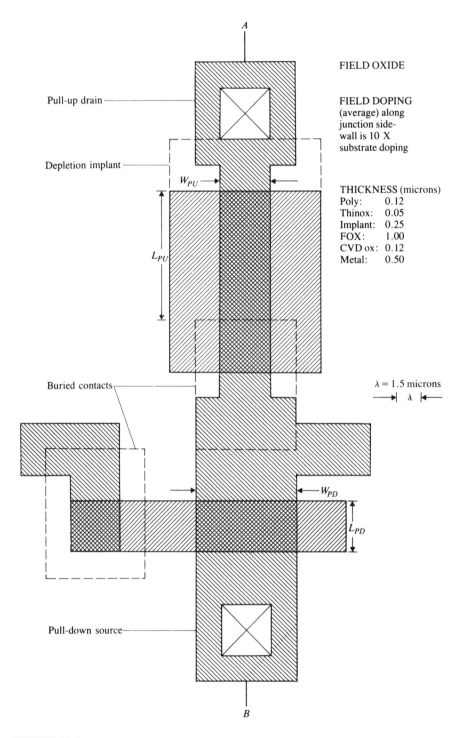

FIGURE P5.4
An NMOS inverter with depletion-mode pull-up and enhancement-mode pull-down.

5.5. Calculate ϕ_0 and specific capacitances C_{jo}, C_{jsw}, C_{ox} and C_{oxLD} for the circuit shown in Fig. P5.4.

5.6. Calculate the nominal areas and perimeters of the sources and drains of both the pull-up and the pull-down devices as shown in Fig. P5.4. Treat the pull-up source and pull-down drain as a single region.

5.7. The nominal aspect ratios are $Z_{pu} = 2.5$ and $Z_{pd} = 0.5$. Calculate the actual aspect ratios, considering lateral diffusion. The diffusion laterally under the field oxide is negligible.

5.8. Repeat Prob. 5.6 for the areas and perimeters when a lateral diffusion of distance $x_j = 1$ micron is included in the calculations.

5.9. For a particular NMOS process, the sheet resistance is $10 \ \text{k}\Omega/\text{sq}$ and the specific capacitance is $10 \ \text{fF/sq}$. Assume the stray wiring capacitance is $20 \ \text{fF}$, and $V_{DD} = 5 \ \text{V}$. Compare the following three inverters for total gate area, speed, and power dissipation:

    (a) $Z_{pu} = 2/1$ and $Z_{pd} = 1/2$
    (b) $Z_{pu} = 4/1$ and $Z_{pd} = 1/1$
    (c) $Z_{pu} = 1/1$ and $Z_{pd} = 1/4$

For Probs. 5.10 through 5.12

Let $V_{DD} = 5 \ \text{V}$, $V_{THE} = 1 \ \text{V}$, $V_{THD} = -3 \ \text{V}$, $V_{THP} = -1 \ \text{V}$, $L_{min} = W_{min} = 2$ microns, $C_{ox} = 0.86 \ \text{fF/micron}^2$, $\mu_n = 800 \ \text{cm}^2/\text{V} \cdot \text{s}$, and $\mu_p = 400 \ \text{cm}^2/\text{V} \cdot \text{s}$.

5.10. (a) Derive Eq. (5.70) from Eq. (5.67), and calculate the rise time, t_{rise}, of a minimum-size NMOS depletion-load inverter.

    (b) Obtain an expression for the rise time of an NMOS inverter driving an identical load device of aspect ratios, $Z_{pu} = 2$ and $Z_{pd} = 1/2$. How does this compare to a transit time, T?

    (c) Calculate the average charging current sourced to the load of the inverter in part b.

5.11. (a) Derive Eq. (5.71) from Eq. (5.67), and calculate the fall time, t_{fall}, of a minimum size NMOS pull-down.

    (b) Obtain an expression for the fall time of an NMOS inverter driving an identical load device of aspect ratios $Z_{pu} = 2$ and $Z_{pd} = 1/2$. How does this compare to a transit time, T?

    (c) Calculate the average discharging current for the inverter in part b.

    (d) The calculation in part b neglects the pull-up current. Repeat part b, including the pull-up current.

5.12. Derive Eq. (5.72) from Eq. (5.67), and calculate the rise time and fall time of a CMOS inverter of minimum gate dimensions, $Z_{pu} = 0.707Z_{pd}$, and $Z_{pu} = 0.5Z_{pd}$.

5.13. If $V_{THD} = -4 \ \text{V}$ and $Z_{pu} = Z_{pd}$, an NMOS depletion-mode pull-up and enhancement-mode pull-down both have the same saturation current when the gate-drive is the same. Calculate the ratio t_{pLH}/t_{pHL} for this inverter.

5.14. For NMOS inverters and $V_{DD} = 5 \ \text{V}$, V_{oL} is typically 0.3 V, and the 50 percent voltage level is 2.65 V. Calculate t_{pLH} and t_{pHL} for the inverter of Example 5.3.

DESIGN PROBLEMS

5.15. Lay out a pair of the 2-input NAND gates previously designed and stored in the cell library. Do a Weinberger layout, with VDD running horizontally across the top and bottom of the layout, and GND running through the middle. (One NAND gate must be inverted with respect to the original gate). Clock the pair of gates with one phase running vertically on the layout.

5.16. Repeat Prob. 5.15 for a pair of 2-input NOR gates.

CHAPTER
6

SUPERBUFFERS, BI-CMOS, AND STEERING LOGIC

6.1 INTRODUCTION

Propagation delays were discussed in Chap. 5. When driving a very large capacitive load, serious delays can occur unless current buffers are used to source and sink large amounts of charge in short times. Devices that can do this are referred to as superbuffers, and can be either inverting or noninverting, NMOS or CMOS.

Often a small-signal gate must drive either a large pad or a long line, usually of polysilicon or metal. Either presents a large capacitive load to the driver. The line acts as a transmission line, with a delay proportional to the square of its length. A method of approximating the delay of the transmission line will be discussed.

Bonding pads are required on every chip to interface it with the rest of the world, and probe pads are often required for testing. Bonding pads are larger than probe pads, but both present a very heavy capacitive load to the pad drivers. One of the main applications of superbuffers is in interfacing between small-signal gates and large pad drivers. Since the stage that actually drives the bonding pad is very large, it should be capable of being turned off, to avoid dissipating standby power.

Superbuffers will be described, and methods of scaling them properly will be investigated. Precharging will be studied as an alternative method of improving performance. Precharging circuitry requires at least two-phase clocking, as well as specially designed precharge drivers.

Bi-CMOS high current drivers will be discussed as alternatives to super-buffers.

Pass-transistor design will be investigated as an alternative to conventional logic. Pass-transistor logic offers no direct path from the plus supply to ground, and thus uses no standby power. Pass transistors can be designed to be minimum size, with channel dimensions of 2λ by 2λ. Pass-transistor circuits must be designed to allow both a pull-up and a pull-down path in order to guarantee that any node driven by them can be discharged as well as charged.

Depletion-mode, enhancement-mode, and CMOS function blocks will be discussed as general forms of pass-transistor logic.

NMOS pass transistors output a logic high that is one threshold voltage below the supply rail, and PMOS pass transistors output a logic low that is one threshold voltage above ground. This leads to a definition of strong and weak ones and zeros, as well as restrictions on driving NMOS and PMOS pass transistors.

6.2 RC DELAY LINES

A long metal line is a low-loss distributed capacitance. A long polysilicon line can be treated as a lumped RC transmission line or delay line as shown in Fig. 6.1. The current charging the capacitance is $C\,dV_2/dt$ which can be approximated as $C\,\Delta V_2/\Delta t$. The current entering node 2 is

$$I_1 = \frac{V_1 - V_2}{R} \tag{6.1}$$

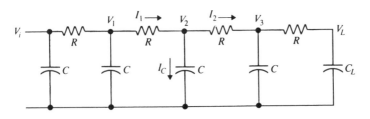

FIGURE 6.1
Lumped equivalent circuit representation of a long polysilicon line.

and the current leaving node 2 is

$$I_2 = \frac{V_2 - V_3}{R} \tag{6.2}$$

Apply Kirchhoff's current law at the node to obtain

$$I_C = C \frac{\Delta V_2}{\Delta t} = I_1 - I_2 = \frac{(V_1 - V_2) - (V_2 - V_3)}{R}$$

Let

$$V_1 - V_2 = \frac{\Delta V_{\text{left}}}{\Delta x} \qquad V_2 - V_3 = \frac{\Delta V_{\text{right}}}{\Delta x}$$

Then

$$RC \frac{\Delta V_2}{\Delta t} = \frac{\Delta V_{\text{left}} - \Delta V_{\text{right}}}{\Delta x} = \frac{\Delta^2 V_2}{\Delta x^2} \tag{6.3}$$

Equation (6.3) is a finite-difference equation. As the number of sections becomes large, the finite-difference equation can be approximated by the differential equation of a distributed model. If this is done, Eq. (6.3) reduces to the diffusion equation

$$RC \frac{dV}{dt} = \frac{d^2 V}{dx^2}$$

where R and C are the resistance and capacitance per lumped element, respectively. The propagation delay is proportional to the total resistance, R_t, and the total capacitance, C_t, of the line, both of which are proportional to the length of line. Hence the propagation time is proportional to the square of the length of the line.

Horowitz (1) shows that, from a discrete analysis of the circuit, the signal delay of N sections with a matched load $C_L = C$ is approximately

$$t_d = 0.7 \frac{N(N + 1)}{2} \frac{R_t}{N} \frac{C_t}{N} \tag{6.4}$$

Let r and c be the resistance and capacitance per length of line, respectively. Then $R_t = rL$ and $C_t = cL$, and the propagation time over a wire of length L is

$$t_d = 0.7 \frac{N(N + 1)}{2} \frac{L^2 rc}{N^2} \tag{6.5}$$

As the number of sections of line approaches infinity, the signal delay reduces to

$$t_d = 0.7 \frac{rcL^2}{2} \tag{6.6}$$

As L becomes very large, the delay becomes unacceptably large. To improve the performance of a very long line, one can insert buffers along the line to restore the signal. The buffer delay depends upon the resistance of the segment driving it, and the capacitance of the segment it drives.

> **Example 6.1.** Find the total resistance, total capacitance, and delay of a 3 mm long polysilicon line of width $3 \, \mu m = 2\lambda$, resistance $50 \, \Omega/\text{sq}$, and capacitance $0.04 \, \text{fF}/\mu m^2 = 0.36 \, \text{fF}/\text{sq}$. Find the improved performance, if one, two, or three inverters of ratio 8 to 1 are inserted in the line. Assume each inverter has a delay, t_I, of 1.0 ns when driving a line 1 mm long. Neglect delay changes with driving resistance. Then the inverter delay is proportional to the load capacitance of the line, which is proportional to the length of line being driven. $t_I = L$ ns when L is in millimeters.

> **Solution.** The length of wire is $3 \, \text{mm}/3 \, \mu m = 1000$ sq, $R_t = 50 \, k\Omega$, and $C_t = 0.36$ pF. $r = 50/3 = 16.67 \, \Omega/\mu m$, $c = 0.04(3) = 0.12 \, \text{fF}/\mu m$, and $t_d = 0.7 r c L^2/2 = 0.7 \times 10^{-15} L^2$.
>
> With no inverters, $t_d = t_{dL} = 6.3$ ns, where t_{dL} is the delay of the 3 mm line.
>
> With one inverter in the line each line segment is 1.5 mm, $t_{dL} = 1.575$ ns per line segment, and $t_I = 1.5$ ns. The total delay, t_d, is $2(1.575) + 1.50 = 4.65$ ns. (74 percent of the unbuffered delay.)
>
> With two inverters in the line, $t_{dL} = 0.70$ ns per section of line, $t_I = 1.0$ ns, and $t_d = 3(0.7) + 2(1.00) = 4.10$ ns. (65 percent of the original delay.)
>
> With three inverters in the line, $t_{dL} = 0.394$ ns per line section, $t_I = 0.75$ ns, and $t_d = 4(0.394) + 3(0.75) = 3.83$ ns. (61 percent of unbuffered delay.)

Three inverters give a slightly faster response than two, while requiring more space and more static power dissipation. In this example, two inverters would probably be a suitable compromise.

The design engineer should also consider widening the bus line. This will reduce the resistance of the line, while increasing the capacitance. When a polysilicon line is very long it might not be feasible to compensate by adding more inverting buffers. In this case, a second metal line, or a silicide of a metal such as molybdenum, titanium, tantalum, or tungston can be deposited on top of a doped polysilicon line. This is referred to as *polysilicide*, and is compatible with thermal oxidation processing.

The above example points out the need to estimate resistances and capacitances before the layout is finalized. To do this, the designer needs a working knowledge of the capacitances and resistances per length, or per square, of bus line. If the process is known, the information can be obtained from test measurements or from the fabricator. Lacking this data, the engineer must proceed with a best guess estimate.

As a rule of thumb diffused lines should never be used and polysilicon lines should be kept as short as possible, or the resistance should be lowered by silicides deposited over the polysilicon.

For a line segment to be treated as a node it must have a unique voltage value. This means the propagation delay on a line must be kept small compared to an inverter delay if the line is to be treated as a node (2). To make the delay of the line, given in Eq. (6.6), small with respect to an inverter propagation delay t_I

$$\frac{0.7L^2rc}{2} \ll t_I$$

$$L \ll \sqrt{\frac{2t_I}{0.7rc}} = 1.69\sqrt{\frac{t_I}{rc}}$$

A suitable maximum length of the line would be:

$$L(\text{max}) = 0.5\sqrt{\frac{t_I}{rc}} \tag{6.7}$$

For the inverter used in example 6.1, the inverter delay was assumed to be 1.0 ns when driving one millimeter of line. Using this value in Eq. (6.7), one obtains for the polysilicon line:

$$L(\text{max}) = 0.5\sqrt{\frac{10^{-9}}{16.67(0.12 \times 10^{-15})}} = 354\,\mu m = 236\,\lambda \tag{6.8}$$

Reasonable estimates for silicon, silicide, and metal lines for this technology would be 300 μm (200 λ), 3000 μm (2000 λ), and 30,000 μm (20,000 λ), respectively.

The line resistance can be minimized by using silicide or metal, but the capacitance remains. It may even get larger if metal is run over poly. To drive these large capacitances, a buffer capable of supplying and sinking large currents is required.

6.3 SUPERBUFFERS

Ratio-type logic suffers from asymmetry in driving capacitive loads because the pull-up device has less drive capability than the pull-down device, and is quite slow when charging a load. The pull-down device has limited current-sinking ability also, and must fight the pull-up device when the output falls. The pull-down is faster than the pull-up by approximately the factor R_{inv}.

A *superbuffer* is a symmetric inverting or noninverting gate that can supply or remove large currents and switch large capacitive loads faster than a standard inverter. Basically, a superbuffer consists of a *totem-pole* or *push-pull* output driven by an inverting or noninverting input that supplies the signal and its complement to the totem-pole. The superbuffer speeds switching both ways, and by proper choice of geometry can be made almost independent of the inverter ratio.

An NMOS superbuffer is rendered ratioless by designing for an inverter ratio of 4 to 1 and driving the totem-pole pull-up with twice the gate bias of a standard depletion-mode pull-up. This gives the inverter equal pull-up and pull-down current capability and identical rise and fall times. The CMOS superbuffer

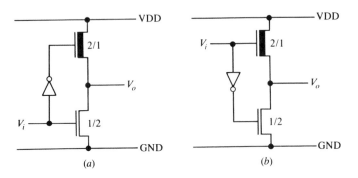

FIGURE 6.2
Mixed-mode diagrams of NMOS superbuffers. (a) Inverting; (b) noninverting.

is rendered ratioless by designing the pull-up aspect ratio to be twice the pull-down aspect ratio, as discussed in Secs. 5.5.1 and 5.10.3, so that it can supply or remove the same amount of current and $t_{rise} = t_{fall}$.

Schematically the two configurations of an NMOS superbuffer can be represented as shown in Fig. 6.2, with the inverted input driving either the pull-up device or the pull-down device. Stick drawings of an inverting and a noninverting superbuffer are shown in Fig. 6.3. Transistors PU_1 and PD_1 form the driving inverter, and transistors PU_2 and PD_2 are the output totem pole.

To analyze the behavior of the inverting superbuffer circuit, consider the following. For the inverting superbuffer of Fig. 6.3a, when the input voltage is low the gates of both pull-down FETs are low, the gates of both pull-up FETs are high, and the output is at the positive rail. When the input goes high the gates of both pull-down FETs switch high, the gates of both pull-up FETs switch low, and the output switches from high to low in approximately t_{fall} seconds.

When the gate of pull-down FET PD_1 goes low, the gate of pull-up FET PU_1 goes to the positive rail very fast, since the load is the gate capacitance of

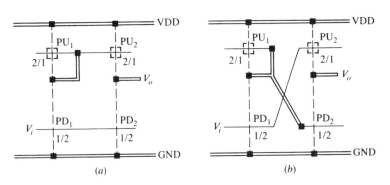

FIGURE 6.3
Stick drawings of (a) an inverting superbuffer, and (b) a noninverting superbuffer.

pull-up FET PU$_2$ only. This drives the push-pull stage very quickly, and the output switches from low to high in approximately t_{fall} seconds also. The superbuffer thus has a propagation delay of t_{fall}, which improves the switching speed.

To examine the switching speed of the noninverting superbuffer, notice that when the input voltage is high, PU$_2$ is on, PD$_2$ is off, and the output is at the positive rail. When the input switches from high to low, PU$_2$ is turned off immediately. With V_i low, the gate of PU$_1$, which is driving the capacitive load of PD$_2$ only, rises rapidly to V_{DD}, turning PD$_2$ on.

In either the inverting or the noninverting case, the depletion-mode FET, PU$_2$, is turned on with about twice the drive of a FET with its gate connected to its source. In the saturation region the drain current is almost proportional to the square of the gate-to-source voltage, and doubling the voltage drive of the depletion-mode FET allows it to supply about four times the current of a standard inverter.

A more precise estimate t_{rise} and t_{fall} is obtained from the average sourcing and sinking current capability. The basic pull-up with its gate and source short circuited together, is in saturation for $V_{DS} > 3$ V, or $V_o < 2$ V. To estimate propagation delay, the device is saturated for $0 < V_o < 2.0$ V, and linear from 2.0 to 2.5 V. The saturation sourcing current at $V_{DS} = 5$ V and the linear current at $V_{DS} = 2.5$ V can be calculated, and the average of these two values can be obtained. Thus:

$$I_D(\text{SAT}) = \frac{k_{pu}}{2}[V_{GS} - V_{THD}]^2 = \frac{k_{pu}}{2}[0 + 3]^2 = 4.50k_{pu} \tag{6.9}$$

$$I_D(\text{LIN}) = \frac{k_{pu}}{2}[2(V_{GS} - V_{THD})V_{DS} - V_{DS}^2]$$

$$= \frac{k_{pu}}{2}[2(0 + 3)2.5 - (2.5)^2] = 4.38\,k_{pu} \tag{6.10}$$

The average current is approximately $4.44k_{pu}$.

The push-pull pull-up is always in the linear region of operation since $V_{GS} = V_{DS}$. The average pull-up current in this case is the average of the linear currents at $V_{DS} = 5$ V and $V_{DS} = 2.5$ V.

$$I_D(5\text{ V}) = \frac{k_{pu}}{2}[2(5 + 3)5 - 5^2] = 27.5\,k_{pu} \tag{6.11}$$

$$I_D(2.5\text{ V}) = \frac{k_{pu}}{2}[2(2.5 + 3)2.5 - (2.5)^2] = 10.62\,k_{pu} \tag{6.12}$$

The average sourcing current for the totem-pole is $(27.5 + 10.62)/2 = 19.06k_{pu}$.

The approximate improvement in pull-up current drive of the totem-pole is $19.06/4.44 = 4.3$. It will be left as an exercise (Prob. 6.1) to calculate more accurate values of both currents, as was done in Chap. 5.

This increase in pull-up current drive of the superbuffer allows it to be almost ratioless when it is designed to have a nominal inverter ratio of 4 to 1, and the effective delay time, t_p, is almost the same whether the output switches from high to low or low to high.

6.3.1 An NMOS Super Superbuffer

An NMOS super superbuffer can be formed as shown in Fig. 6.4, by combining an inverting superbuffer composed of transistors Q_{1A} through Q_{4A}, with a noninverting superbuffer, composed of Q_{1B} through Q_{4B}, both driving the totem-pole output stage Q_5 and Q_6.

Transistors Q_{3A}, Q_{3B}, and Q_5 are zero-threshold devices that have replaced the normal depletion-mode devices. The *zero-threshold device* has a threshold voltage that is nominally zero volts. When the zero-threshold device is used as a source follower it pulls up to V_{DD}. When the gate bias is low, the zero-threshold device is at or quite near cutoff, and the power dissipation of Q_5 approximates that of a PMOS pull-up, rather than a depletion-mode pull-up (3). This buffer can drive large capacitive loads faster than either the inverting or noninverting superbuffer and it exhibits low power consumption under no-load conditions.

An extra masking step is needed to create the zero-threshold transistors.

6.3.2 NMOS TriState Superbuffers and Pad Drivers

Tristate drivers are desirable to multiplex a bus, and to drive large capacitive loads such as pads. A *tristate pad-driver* circuit consists of a suitable number of tristate buffer stages, followed by a pad-driver stage. An NMOS tristate super-buffer stage is shown in Fig. 6.5. A disable signal, ENABLE-BAR, forces both

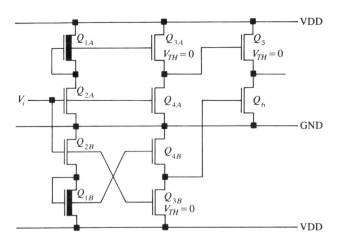

FIGURE 6.4
An NMOS super superbuffer circuit layout.

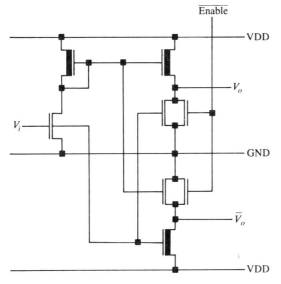

FIGURE 6.5
An NMOS noninverting, tristatable superbuffer.

V_o-BAR and V_o to be low, but it does not cause all current to cease, since the pull-up devices are depletion type, and their sources go to ground when the gate is disabled.

The outputs of this stage feed a pad-driver load such as the circuit shown in Fig. 6.6, and will tristate the pad driver when the superbuffer is disabled. When the gate is enabled, V_o follows V_i and V_o-BAR is the logical complement of V_o.

The *NMOS tristatable superbuffer* draws standby current, but it is desirable that the pad driver which must handle very large currents be truly tristatable. The pad driver is not an NMOS superbuffer because both the pull-up and the pull-down are enhancement-mode devices. However, when both transistor gates are low, the output pad is truly tristated and draws negligible standby current.

As in the output stage of a superbuffer, the pull-up and pull-down of the pad driver form a totem pole. The pad driver devices are normally wrapped around the pads they are driving in order to accommodate the extremely large width of both the pull-up and the pull-down gates. An example of a pad-driver wrapped around its pad is shown in Fig. 6.7.

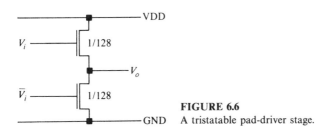

FIGURE 6.6
A tristatable pad-driver stage.

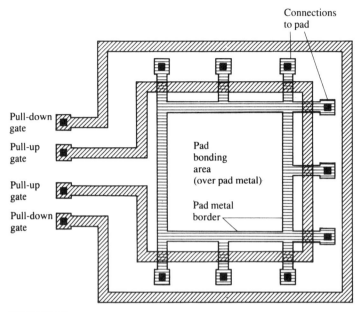

FIGURE 6.7
A pad with pull-up and pull-down devices wrapped around it.

6.3.3 CMOS Superbuffers

By doubling the width of the PMOS channel, the CMOS inverter can be made ratioless with respect to performance, as discussed in Chap. 5. A CMOS super-buffer is simply a wide-channel CMOS inverter, or pair of inverters, that can supply or remove large currents. The CMOS superbuffer should have the capability of tristating the pad driver also.

A *CMOS tristatable superbuffer* is shown in Fig. 6.8. When the enable signal EN is true, EN-BAR is false, Q_{1B} and Q_{3B} are off, Q_{2A} and Q_{2B} are on, V_{o1} is connected to V_{o2}, and the single output signal is the complement of the input signal. When EN is false the inverter is disabled, Q_{2A} and Q_{2B} are both off, while Q_{1B} and Q_{3B} are both on, and V_{o1} is pulled to the positive rail, while V_{o2} is pulled to the negative rail. This forces both the PMOS pull-up and the NMOS pull-down transistors of the CMOS pad-driver totem pole to be off. The CMOS superbuffer is truly tristated.

6.3.4 Bi-CMOS Gates

High-gain vertical *npn* transistors with their collectors tied to the positive rail, and medium-gain lateral *npn* transistors, are both compatible with conventional CMOS processing. When bipolar and MOS technology are merged the resulting circuits are referred to as *bi-CMOS circuits*.

Bi-CMOS gates can be used to improve the performance of line drivers and sense amplifiers. They combine the traditional low power dissipation of CMOS with the output drive capability and low propagation delay of bipolar technolo-

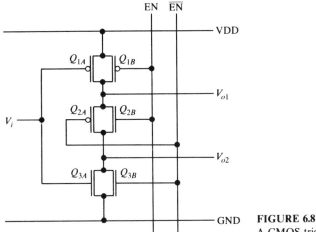

FIGURE 6.8
A CMOS tristatable inverting superbuffer.

gy. The load degradation is practically the same for all circuit functions because the bipolar push-pull devices isolate the CMOS circuits from the loading. Bipolar devices also make it much easier to interface with current-mode or emitter-coupled logic (ECL), which is required in high-speed systems.

Bi-CMOS inverters are shown in Fig. 6.9, and use a pair of push-pull bipolar devices to provide driving capability. The MOS devices provide a high input impedance, while the BJT devices provide current drive and low output impedance. When the input signal is high, the pull-down FET short circuits the base of Q_2 to its collector, converting it to a diode. The pull-up FET is off and Q_1 has no base drive. The output sees a very high resistance to the plus rail and a low resistance to the ground rail, resulting in a low output value. Q_2 can sink

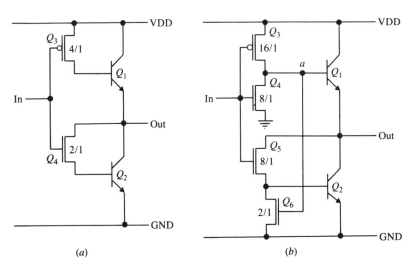

FIGURE 6.9
Bi-CMOS inverters. (*a*) A minimum geometry inverter; (*b*) a faster inverter.

large amounts of current. The reverse happens when the input signal goes low, causing Q_1 to source current and pull the output high, while Q_2 is cut off.

The circuit dissipates essentially no standby power and the low power consumption of the CMOS circuit is preserved. Figure 6.9*b* shows an improved bi-CMOS inverter (4). In the improved bi-CMOS inverter, Q_4 turns on when the input signal goes high, pulling node *a* down and discharging Q_1 quickly. As the potential at node *a* drops, Q_6 is turned off, allowing Q_5 to drive Q_2 on hard and pull the output low. When the input goes low, Q_3 turns on while Q_4 turns off. This allows Q_1 to turn on fast. Q_5 is off and Q_6 turns on when the voltage at node *a* rises, allowing Q_2 to discharge quickly.

$V_{oH} = V_{DD} - V_{BE}$, where V_{BE} is the voltage drop across the base emitter junction of Q_1, while $V_{oL} = V_{BE}$ of Q_2 when the output is short circuited to the base of Q_2 through Q_5 which is conducting when the input is high. When a load capacitance connected to the inverter output is fully charged (discharged) transistor Q_1 (Q_2) is drawing a low collector current, and its V_{BE} is small. The noise margins are then a few tenths of a volt less than half of the V_{DD} supply voltage, or almost as good as those of a CMOS gate.

When the bi-CMOS gate is switching all the FET devices are conducting, and there is a path from V_{DD} to ground. During transition, the two BJT devices are also on, providing another low-impedance path between the supply rails, which is in parallel with the MOS path. This causes the switching current spikes to be larger than those of a conventional CMOS gate. Because of the low output impedance of a bi-CMOS gate, the output switches much faster than the output of a CMOS gate. This causes a load gate driven by a bipolar output to switch faster than it would normally switch when driven by a CMOS gate, and the switching current spikes to be narrower for the bi-CMOS. The overall result is a lowered power dissipation per gate per frequency (4).

The bi-CMOS implementations of a 2-input NAND gate and a 2-input NOR gate are shown in Figs. 6.10 and 6.11, respectively. Typical FET width-to-length conductance ratios are shown in Figs. 6.9, 6.10, and 6.11.

Under no-load conditions, CMOS is faster than bi-CMOS, but as the circuit loading increases, the bi-CMOS easily outperforms the standard CMOS gate due to its superior current capability. Bi-CMOS circuits consume only slightly more power than their standard CMOS counterparts while providing much better switching response.

Bi-CMOS circuits can be used wherever superbuffers can be used. One advantage of bi-CMOS gates is that the pull-up and pull-down current capabilities are determined only by the current gains (betas) of the bipolar devices. When driving heavy loads, bi-CMOS has a big real-estate advantage over superbuffers which do best when scaled up by a factor of no more than four each, and require many buffers in series for heavy loads, as discussed in Sec. 6.5.

The bi-CMOS process merges bipolar transistors that are built into a CMOS process structure without an epitaxial layer. The basic technology is an *n*-well, 2-micron, double-metallization CMOS process, the bipolar devices built with polysilicon emitters. The complete process requires the addition of three mask steps to the ten-mask CMOS *n*-well fabrication process (5).

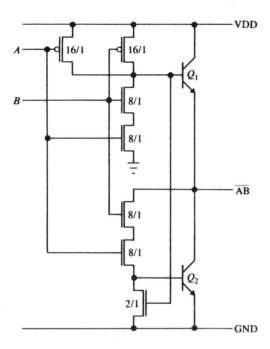

FIGURE 6.10
A bi-CMOS 2-input NAND gate.

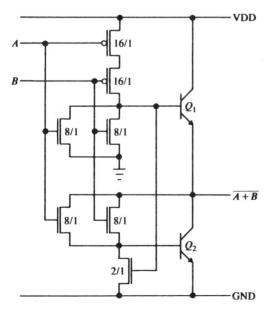

FIGURE 6.11
A bi-CMOS 2-input NOR gate.

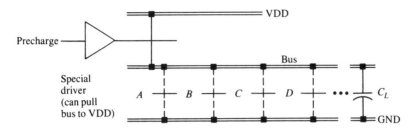

FIGURE 6.12
A mixed-mode drawing of a precharge driver and bus line.

6.4 DYNAMIC RATIOLESS INVERTERS

Precharging is another approach used to improve switching performance. For NMOS circuits, the output can be precharged high (the slow transition) and selectively discharged low. This method requires a minimum of two clock phases, so that all the loads can be precharged on one phase, and selective loads can be discharged on the other phase. This is a dynamic approach to avoiding ratio logic.

A typical example is shown in Fig. 6.12, where a bus line is precharged high. The pull-down devices must be multiplexed, since they are in parallel, and only one pull-down at a time can be allowed to selectively discharge the load. Both the pull-up and the pull-down can be minimum geometry, giving a saving in real estate as well as in speed.

A basic problem with NMOS precharging circuitry is that the driver that precharges the line must have an output that is at least a threshold voltage above plus supply, so that the output line is pulled up to plus supply. This problem will be treated later. For now, assume that appropriate circuitry exists, such that the bus line can be pulled all the way up to V_{DD}. The special driver shown in Fig. 6.12 is assumed to accomplish this. A signal on any input line discharges the bus fast if its input is high, while it has no effect if its input is low.

6.5 LARGE CAPACITIVE LOADS

Driving large capacitive loads such as output pads presents a severe mismatch problem. For example, a two-input NOR gate driving a capacitive load, C_L, of one hundred times the NORs gate capacitance (an equivalent ac fan-out of 100), will have an effective propagation delay of $100t_d$, as shown in Fig. 6.13. This is very slow.

An inverting or noninverting superbuffer can supply much more current

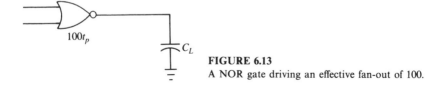

FIGURE 6.13
A NOR gate driving an effective fan-out of 100.

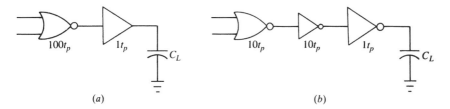

FIGURE 6.14
(a) A NOR gate driving a superbuffer which drives a fan-out of 1; (b) a NOR gate driving a 10 × larger superbuffer, which drives a 100 × larger superbuffer.

than a standard MOS gate, and can be designed to charge the load capacitance with a delay of t_{pLH}, or discharge the load with a delay of $t_{pHL} = t_{pLH} = t_p$, as shown in Fig. 6.14a. However, the superbuffer presents a load equivalent to a fan-out of 100 to the NOR gate, and the effective propagation delay of the super-buffer plus load is now at least $101t_p$. This is worse than the original situation.

Inserting an intermediate-sized superbuffer between the NOR gate and the output superbuffer gives an effective delay of $21t_p$, as shown in Fig. 6.14b. This indicates that using more than one buffer and gradually increasing the buffer sizes is faster because it gradually increases the load at all nodes of the circuit.

Since superbuffers are not ratio devices their propagation delays low-to-high and high-to-low are both the same. Let each superbuffer be scaled up in area by a factor f, so that its gate capacitance is f times larger than the driver gate capacitance. Then each stage is driving a load scaled up by f, with a stage delay of ft_p. For N such stages, the delay is Nft_p. Let Y be the ratio of the load capacitance to one gate capacitance. For N superbuffer stages in cascade (6)

$$Y = \frac{C_L}{C_g} = \frac{C_{g2}}{C_{g1}}\frac{C_{g3}}{C_{g2}}\cdots\frac{C_{gN}}{C_{gN-1}} = f^N \tag{6.13}$$

Take the natural logarithm of both sides of Eq. (6.13) and solve for N.

$$\ln Y = N \ln f \quad \text{and} \quad N = \frac{\ln Y}{\ln f} \tag{6.14}$$

Each stage has a delay of ft_p, the total delay of N stages is

$$Nft_p = f\left[\frac{\ln Y}{\ln f}\right]t_p.$$

The delay is always proportional to $\ln(Y)$, which is determined by the capacitive load. For a given load Y is constant, and the derivative of the total delay with respect to f is proportional to the derivative of $f/\ln(f)$ with respect to f.

$$\frac{d(f/\ln f)}{df} = \frac{\ln f - f(1/f)}{\ln^2 f} \tag{6.15}$$

Set

$$\frac{d(f/\ln f)}{df} = 0$$

TABLE 6.1

f	$\dfrac{f}{e(\ln f)}$
2	1.062
e	1.000
3	1.005
4	1.062
5	1.143
6	1.232

and the minimum total delay for a fixed load capacitance occurs when

$$\ln f = 1 \quad \text{or} \quad f = e \tag{6.16}$$

where e is the base of natural logarithms. The minimum total delay is equal to Nft_p which is

$$Nft_p = \frac{\ln Y}{\ln \epsilon} et_p = et_p \ln\left(\frac{C_L}{C_g}\right) \tag{6.17}$$

The minimum total delay time is a slowly varying function of f for f slightly larger than e, as seen from Table 6.1.

Often the real estate saved by using a ratio of 4 to 1 when scaling up more than justifies the 6 percent penalty in delay time. In fact when driving an output pad or other very large capacitive load, it might be worthwhile to scale the superbuffers by 5 to 1 in order to use less buffers and save space. The speed penalty for this is seen from Table 6.1 to be 14 percent. Unless otherwise specified, a scale factor of 4 to 1 will be assumed in future calculations (6).

The capacitance of a pad can be extremely large, and can require very large pad-driving circuitry. Since buffers should be scaled by 4 to 1, the pad driver should also be scaled to drive an effective fan-out of 4. The NMOS superbuffer shown in Fig. 6.5 is not truly tristatable. When power dissipation is more important than speed, the NMOS pad-driver can be scaled up by more than 4 to 1 with respect to the superbuffer driving it. The CMOS superbuffer of Fig. 6.8 is truly tristatable, and should be scaled up by 4 to 1 with respect to its driver.

A NOR gate driving a fan-out of 100 with three superbuffers, each scaled up by a factor of 4 to 1, can charge the load capacitance in a time of $4t_p$ of the NOR gate, $4t_p$ delay for each of the first two superbuffers, and $100/64 = 1.56t_p$ for the third superbuffer, giving a total time of $13.6t_p$, which is much better than the $21t_p$ of Fig. 6.14b.

> **Example 6.2.** Calculate the propagation delay for an inverter to drive a pad with a capacitive load of 50 pF, if the inverter has a gate capacitance of 15 fF, and the parasitic capacitances of each stage are equal to one gate capacitance.
>
> **Solution.** The load is equivalent to a fan-out of $50{,}000/30 = 1667$. Scaling each stage by 4 to 1, a total of 5.35 stages is required. Each stage, including the pad-driver stage, should be larger than the previous stage by a factor of 4. If the pull-up of the

inverter has a channel width-to-length ratio of 0.5, the superbuffer width-to-length ratios needed are 2, 8, 32, 128, and 512. The pad driver drives an effective load of $1667/512 = 3.26$. The tristate pad stage should be driven by five superbuffer stages, each driving a fan-out of 4, for a delay of $20t_p$, plus $3.26t_p$ for the pad driver, for a total delay of $23.26t_p$.

If area is critical, the buffers can be scaled up by 5 to 1. This requires 4 superbuffers of reciprocal aspect ratios 2.5, 12.5, 62.5, and 312.5, with the pad driver driving a load of $1667/312.5 = 5.33$. The total delay is now $4 \times 5t_p + 5.33t_p = 25.33t_p$, which is not much worse.

6.6 PASS-TRANSISTOR LOGIC

An NMOS or PMOS pass transistor, or a CMOS transmission gate, can be used to steer or transfer charge from one node of a circuit to another node, under the control of the FETs gate voltage. Pass transistor chains are used in designing regular arrays, such as ROMs, PLAs, and multiplexers. When used in regular arrays, depletion-mode pass transistors created by an ion-implant step can be used to remove control from a given FET by short circuiting its drain to its source as shown in Sec. 6.8.1. Thus, both enhancement-mode and depletion-mode devices can appear in pass-transistor chains.

Some problems associated with pass-transistor logic will be discussed in this section, followed by design aspects in Sec. 6.7. Pass transistors have several advantages over inverters. Two major advantages of pass transistors over standard NMOS gate logic are:

1. They are not "ratioed" devices and can be minimum geometry.
2. They do not have a path from plus supply to ground, and do not dissipate standby power.

If the gate and drain of a pass transistor are both high, the source will rise to the lower of the two potentials V_{DD} and $V_{GS} - V_{TH}$. If the gate and drain are both at V_{DD}, the source can only rise to one threshold voltage below the gate. If the source tries to rise higher the device cuts off. If the gate is at least a threshold voltage higher than the drain, the source will rise to within a few millivolts of the drain potential. This is shown in Fig. 6.15.

Three pass transistors driving an inverter are shown in Fig. 6.16. Let the threshold voltage of enhancement-mode pass transistors be 1 V with no back-gate bias, and 1.5 V with a back-gate bias of 3.5 V. Then the node voltages are as shown in Fig. 6.16. With the gate and drain of the first pass transistor at 5 V, its source rises to 3.5 V and the device is at the onset of pinching off. With the gate bias of the second FET at 5 V and its drain at 3.5 V, its source rises to the drain potential 3.5 V, and the device passes the input voltage to its output. Any depletion-mode devices are short circuits and can be omitted from the discussion.

Each additional input requires only a minimum-geometry FET, and adds no dc power dissipation to the circuit. However, there are disadvantages to charge steering. For the circuit shown in Fig. 6.16, and inputs A, B, C, and D all

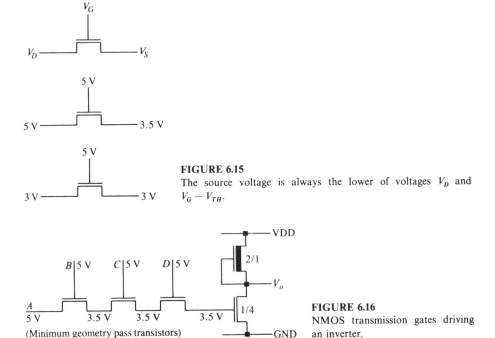

FIGURE 6.15
The source voltage is always the lower of voltages V_D and $V_G - V_{TH}$.

FIGURE 6.16
NMOS transmission gates driving an inverter.

at 5 V, the voltage presented to the inverter input is only 3.5 V. This must be sufficient to drive the inverter output low.

In fact, if a pass transistor is driven by a voltage less than 5 V, the source of that FET will be at one threshold voltage less than the corresponding gate voltage, and the voltage presented to the inverter input will be lower than the lowest gate voltage of the pass transistor chain by one threshold voltage drop. Figure 6.17 shows the situation when input C is 3.5 V, which would be the case if it were driven by a pass transistor. Even though input D is 5 V, the voltage to the inverter is only 2 V. This is below the inverter threshold voltage, and will most likely be treated by the inverter as a logic 0 when it should have been a logic 1.

A sufficiently high inverter ratio will solve this problem, but at the expense of a long pull-up. If NMOS pass-transistor logic circuits are designed such that one pass transistor never drives the gate of another pass transistor, the output high from a pass-transistor logic string will be about 3.5 V. An inverter with a ratio of 8 to 1, as shown in Figs. 6.16 and 6.17, will suffice to restore the signal to a logic high of 5 V. This leads to the first major rule in designing NMOS pass-transistor logic.

> In designing NMOS pass-transistor logic, one must never drive a pass transistor with the output of another pass transistor!

This is not a problem when using CMOS transmission gates.

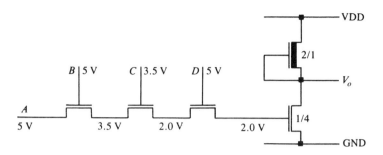

FIGURE 6.17
The circuit of Fig. 6.16 with input C at 3.5 V.

There is another problem associated with pass-transistor logic that the designer must be aware of. If control D in Fig. 6.16 goes from logic 1 to logic 0, the gate-to-drain capacitance of the pass transistor driven by signal D couples a negative voltage step to the inverter input. When the voltage at D drops from 5 to 0 V, the input voltage to the inverter drops from 3.5 to -1.5 V. The pass transistor is turned off by the logic 0 at D and there is no discharge path for the pull-down device of the inverter. Thus the second major rule in designing NMOS pass-transistor chains.

> In designing pass-transistor logic, care must be taken
> to ensure the existence of both charging
> and discharging paths to the inputs of all inverters!

Charge sharing is a serious problem which occurs when two or more capacitors at different potentials are tied together. A node of a network must never be driven simultaneously by signals of opposed polarity, as this can leave the node in an erroneous or undefined state. One must beware of "sneak paths" which allow charge to leak. Pass transistors are bilateral, and charge can flow from output to input also. This is not a problem if all the inputs are designed to connect to the output via mutually disjoint paths.

A *sneak path* is created when two pass transistors are both on at the same time and one is connected to VDD while the other is connected to GND, as shown in Fig. 6.18. Pass transistors are usually designed to be of minimum size, 2λ by 2λ. If, further, the two devices have the same gate-to-source bias, their on resistances will be approximately equal and the output voltage will be about VDD/2.

There is also a timing problem associated with the circuit shown in Fig. 6.16. If all four signals are high, the inverter input is high. If B, C, or D goes low while A is high, the inverter input will remain high when A goes low, and the output will be low. However, if A goes low first, a low is presented to the inverter, and when any of the pass transistors turn off, a low will be latched to the inverter

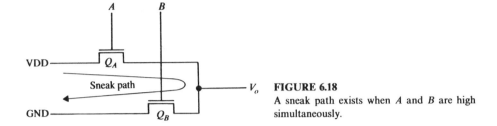

FIGURE 6.18
A sneak path exists when A and B are high simultaneously.

input, keeping its output high. This problem is avoided by either tying A to the positive rail and not using it as a data input, or by providing A with both charging and discharging paths to the inverter.

> One must always provide both a charging
> and a discharging path for all input variables!

In designing pass-transistor circuits, both true and false input variables must be passed to the output in order to provide pull-up and pull-down paths and avoid undefined states. Inverters are needed to drive control inputs because they output strong ones, and superbuffers are required to drive long chains.

A pass-transistor chain driving a capacitive load is shown in Fig. 6.19. As with the long transmission line of Sec. 6.2, the pass-transistor chain can be approximated as a lumped RC equivalent circuit, as shown in Fig. 6.1. In this approximation, C is the gate-to-channel capacitance plus any parasitic capacitance of the gate node; and R is the series resistance of the channel with the FET operating in the linear region, plus any parasitic resistance between nodes.

The distributed model is as discussed in Sec. 6.2. The rise time is proportional to the total resistance, R_t, and the total capacitance, C_t, of the line, both of which double when the number of pass transistors doubles. Hence the propagation time is proportional to the square of the number of pass transistors in the chain. As with the finite transmission line consisting of N elements, a string of N

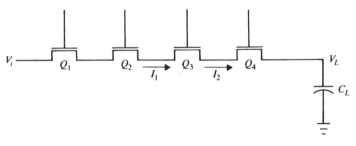

FIGURE 6.19
A pass-transistor chain driving a capacitive load C_L.

TABLE 6.2

N	$\dfrac{N(N+1)}{2}$	t_{pLH}	t_{pHL}	$P = t_{pLH} + t_{pHL}$
1	1	$0.63RC_L$	$0.79RC_L$	$1.42RC_L$
2	3	$1.89RC_L$	$2.37RC_L$	$4.26RC_L$
3	6	$3.78RC_L$	$4.74RC_L$	$8.52RC_L$
4	10	$6.30RC_L$	$7.90RC_L$	$14.20RC_L$
5	15	$9.45RC_L$	$11.85RC_L$	$21.30RC_L$

identical pass transistors driving a matched load, $C_L = C_g$, exhibits a delay of approximately

$$t_p = 0.7 \frac{N(N+1)}{2} RC_L \tag{6.18}$$

Again, more accurate estimates for the propagation delay times low-to-high, t_{pLH}, and high-to-low, t_{pHL} are (1)

$$t_{pLH} = 0.63 \frac{N(N+1)}{2} RC_L \quad \text{and} \quad t_{pHL} = 0.79 \frac{N(N+1)}{2} RC_L \tag{6.19}$$

In Table 6.2, rising and falling propagation delay times and pair delay are calculated for short pass-transistor chains. Periodic restoration of the full signal voltage swing will improve the speed of the circuit. A cascade of more than four steering gates produces a very slow circuit, and the signal should be restored by an inverter after every three or four steering gates. This can be a severe problem in designing large PLAs.

6.7 DESIGNING PASS-TRANSISTOR LOGIC

The VLSI designer must minimize power, delay, and chip area. Good pass-transistor design can often give faster logic than conventional MOS design, with very low power loss and much less chip area.

Define a strong one as an output very close to the positive rail, and a strong zero as an output very close to the negative rail. A weak one can then be defined as an output voltage that is above V_{iH} but lower than a strong one, and a weak zero as an output that is below V_{iL} but higher than a strong zero. Typical values for 5 V logic are shown in Table 6.3.

TABLE 6.3

Signal	Range, V
Strong one	4.5–5.0
Weak one	3.5–4.5
Weak zero	0.5–1.5
Strong zero	0.0–0.5

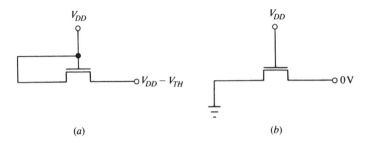

FIGURE 6.20
The NMOS pass transistor passes (a) weak ones, and (b) strong zeros.

An NMOS pass transistor can pull down to the negative rail, but it can only pull up to a threshold voltage below the positive rail, as shown in Fig. 6.20. It can output a strong zero, but only a weak one. By contrast, a PMOS pass transistor can pull up to the positive rail, but can only pull down to a threshold voltage above the negative rail. It can output a strong one, but only a weak zero, as shown in Fig. 6.21.

NMOS and PMOS depletion-mode devices can both pass strong ones and zeros, but they never turn off and can only be used to remove control from a gate signal.

CMOS transmission gates can be used whenever PMOS devices are available. CMOS transmission gates are superior to NMOS pass transistors in two significant ways. First, they output both strong ones and strong zeros. Second, the transmission gate consists of two transistors in parallel, and except near the positive and negative rails, it has about half the resistance of a single pass transistor. Halving the resistance halves the propagation delay of the string.

There are two disadvantages to CMOS transmission gates. They require more area than NMOS pass circuitry, and they require complemented control signals. They also differ from NMOS pass transistors in that, in conventional CMOS design, the PMOS pass function is the dual of the NMOS structure, whereas in NMOS design the pull-up and pull-down are complementary functions. The circuit diagram, stick drawing, and one possible layout of a CMOS transmission gate, are shown in Fig. 6.22. See Plate 4 also.

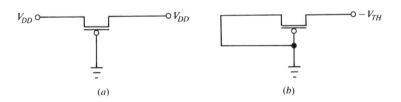

FIGURE 6.21
The PMOS pass transistor passes (a) strong ones, and (b) weak zeros.

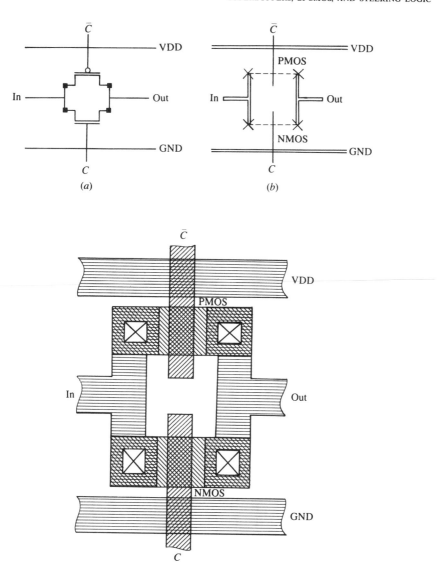

FIGURE 6.22
CMOS transmission gate. (*a*) Circuit diagram; (*b*) stick drawing; (*c*) physical layout.

With four or less pass gates, the pass-transistor network dissipates negligible switching power. For more pass gates in series, signal-restoring buffers which dissipate static and switching power must be added. Four pass gates typically have less than half the dynamic power dissipation of one inverter, and using pass-transistor strings to replace four of every five inverters in a circuit reduces the total power dissipation by a factor of better than two to one.

A Karnaugh mapping which ensures pull-up and pull-down pass logic for all input combinations has been reported by Whitaker (7). In this approach, groupings that pass both true and false input variables are made in order to avoid undefined states.

The Karnaugh maps are obtained by adding to the truth table a column which gives the desired pass function. This column contains an OR-function of the input variables that guarantees that the desired output is realized for each minterm. This column is then mapped, and looped in such a manner as to obtain the pass functions required for each control variable.

The K-map and pass-transistor circuitry for a 2-input NAND gate are shown in Fig. 6.23, and those of a 2-input NOR gate are shown in Fig. 6.24. From the first row of the 2-input NAND gate truth table, it can be seen that the output can go high through either A' or B'. Likewise, from the second row, the output can go high through either A' or B. Continuing in this manner, one can design both pull-up and pull-down paths for the circuit, and there is no danger of tristating the output. The gating signals are disjoint and there is no danger of charge sharing either.

Since the desired pass function can be achieved as a function of A or of B, either A or B can be used as the control signal, and the other variable as the input signal. In Figs. 6.23 and 6.24 both possible realizations are shown.

NAND gate

Inputs		Output	
A	B	Y	Pass FN
0	0	1	$\bar{A} + \bar{B}$
0	1	1	$\bar{A} + B$
1	0	1	$A + \bar{B}$
1	1	0	$\bar{A} + \bar{B}$

(a)

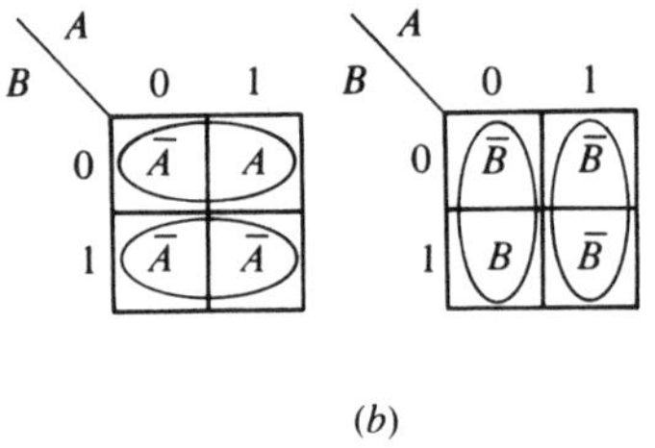

(b)

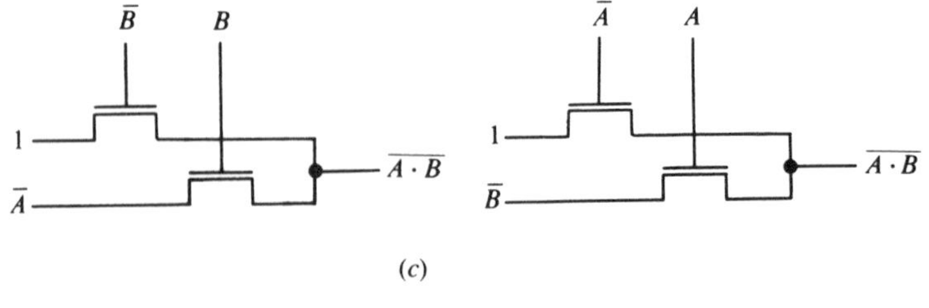

(c)

FIGURE 6.23
Pass-transistor 2-input NAND Gate. (a) Truth table; (b) maps; (c) two realizations.

NOR gate

Inputs		Output	
A	B	Y	Pass FN
0	0	1	$\bar{A} + \bar{B}$
0	1	0	$A + \bar{B}$
1	0	0	$\bar{A} + B$
1	1	0	$\bar{A} + \bar{B}$

(a)

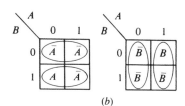

(b)

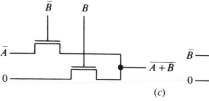

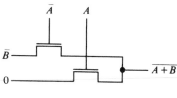

(c)

FIGURE 6.24
Pass-transistor 2-input NOR gate. (a) Truth table; (b) map, (c) two realizations.

6.8 GENERAL FUNCTION BLOCKS

One application of pass-transistor logic is the *universal logic module*, or *general function block*, which is a close relative of the PLA. It is often less costly in area, time, and power to implement a general function block than it is to implement a specific function. The function block can be either NMOS or CMOS and, if implemented, the details of its operation can be left unbounded until later. This provides a cleaner interface to the next level of design. The general two-variable function block that implements all 16 logic functions of two input variables A and B, and is controlled by inputs C_0 through C_3, is shown in Fig. 6.25.

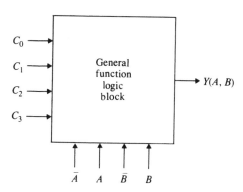

FIGURE 6.25
Symbol for a 2-variable function block for variables A and B, controlled by C_0 through C_3.

6.8.1 NMOS Function Blocks

Examination of Figs. 6.23 and 6.24 shows the same structure for NAND and NOR gates, regardless of the control variables. Examination of 2-input NAND, NOR, AND, OR, EOR, and ENOR pass networks shows that they all are of the same topological structure, with only the inputs, controls, and outputs changing. These six functions are special cases of the sixteen possible logic functions realizable with a 2-input function block, or logic block, as shown in Fig. 6.26.

There are two possible realizations of a two-input function block, one consisting of enhancement-mode transistors only and one made with both depletion-mode and enhancement-mode transistors. The first approach is the conventional steering logic that has been under discussion, the second realization is an alternative approach. The two possible realizations are shown in Figs. 6.27 and 6.28.

The mask sets for the circuits in Figs. 6.27 and 6.28 are complementary in the sense that an enhancement-mode device loses control if it is missing, while an ion-implant removes control from a depletion-mode device. Thus, implants in Fig. 6.28 are placed where transistors were omitted in Fig. 6.27.

As mentioned earlier, timing problems can occur when variables are used as inputs to pass-transistor chains as well as control signals. The timing problems can be eliminated by using only VDD and GND as inputs to the pass-transistor chains, but this doubles the size of the gate. For example, to design an exclusive-OR gate with 0 and 1 inputs requires four controls, A, $\bar{A}$, B, and $\bar{B}$. This requires a 4-to-1 multiplexer in either NAND or NOR form. Two realizations of an EOR gate with fixed inputs are shown in Fig. 6.29 and are seen to require a 4×4 matrix of transistors.

To complete the discussion, stick drawings of NMOS pass-transistor 2-variable function blocks are shown in Fig. 6.30. Figure 6.30a shows the function block realized with NOR logic consisting of enhancement-mode devices only, and Fig. 6.30b shows the function block realized with NAND logic consisting of enhancement-mode and depletion-mode transistors.

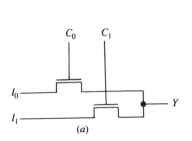

General function block

Output	Inputs		Controls		Logic
Y	I_0	I_1	C_0	C_1	Function
AB	0	B	$\bar{A}$	A	AND
$\overline{AB}$	1	$\bar{B}$	$\bar{A}$	A	NAND
$A + B$	B	1	$\bar{A}$	A	OR
$\overline{A + B}$	$\bar{B}$	0	$\bar{A}$	A	NOR
$A \oplus B$	B	$\bar{B}$	$\bar{A}$	A	EOR
$A \odot B$	$\bar{B}$	B	$\bar{A}$	A	ENOR

(a)   (b)

FIGURE 6.26
The general two-variable function block. (a) Circuit, and (b) control and input variables for six output functions.

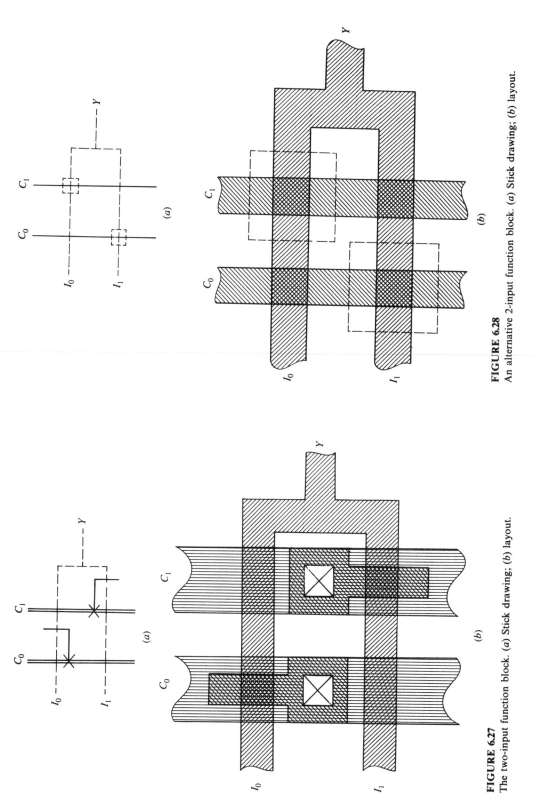

FIGURE 6.28
An alternative 2-input function block. (a) Stick drawing; (b) layout.

FIGURE 6.27
The two-input function block. (a) Stick drawing; (b) layout.

171

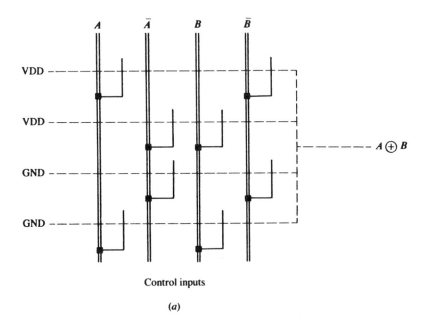

Control inputs

(a)

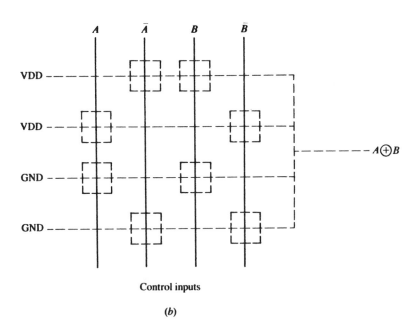

Control inputs

(b)

FIGURE 6.29
NMOS exclusive-OR gates realized with fixed inputs. (a) NOR structure; (b) NAND structure.

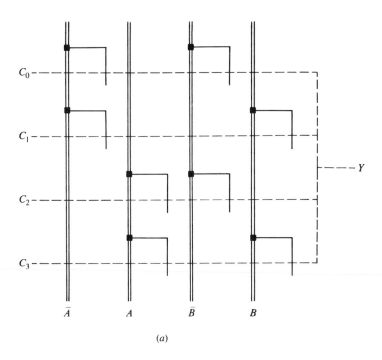

(a)

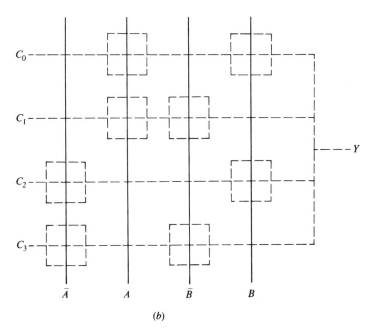

(b)

FIGURE 6.30
Stick drawings of NMOS pass-transistor 2-variable function blocks. (a) NOR, and (b) NAND realizations.

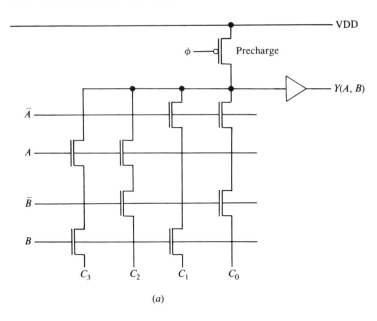

(a)

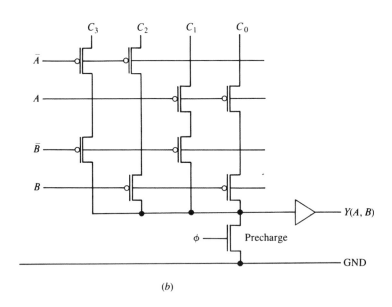

(b)

FIGURE 6.31
Two-variable CMOS function blocks. (a) Mostly-NMOS; (b) mostly-PMOS.

6.8.2 CMOS Function Blocks

A CMOS function block that implements all 16 logic functions of two input variables, A and B, and is controlled by inputs C_0 through C_3, would be structurally similar to the NMOS block in Fig. 6.30a. A complementary CMOS design would consist of eight transmission gates replacing the eight pass transistors of the NMOS design. When the CMOS function block is laid out the transmission gates would be split. The PMOS transistors would be grouped in an n-well and the NMOS transistors would be grouped in a p-well. This gives rise to a structure twice the size of an NMOS function block, containing twice as many transistors. Depletion-mode devices are not used in CMOS design, and there is no CMOS equivalent of the NMOS NAND structure of Fig. 6.30b.

The CMOS function block can be reduced in size by using precharge logic. It can be precharged either high or low. A precharged-high mostly-NMOS function block and a precharged-low mostly-PMOS function block are shown in Fig. 6.31. A mostly NMOS pull-down circuit for a four-variable function block is shown in Plate 5. The output of the function block is precharged on phase 1, and is controlled by the four signals labeled C_0, C_1, C_2, and C_3. During precharge the controls are kept at the same logic level as the output, thus eliminating the need to disconnect the evaluation block during precharge. The four controls are kept low in the case of the mostly-NMOS circuit of Fig. 6.31a, and high in the case of the mostly-PMOS circuit of Fig. 6.31b.

6.9 SUMMARY

MOS transistors often must drive large capacitive loads. Superbuffers are inverting and noninverting gates built of larger transistors which can source and sink more current than standard-sized devices. If an exponentially increasing driving circuitry is scaled such that each FET drives an effective load of $e = 2.72$, the propagation delay is a minimum. For most applications scaling up by 4 is satisfactory and saves space.

Bi-CMOS draws negligible standby power and uses bipolar transistors with high current gain to enhance switching speed without causing power-dissipation problems. This approach does increase input loading, but interconnect capacitance often dominates layouts that require bi-CMOS drivers.

Increasing the transistor width, as in superbuffer design, can make the circuit run faster without significantly increasing the overall power consumption, but bi-CMOS can source and sink large currents while taking up much less space than a series of superbuffers. Bi-CMOS does add three masking steps to the process.

Pass transistors can be minimum size and they dissipate no standby power. A pass transistor is faster than an inverter, but a long string of steering logic begins to act as a transmission line and delays become unacceptably large. Inserting inverters to restore the signal after about four pass transistors gives shorter propagation delay.

NMOS steering gates output a weak 1 of about 3.5 V, and PMOS steering gates output a weak 0 of about 1.5 V. NMOS pass transistors must never be driven by weak ones, nor for that matter, can PMOS pass transistors be driven by weak zeros. Inverters driven by pass transistors must have at least an 8-to-1 inverter ratio, and one must ensure that both charging and discharging paths are available at the input of each inverter.

Steering logic can be mapped into general function blocks which can realize all the possible combinations of the input variables. They can be designed with enhancement-mode devices only, or with enhancement-mode and depletion-mode devices. To avoid timing problems, function blocks should have inputs connected to the appropriate supply rails, and use data signals only for controls. For two variables, this approach gives a 4×4 matrix. Larger matrices will require restoring logic after every four pass transistors.

REFERENCES

1. M. Horowitz, "Timing Models for MOS Pass Networks," *Proc. IEEE Symp. Circuits and Systems*, 1983, pp. 198–201.
2. N. Weste and K. Eshraghian, *Principles of CMOS VLSI Design*, Addison-Wesley, Reading, Mass., 1985, pp. 131–137.
3. D. A. Pucknell and K. Eshraghian, *Basic VLSI Design, Principles, and Applications*, Prentice-Hall of Australia, Sydney, Aus., 1985, pp. 282–283.
4. E. W. Greenwich and K. L. McLaughlin, "Analysis and Characterization of BiCMOS for High-Speed Digital Logic," *IEEE J. Solid-State Circuits*, vol. 23, April, 1988, pp. 558–565.
5. S. C. Lee, D. W. Schucker, and P. T. Hickman, "Bi-CMOS Technology for High-Performance VLSI Circuits," *VLSI Design*, August, 1984, pp. 98–100.
6. C. A. Mead and L. A. Conway, *Introduction to VLSI Systems*, Addison-Wesley Publishing Co., Reading, Mass., 1980, pp. 12–14.
7. S. Whitaker, "Pass-Transistor Networks Optimize *n*-MOS Logic," *Electronics*, Sept. 22, 1983, pp. 144–148.

PROBLEMS

6.1. Use Eq. (5.67) to calculate more accurate sourcing currents for a normal pull-up with its gate short circuited to its source, and a push-pull pull-up with $V_{GS} = V_{DS}$. Compare your answers with those in Eqs. (6.9) through (6.12).

6.2. A push-pull gate, sometimes called "poor man's CMOS," is shown in Fig. P6.2. Compare the speed and power consumption of this gate to a conventional NMOS NOR gate of the same size.

6.3. Consider a minimum geometry gate of size $2\lambda \times 2\lambda$ to define one unit of area. A minimum geometry gate size ($2\lambda \times 2\lambda$) is capacitively equivalent to a contact area of the same size, to about 5 units of area of a polysilicon line, and to about 10 units of area of first or second metal lines. Calculate the rising and falling propagation times for the NMOS example of Fig. P6.3a and the CMOS example of Fig. P6.3b. The aspect ratios of the NMOS are $Z_{pu} = 4$ and $Z_{pd} = 1/2$, the aspect ratios of the CMOS inverters are $Z_{pu} = 1/4$ and $Z_{pd} = 1/2$, and the propagation delays of minimum size NMOS and PMOS devices are $t_n = 0.3$ ns and $t_p = 0.6$ ns.

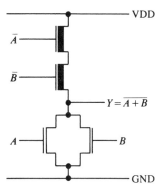

FIGURE P6.2
An NMOS push-pull NOR gate.

6.4. (a) Show that for $N_a = 10^{15}$ atoms/cm^3, and $t_{ox} = 700$ angstroms, the value of the threshold voltage for a pass-FET is approximately 1.5 V and a "weak 1" is about 3.5 V. Assume the threshold voltage is 1 V when there is no body effect.
  (b) Does it help to increase the gate-oxide thickness to 1000 angstroms?
  (c) Does increasing N_a improve a "weak 1"?

6.5. For a level restoring inverter driven by a pass transistor, determine the value of $R_{inv} = Z_{pu}/Z_{pd}$ that will yield a V_{oL} at least as small as the value of V_{oL} for an inverter driven by a 5 V signal. Assume $V_{THE} = 0.2\ V_{DD}$ for the pull-down device and $V_{THD} = 0.3\ V_{DD}$ for the pull-up device.

6.6. For an NMOS pass transistor of length 3 μm, threshold voltage 1 V, and electron mobility 800 cm^2/V·s, calculate the channel transit time as a function of bias voltage.

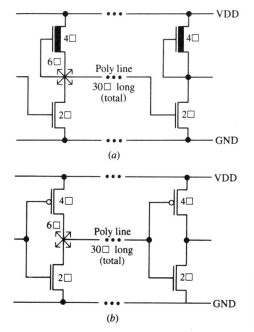

FIGURE P6.3
(a) An NMOS, and (b) a CMOS inverter, driving an identical load over a polysilicon line of length 30 squares.

Input			Output	
A	B	C	Y_1	Y_0
0	0	0	0	0
0	0	1	0	1
0	1	0	1	0
0	1	1	1	0
1	0	0	1	1
1	0	1	1	1
1	1	0	1	1
1	1	1	1	1

Truth table for Problem P6.8

6.7. Design pass-transistor circuits with depletion-mode devices for the NAND gate of Fig. 6.23 and the NOR gate of Fig. 6.24 using VDD and GND as inputs. How do these gates compare in size to those shown in Figs. 6.27 and 6.28?

6.8. Design a pass-transistor circuit for the priority encoder whose truth table is given. The controls are A and B. Show the Karnaugh maps and a circuit diagram. Realize Y_1 and Y_2 simultaneously. Which form of pass-transistor circuit is better suited for this realization, and why?

6.9. Design a pass-transistor circuit for a three-input majority gate. The output of a 3-input majority gate is true if at least two inputs are true. The controls are A and B. Show the Karnaugh map and a circuit diagram.

6.10. Consider a string of three pass transistors controlled by input signal A, and gate signals B, C, and D, which are all high (5 V) as shown in Fig. 6.16. Let signals B and D both switch low (0 V), after which signal C switches low. When transistors B and D turn off, transistor C has no discharge path to left or right. With 5 V on the gate of transistor C its capacitance gate-to-ground is charged.
(a) Where does this charge go when the gate of transistor C goes low?
(b) If these transistors are in the same well, what should be done to avoid problems caused by the charge on gate C?

6.11. Give the truth table for the function blocks shown in Fig. 6.30. The C_i are the controls and the outputs are functions of A and B.

For Probs. 6.12 through 6.17

SPICE simulation is to be used to obtain the transient response of the circuits given in Probs. 6.12 through 6.17 to determine propagation delays and rise and fall times of the output voltage. The SPICE circuit is shown in Fig. 2.10, and the parameters needed for the transistors are:

$k' = KP = 69$ μA/V^2 for NMOS devices and 34.5 μA/V^2 for PMOS devices. GAMMA = 0.37 V$^{1/2}$, LAMBDA = 0.06 V^{-1}, TOX = 0.04 μm, R_d = RD = 1 Ω, and R_s = RS = 1 Ω. C_{bd} = CBD = 2 fF, C_{bs} = CBS = 2 fF, C_j = CJ = 200 μF/m^2, C_{gbo} = CGB0 = 200 pF/m, C_{gso} = CGS0 = 40 pF/m, and C_{gdo} = CGD0 = 40 pF/m. For NMOS enhancement-mode transistors, $V_{THE} = $ VT0 $= 1$ V, for NMOS depletion-mode devices, $V_{THD} = $ VT0 $= -3$ V, and for PMOS enhancement-mode devices, $V_{THP} = $ VT0 $= -1$ V. $AS = AD = 36$ pm, and $PD = PS = 24$ μm.

The input signal is a voltage pulse from 0 to 5 V, with a delay of 1 ps, a rise time and a fall time of 10 ps each, a pulse width of 3 ns, and a period of 6 ns. Plot the output voltages of each inverter (V_{01} and V_{02}) versus time and determine t_{rise}, t_{fall}, t_{pLH}, and t_{pHL} for each inverter.

6.12. The NMOS inverter consists of an NMOS enhancement-mode pull-up device, $Q1$, with $L = 6$ μm and $W = 3$ μm, an NMOS enhancement-mode pull-down device, $Q2$, with $L = 3$ μm and $W = 6$ μm, and a load capacitance of 31 fF. The circuit is shown in Fig. P6.12.

6.13. The NMOS inverter consists of an NMOS depletion-mode pull-up device, $Q1$, with $L = 6$ μm and $W = 3$ μm, an NMOS enhancement-mode pull-down device, $Q2$, with $L = 3$ μm and $W = 6$ μm, and a load capacitance of 31 fF. The circuit is shown in Fig. P6.13.

6.14. The conventional CMOS inverter consists of a PMOS enhancement-mode pull-up device, $Q1$, with $L = W = 3$ μm, an NMOS enhancement-mode pull-down device, $Q2$, with $L = W = 3$ μm, and a load capacitance of 31 fF. The circuit is shown in Fig. P6.14.

6.15. The CMOS inverter with minimum pair delay consists of a PMOS enhancement-mode pull-up device, $Q1$, with $L = 3$ μm and $W = 4.24$ μm, an NMOS enhancement-mode pull-down device, $Q2$, with $L = W = 3$ μm, and a load capacitance of 37.4 fF. The circuit is shown in Fig. P6.14.

6.16. The CMOS inverter with equal rise and fall times consists of a PMOS enhancement-mode pull-up device, $Q1$, with $L = 3$ μm and $W = 6$ μm, an NMOS enhancement-mode pull-down device, $Q2$, with $L = W = 3$ μm, and a load capacitance of 46.5 fF. The circuit is shown in Fig. P6.14.

6.17. The pseudo-NMOS CMOS inverter consists of a PMOS enhancement-mode pull-up device, $Q1$, with $L = 9$ μm, $W = 3$ μm, an NMOS enhancement-mode pull-down device, $Q2$, with $L = W = 3$ μm, and a load capacitance of 15.5 fF. The circuit is shown in Fig. P6.17.

DESIGN PROBLEMS

6.18. Design an inverting NMOS superbuffer for the cell library.

6.19. Design a noninverting NMOS superbuffer for the cell library.

6.20. Design a CMOS superbuffer for the cell library.

6.21. A totem-pole pad driver is to drive an effective fan-out of 50 pF. The pad dimensions are 100 μm on an edge, $\lambda = 2$ μm, and $C_L = 31$ fF for a normal fanout of 1. Design the pad driver to wrap around the pad. Count corner squares as half squares.

6.22. Repeat Prob. 6.21 for a pad size of 90 μm $\times$ 90 μm. The pad specific capacitance and the load capacitance remain the same as in Prob. 6.21.

6.23. Lay out the general function blocks shown in Fig. 6.30.

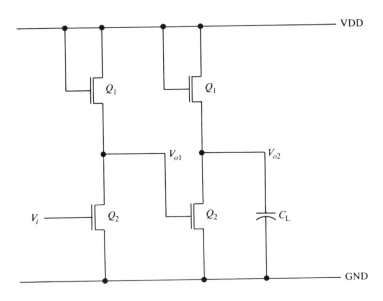

FIGURE P6.12
An NMOS inverter with enhancement-mode pull-up driving an identical inverter with a capacitive load.

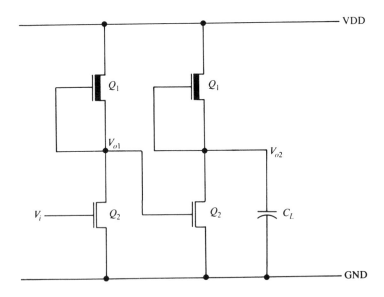

FIGURE P6.13
An NMOS inverter with depletion-mode pull-up driving an identical inverter with a capacitive load.

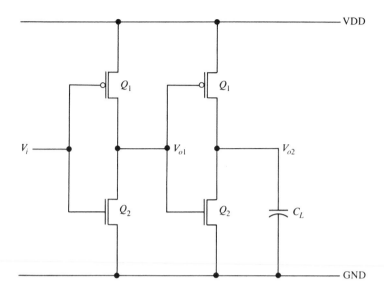

FIGURE P6.14
A CMOS inverter driving an identical inverter with a capacitive load.

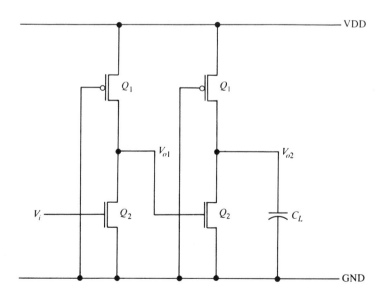

FIGURE P6.17
A pseudo-NMOS CMOS inverter driving an identical inverter with a capacitive load.

CHAPTER
7

DYNAMIC CMOS AND CLOCKING

7.1 INTRODUCTION

As system complexity and circuit density increase, power dissipation becomes a limiting factor, causing a shift from NMOS to CMOS technology. Modern NMOS process sequences have become longer and more complex, while at the same time CMOS processes have been simplified and new techniques have reduced the area penalty significantly. Much effort has been expended to minimize the relative disadvantages of CMOS because of its desirable speed-power product. New circuit techniques, low-temperature processing techniques replacing high-temperature operations, and dry etching replacing wet etching, have all contributed to the drive for low-cost, high-reliability CMOS fabrication.

This chapter begins with an examination of the four major CMOS technologies. The relative merits of each CMOS layout, and the process steps required, will be discussed. CMOS will be compared to NMOS, and CMOS/bulk will be compared to CMOS/SOS, for speed and relative power dissipation. In addition to the normal MOS surface parasitics that are due to layout characteristics and design rules, there are several parasitic bipolar transistors possible within the bulk of the wafer. These become more of a problem as the structures are scaled down, since decreasing the base-widths of the parasitic bipolar transistors increases their current gains. These transistors can cause latchup, and methods of avoiding or minimizing latchup will be considered.

Static, dynamic precharge, and precharge-evaluate CMOS circuitry will be examined, including Domino CMOS logic. Charge-sharing is a major problem in precharge logic, and methods of avoiding it will be examined.

There are three basic requirements of a clocking system. The signals must occur at the correct time, the clock must be able to drive the fan-out, and the rise and fall times of the clock pulses must be as short as possible. Long transition times not only slow the circuit but also increase power consumption.

To avoid oscillation, asynchronous latching, and both static and dynamic hazards, every closed signal path must pass through a clocked storage register. The only dynamic characteristic of the combinational logic network is its propagation delay time, all other timing being controlled by the clocked registers. This approach often simplifies design and testing.

Two-phase, nonoverlapping clocking was proposed by Mead and Conway. It remains popular, due to its simplicity and reliability, and will be employed in this text whenever possible.

7.2 ADVANTAGES OF CMOS OVER NMOS

Reduction in transistor size over the last two decades has greatly increased memory density and speed while concurrently reducing power consumption, but there are fundamental technical limits to scaling due to resolution limitations of the photographic and other equipment used to make circuits. There are also electrical limitations such as junction and oxide breakdown, hot-electron effects, latchup and short-channel effects within the devices themselves.

These limitations apply to both CMOS and NMOS, but a major limitation to the scaling of NMOS circuits is heat generation which increases with transistor count and becomes a serious problem for densities in excess of about 250,000 transistors per chip. Heat also accelerates failure mechanisms within the silicon, leading to reduced device and system reliability.

When the input to an NMOS gate is low, the gate is off and no dc power is being dissipated. When the gate input is high, the depletion-mode pull-up is drawing a quiescent saturation current, I_{SAT}, and the power dissipation is $I_{SAT}V_{DD}$.

To estimate the worst-case current and power needs, assume that all NMOS pull-ups are conducting. To estimate the average power dissipation, assume one-half of all the branches from VDD to GND are on and drawing current since, on the average, one-half of all the inputs will be high and one-half of all the inputs will be low.

Most of the current from a CMOS inverter is used to charge or discharge the load. There is a small current spike from plus supply to ground through the inverter because both the p-channel and n-channel transistors are on for a short period of time during input voltage transitions.

CMOS achieves a significant reduction in low-frequency power dissipation, as compared to an equivalent NMOS circuit. Since a CMOS gate draws one current spike each time it is switched, its power dissipation is proportional to the switching frequency. At clocking frequencies in the range of 1 to 10 MHz the CMOS advantage vanishes, and at high frequencies both circuits dissipate an equivalent amount of power.

The CMOS inverter draws negligible quiescent current, but when the output switches high, a charge $C_L V_{DD}$ is placed on the load capacitance, and when the output switches low this charge is transferred to ground. The net result is a transfer of charge $Q_L = C_L V_{DD}$ from plus supply to ground. If the output switches at a frequency f Hz, then a charge fQ_L is transferred every second, and the average current from VDD to GND is:

$$I_{AV} = fQ_L = fC_L V_{DD}$$

The average ac power dissipated is $I_{AV} V_{DD}$ per switching gate, or $P_{(AV)} = fC_L V_{DD}^2$. If D devices switch during each clock period, the total power dissipation is

$$P_{AV} = Df C_L V_{DD}^2$$

Typically, one-half the total number of devices switch during any given clock cycle. If there are a total of N devices on the chip, the average power dissipation would occur when $D = 0.5N$, and the worst-case power dissipation would be if all the devices switch simultaneously, and $D = N$.

Reduced power requirements lead to reduced cost and improved reliability of the final circuit. Low power allows smaller, lower-cost power supplies, simplifies power distribution throughout the system, eliminates cooling fans, and allows printed-circuit boards to be packed more densely. Smaller power supplies, no fans, and denser circuit boards allow smaller cabinets to be used, leading to savings in chassis and enclosure costs. Low power makes battery operation practical and allows for safe hand-held devices. A comparison between the power dissipation of typical NMOS and CMOS inverters is given in Fig. 7.1.

CMOS has two major cost disadvantages with respect to NMOS, the larger number of process steps required to fabricate CMOS circuits and the larger die required because CMOS has lower gate density, even when skillful design and scaling are employed. Size is the more significant factor in VLSI because cost tends to increase faster with size than with process steps. The larger area of CMOS is due to three causes: the area used to prevent or minimize latchup, the CMOS logic-gate structure which can take up to twice the number of transistors that a comparable NMOS circuit requires, and static design techniques. CMOS has more layout rules and designing is generally more complicated in CMOS than in NMOS.

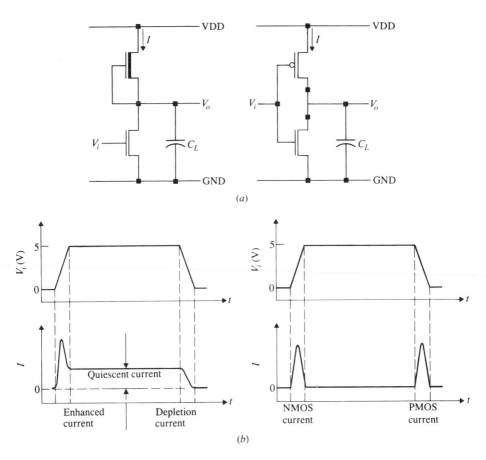

FIGURE 7.1
NMOS vs. CMOS power dissipation. (*a*) NMOS and CMOS inverters; (*b*) their current responses.

7.3 CMOS TECHNOLOGIES

There are two principal categories of CMOS: *CMOS/SOI* or *silicon-on-insulator CMOS*, and *CMOS/bulk* or CMOS on a silicon substrate. A major benefit of CMOS/SOI structures is the reduced load due to the absence of well-to-substrate capacitance and very small interconnect-substrate capacitance. CMOS/SOI is better suited for layout design automation since transistors can be located more appropriately, and it has a speed advantage over CMOS/bulk in interconnect-dominated design methodologies such as gate arrays or standard cell designs. Power dissipation in CMOS/SOI can be up to a third less than in equivalent CMOS/bulk designs due to the lower load capacitance.

CMOS/bulk requires a *well* (also called a *tub* or an *island*) for at least one type FET to provide electrical isolation. For this reason, CMOS/SOI design rules are simpler than CMOS/bulk rules, and CMOS/SOI offers the NMOS designer an easy transition to CMOS technology.

TABLE 7.1
Devices per gate

Inputs	NMOS	Standard CMOS	Precharge CMOS	Precharge and evaluate CMOS	Domino CMOS
2	3	4	3	4	6
3	4	6	4	5	7
4	5	8	5	6	8
5	6	10	6	7	9
6	7	12	7	8	10

NMOS requires one pull-down device for each input, plus a single pull-up device, whereas conventional CMOS design requires one pull-down and one pull-up device per input signal. Clocked CMOS, by precharging certain nodes and then conditionally discharging them, requires only one transistor per input signal plus one common pull-up device and requires only slightly more area than NMOS circuitry due to the need for n wells in which to place the pull-up devices.

For M inputs, static NMOS design requires $M + 1$ transistors, conventional CMOS requires $2M$ transistors, dynamic precharge CMOS requires $M + 1$ transistors, and clocked precharge and evaluate CMOS requires $M + 2$ transistors. One can consider $2M$ as an upper limit on the number of devices required for a design, and $(M + 1)$ devices as a lower limit on the device count. Table 7.1 offers a comparison of the number of transistors per gate for different CMOS technologies.

Precharge-NOR circuitry with several pull-down paths opposing the pull-up is still slow, and adding an *evaluation transistor* to the circuit speeds the precharging by disconnecting the pull-down evaluation circuitry during precharge. PLA design with clocked CMOS has been developed with these ideas in mind. Precharge and evaluate circuits are shown in Figs. 7.13 through 7.16.

Domino CMOS is a special form of precharge and evaluate CMOS with an inverting buffer at the output. It requires two more transistors per gate than ordinary precharge and evaluate CMOS. A domino circuit is shown in Fig. 7.22.

In PLAs and memories, PMOS can be limited to static and precharge pull-up devices used around the periphery of the circuit, where few devices are required and the PMOS devices can be made much larger if necessary. The evaluation pull-down circuitry, including the AND- and OR-plane circuitry of PLAs, is implemented in NMOS. This yields a design with few PMOS devices surrounding a large central array of NMOS devices, is referred to as a *mostly NMOS structure*, and is quite fast. The mostly-NMOS implementation approaches the speed and chip density of NMOS circuitry while retaining the lower power consumption capability of CMOS.

7.3.1 The CMOS/SOS Technology

Silicon-on-sapphire (SOS) is the highest-performance SOI technology today. In this approach, silicon is grown on a sapphire substrate, and islands are formed by implant or diffusion. *N*-channel and *p*-channel transistors are built on the islands.

High performance is achieved due to a significant reduction in parasitic capacitance, and high gate density is achieved because no guard rings are needed. (Guard rings are explained in Sec. 7.3.3.)

Sapphire (Al_2O_3) is a good insulator and the lattice constants of silicon and sapphire match well. When sapphire is used as the substrate, the epitaxial growth of silicon yields monocrystalline material. Sapphire is also not affected as much by radiation as bulk silicon is, which makes it a preferred material for military applications which require radiation-hardened devices.

The SOS process can use self-aligned implants for PMOS and NMOS, and the dielectric constant of sapphire is much greater than that of SiO_2. Manufacturing difficulty is a major disadvantage of SOS technology. Cost is also a serious problem due primarily to the high cost of sapphire wafers, about an order of magnitude more expensive than silicon wafers. For these reasons SOS is not competitive in high-volume, low-cost markets. This limits the commercial sources of SOS as compared to CMOS/bulk.

7.3.2 CMOS/Bulk Technologies

CMOS/bulk is divisible into three technologies in use today, p well, n well, and twin-tub. P-well CMOS/bulk uses a p-type diffusion into an n-type bulk silicon substrate to form a p well for n-channel transistors. The p-channel transistors are built directly into the substrate.

The n-well process starts with a p-type substrate, into which n-type material is diffused to form the n well in which p-channel devices are built. N-channel devices are built directly into the bulk substrate. Devices built in wells are not as good as bulk devices, and the n-well approach places NMOS devices directly in the substrate to give good NMOS performance at the expense of PMOS. An n-well CMOS process is usually derived from, and is compatible with, NMOS processing. It gives superior n-channel transistors, and when used with a mostly NMOS design, it can yield a faster circuit than one obtained from a p-well CMOS process.

In CMOS layouts, p wells and n wells need contacts and can abut, but active devices must be spaced some minimum distance from the edges of their wells. This leaves a "dead space" between the PMOS and the NMOS devices, which can be used to run metal. A p-well CMOS layout with contacts to the substrate and the p-well is shown in Fig. 7.2. If the PMOS FET is in an n well, the upper contact is the n-well contact and the process is twin-tub.

The twin-tub process combines n-well and p-well technologies and is slightly more complex and costly than either. The wells are usually formed in a lightly doped n-type substrate. It allows the designer more freedom to optimize the performance of both the n-channel and p-channel devices, and gives the highest overall performance of the three CMOS/bulk technologies. Seven or eight implants will form the twin-tubs and give complete control over device parameters such as threshold voltages and surface doping. The four basic CMOS processes are shown in cross section in Fig. 7.3.

The twin-tub structure is examined in more detail in Fig. 7.4. The n^+

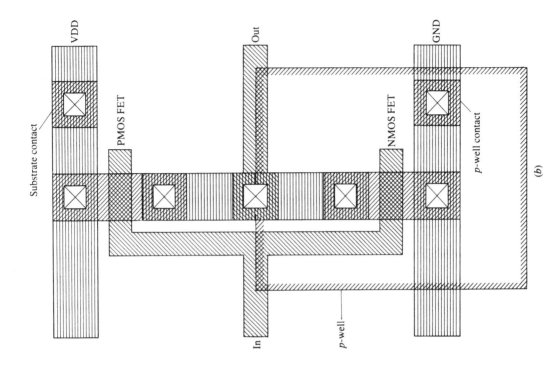

FIGURE 7.2

The p-well CMOS inverter. (a) Stick drawing; (b) layout including well contacts.

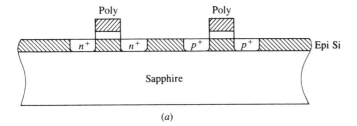

(a)

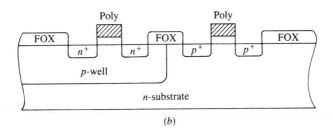

(b)

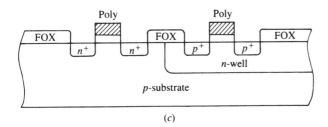

(c)

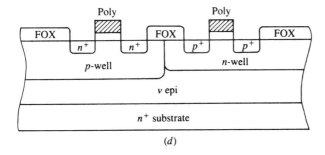

(d)

FIGURE 7.3
The four CMOS technologies. (a) SOS; (b) p-well; (c) n-well; (d) twin-tub.

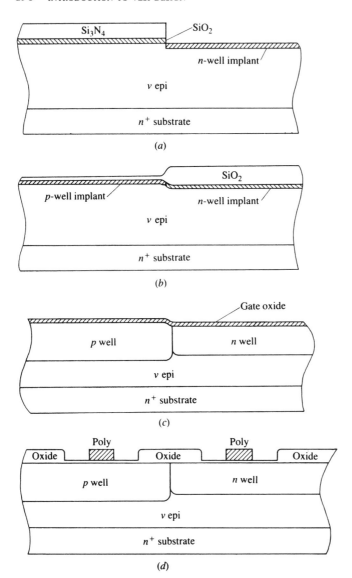

FIGURE 7.4
The twin-tub CMOS structure. (*a*) *n*-well implant; (*b*) *p*-well implant; (*c*) twin-tub drive-in; (*d*) ready for source/drain implant.

substrate covered by a low-conductivity *n*-type epitaxial layer is shown in Fig. 7.4*a*. Silicon dioxide and silicon nitride protect the future *p* well, while an *n*-type ion implant is used to form the *n* well. In Fig. 7.4*b* an oxide layer has been grown over the *n* well to shield it, and the *p* well has been ion implanted. In Fig. 7.4*c* the oxide has been stripped, both wells have been formed by a drive-in diffusion, and an oxide layer has been grown over the surface to form the gate oxide.

Next, the n-channel and p-channel gates are deposited and the field oxide is grown as shown in Fig. 7.4d. PMOS source and drain regions are next implanted, followed by n-type source/drain regions, to yield the finished circuit shown in Fig. 7.3d. (The surface step discontinuity has been ignored in both Figs. 7.3d and 7.4d.)

An n^+ substrate and a lightly doped n-type or v-type epitaxial layer were used in Fig. 7.4, and the substrate must be connected to the most positive potential. If a p^+ substrate and a lightly doped p-type epitaxial layer had been used, the substrate would have had to be connected to the most negative potential. A p substrate would be compatible with the basic NMOS structure.

7.3.3 Latchup in Bulk CMOS

CMOS/bulk devices have parasitic bipolar transistors which can cause *latchup*, a condition in which high currents exist between VDD and GND. In latchup, each collector of a parasitic BJT is feeding the base of another parasitic BJT in a positive feedback configuration, forming a silicon controlled rectifier or thyristor. Latchup can cause malfunctioning and even destruction of the devices, and is terminated only when power to the circuit, and hence power to the thyristor, is interrupted.

Latchup is most likely to occur in I/O circuitry where large voltages can be applied. Two well-defined conditions must exist before latchup can occur. First, for the SCR to be triggered, the voltage drop across the n-well material, or the voltage drop across the substrate, must be at least a diode drop, about 0.7 V, in order to forward-bias the base emitter junction of one parasitic bipolar transistor. Second, to sustain the latchup condition, the product of the current gains of both transistors must be at least unity.

A cross section of a CMOS inverter in an n well is shown in Fig. 7.5. There are two parasitic bipolar transistors, a vertical pnp transistor, Q_1, and a lateral npn transistor, Q_2. Latchup is initiated when the output terminal drops about 0.7 V below GND due to a noise spike or an erroneous output hookup. If electron current from the NMOS drain produces a sufficient voltage drop across R_{sub} to lower the substrate potential by one diode drop under the NMOS source, then hole current from the PMOS source to the n-type well can reach the p substrate, which forms the pnp collector, and drift out of the GND terminal. This also produces an IR drop to maintain electron flow from the heavily doped NMOS source to the p substrate.

One method of preventing latchup consists of decreasing the current gains of the parasitic transistors. If the product of the two current gains, $\beta_1\beta_2$, is less than unity, feedback is not self-sustaining and the device cannot latch. The current gain of the vertical pnp transistor is determined by the process design, and can be reduced by using buried layers of n^+ material under the n wells.

The lateral npn device is controllable by the design engineer, and its β can be reduced by increasing the spacing between the n well and the n^+ source/drain diffusion of the n-channel FET. This approach reduces β by increasing the width of the npn transistor's base, but this also reduces the gate density. Gold doping

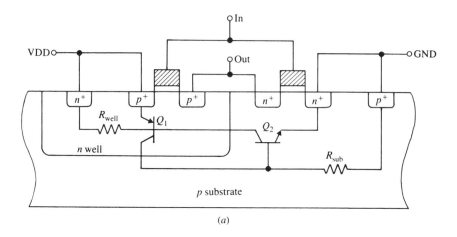

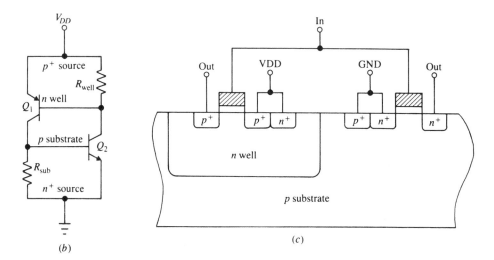

FIGURE 7.5
(a) Parasitic BJT devices in n-well CMOS; (b) the SCR formed of parasitic BJTs; (c) a layout more resistant to latchup.

and neutron irradiation can lower β by killing minority-carrier lifetimes, but these techniques are difficult to control and cause deleterious side effects such as increased leakage currents. Placing the VDD and GND contacts as shown in Fig. 7.5c helps reduce latchup also.

Increasing the well depth raises the pinch-off voltage of the parasitic n-channel JFET formed between the p^+ source/drain and the p substrate, and keeps a conductive path open to well contacts, keeping R_{well} small. A deep well also reduces the forward current gain of the vertical pnp transistor and helps to suppress latchup. However, as the n well is deepened, it also spreads laterally, forcing larger spacings between NMOS and PMOS devices and reducing packing density. As line widths continue to shrink, the safety margin for internal latchup continues to diminish and the chance of impact-ionization induced latchup increases.

The tendency of CMOS/bulk circuits to latch up is reduced by putting *guard rings* around the the p and/or n wells, and making frequent contacts to the rings. This reduces parasitic resistance values, and these contacts drain excess well or substrate leakage current away from active devices. In this manner, the trigger current for latchup can be greatly increased over that of unprotected devices.

While guard rings reduce parasitic resistor values, they also increase the space between n-channel and p-channel devices and reduce the gate density. To partially offset this increased surface area, sensitive areas such as devices connected to I/O pins are guard-ringed while the less susceptible internal circuitry is not ringed. A typical guard-ring layout is shown in Fig. 7.6. The real-estate penalty required to prevent latchup by using guard rings won't be prohibitive in designs where the internal circuitry is predominantly NMOS, with no p^+ diffusion or well structure, but a good CMOS design should sacrifice the area necessary to ensure a safety margin against latchup in normal operation.

Some current goes into the substrate near the FET drain regions, because of high electric fields. This causes avalanche multiplication and electron-hole pairs are generated, with the holes going to the n well. The worst case occurs when V_{DS} is high and V_{GS} is medium in value. Many well contacts are needed to prevent this substrate current from triggering latchup.

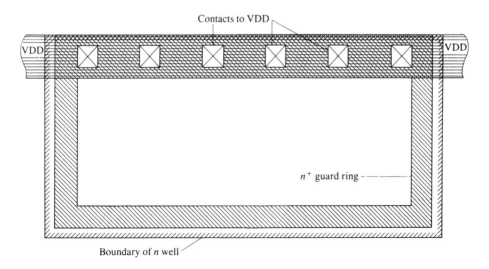

FIGURE 7.6
A guard-ring layout for an n well.

7.4 STATIC CMOS DESIGN

For low operating frequencies, CMOS static logic is used to obtain a relatively small die size. More complex, higher-performance VLSI components require the use of dynamic logic for large arrays in order to keep the die cost down.

There are different arrangements of CMOS gates that can realize a function. Any function can be realized as a sum of products (SOP) or a product of sums (POS). If an SOP function pulls the output high, then an SOP-BAR function will pull the output low. A POS function can pull the output high, while a POS-BAR function can pull the output low, as shown in Fig. 7.7. There is nothing to prevent a hybrid combination of SOP pull-up and POS-BAR pull-down or POS pull-up and SOP-BAR pull-down as shown in Fig. 7.8 (1).

> **Example 7.1.** Let the sum over m be the *care minterm set* and the sum over d be the *don't care minterm set*. Realize the function $f = \sum m(3, 7, 11, 12, 13, 14, 15) + \sum d(6, 9)$ in a CMOS circuit in all four possible combinations of SOP and POS gates.
>
> **Solution.** Mapping and simplifying the function gives minimum sum-of-product and product-of-sum solutions
>
> $$SOP = AB + CD$$
>
> $$SOP\text{-}BAR = (\bar{A} + \bar{B})(\bar{C} + \bar{D})$$
>
> $$POS = (A + C)(B + D)$$
>
> $$POS\text{-}BAR = \bar{A}\bar{C} + \bar{B}\bar{D}$$

The four solutions are shown in Figs. 7.9 and 7.10.

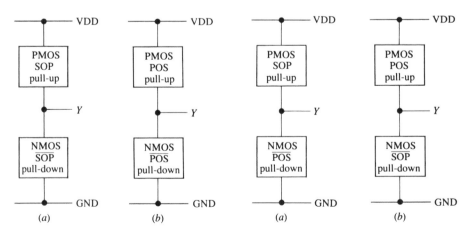

FIGURE 7.7
(a) An SOP pull-up and SOP-BAR pull-down;
(b) a POS pull-up and POS-BAR pull-down.

FIGURE 7.8
(a) An SOP pull-up and POS-BAR pull-down;
(b) a POS pull-up and SOP-BAR pull-down.

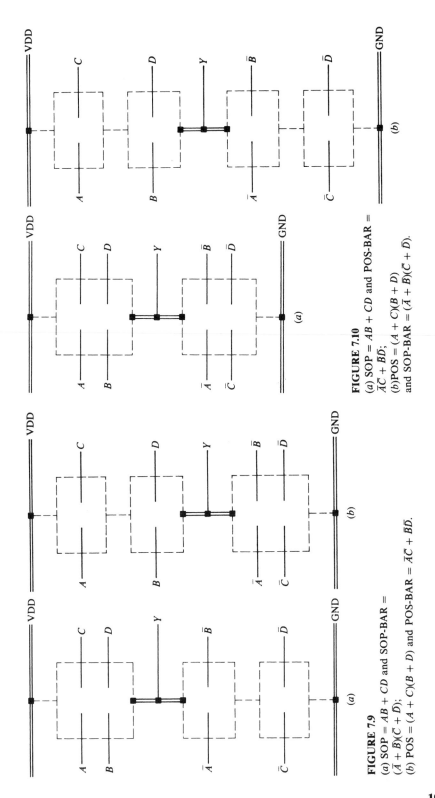

FIGURE 7.9

(a) SOP = $AB + CD$ and SOP-BAR = $(\bar{A} + \bar{B})(\bar{C} + \bar{D})$;

(b) POS = $(A + C)(B + D)$ and POS-BAR = $\bar{A}\bar{C} + \bar{B}\bar{D}$.

FIGURE 7.10

(a) SOP = $AB + CD$ and POS-BAR = $\bar{A}\bar{C} + \bar{B}\bar{D}$;

(b)POS = $(A + C)(B + D)$ and SOP-BAR = $(\bar{A} + \bar{B})(\bar{C} + \bar{D})$.

195

7.5 DYNAMIC CMOS DESIGN

A dynamic CMOS circuit avoids the area penalty of static CMOS, yet has the low power dissipation of a standard CMOS cell. There are two types of clocked bistable elements, the latch and the edge-triggered flip-flop. The latch output reflects its data inputs when the clock is active. Edge-triggered elements such as the *D* flip-flop respond to their inputs on the rising or falling edge of the clock signal.

Modern VLSI design relies heavily on dynamic logic which uses clocked evaluation devices, and dynamic storage which uses a small capacitor as a dynamic latch to store logic values. These techniques save area by reducing the number of transistors per gate, and save power by reducing the number of gates and the static current in structures such as flip-flops and shift registers.

The major disadvantage of dynamic storage is the use of small-sized, leaky capacitors for storing logic values. They must be clocked at a minimum operating frequency in order to maintain their charge, and this increases the power dissipation of the circuit as compared to a static CMOS circuit.

Dynamic CMOS circuits save chip area while enhancing speed over conventional CMOS circuits, but precautions must be taken to ensure proper operation. For a system to operate correctly, the setup time, hold time, and pulsewidth must be sufficient for each bistable element. *Setup time* is the minimum time that the data input of a bistable element must be held stable prior to the active clock signal. *Hold time* is the minimum time that the data input of the bistable element must be held stable after the active clock signal disappears. Setup and hold times for an SR flip-flop are shown in Fig. 7.11, along with the clock pulsewidth and propagation delay. In Fig. 7.11, *S* is the synchronous set

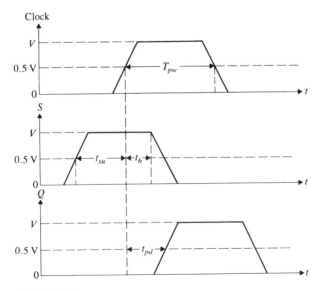

FIGURE 7.11
An example of setup, hold, and propagation delay for an SR flip-flop.

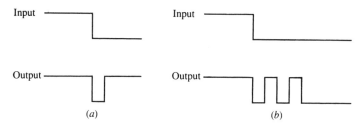

FIGURE 7.12
An example of (*a*) a static hazard, and (*b*) a dynamic hazard.

input signal and Q is the output state of the flip-flop. The clock pulsewidth must be sufficient for the energy under the clock pulse to switch the bistable element.

A *race* is said to exist when more than one feedback variable is in transition at the same time. A noncritical race is one for which the outcome is the same regardless of which path is taken, whereas a critical race is one for which the output might be either of two nonequivalent stable states. An SR flip-flop (cross-connected NOR gates) with inputs that change from 11 to 00 is an example of a critical race, since the next state of the flip-flop can be either SET or RESET.

A *static hazard* is a single momentary transient in an output signal that should have remained static in response to an input change. A *dynamic hazard* consists of multiple momentary transients in an output signal that should have changed only once in response to an input signal. Static and dynamic hazards are shown in Fig. 7.12. An *essential hazard* causes a transition to an improper state in response to an input change. Toggling-type circuits possess the potential for essential hazards. A toggle flip-flop with too long a toggle pulse can toggle an unknown number of times, resulting in an unpredictable output state.

CMOS can use dynamic circuitry to replace the pull-up circuit by one transistor and increase the ratio of *n*-channel to *p*-channel transistors, as shown in Table 7.1. Dynamic CMOS designs use less chip area and tend to be more cost-effective, whereas static CMOS designs consume less power. A tradeoff can be achieved, wherein the circuit is designed to keep the operating power under a specific level and guarantee reasonable junction temperatures and high performance levels, while allowing the use of low-cost packages.

It seems redundant to have to realize the same function twice as in static CMOS logic, once for the pull-up and once for the pull-down, as shown in Figs. 7.7 and 7.8. *Precharge logic* eliminates this need for redundancy by using one clocked PMOS pull-up to precharge the outputs high, as shown in Figs. 7.13 and 7.14, or one clocked NMOS pull-down to precharge the outputs low, as in Figs. 7.15 and 7.16.

Precharge notation indicates the logic value to which the output is precharged, followed by the response to the conditional discharge circuitry. For example, the output of a 2-input AND gate that is precharged high would be written as $(1, AB)$, and the output of a 2-input OR gate that is precharged low would be written as $(0, A + B)$.

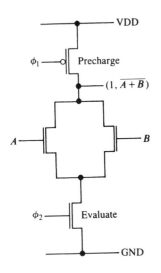

FIGURE 7.13
A clocked, precharged-high, 2-input, mostly NMOS NOR gate.

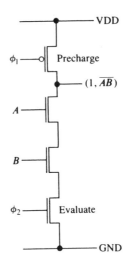

FIGURE 7.14
A clocked, precharged-high, 2-input, mostly NMOS NAND gate.

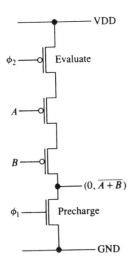

FIGURE 7.15
A gated, precharged-low, 2-input, mostly PMOS NOR gate.

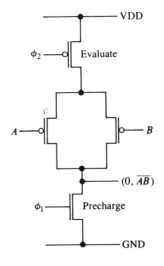

FIGURE 7.16
A gated, precharged-low, 2-input, mostly PMOS NAND gate.

The addition of a transistor in series with the logic evaluation block of a CMOS gate allows precharging while disabling the evaluation circuitry to prevent it from opposing the precharging process. This reduces power consumption during the precharging. The *evaluate transistor* is gated with an enable signal which does not overlap the precharge signal, allowing the circuit to perform the evaluation of the input data with the precharge FET off. The only static power drain is due to leakage through the off devices. Call this additional FET the evaluation device since it enables the evaluation logic block, allowing the circuit to evaluate the inputs and respond with an output.

A mostly NMOS circuit is precharged high by a PMOS device, and a mostly PMOS circuit is precharged low by an NMOS device. The mostly PMOS gate uses PMOS transistors to evaluate the logic, and conditionally charge the output node high when the PMOS evaluation transistor is enabled. Precharged-high, 2-input, mostly NMOS NOR and NAND gates, with evaluation transistors to conditionally pull the output low, are shown in Figs. 7.13 and 7.14. Precharged-low, 2-input, mostly PMOS NOR and NAND circuits, with evaluation transistors to conditionally pull the output high, are shown in Figs. 7.15 and 7.16.

An M-input NAND gate can be implemented with M NMOS pull-down transistors in series with an NMOS evaluation FET, and a single PMOS precharge pull-up. The gate can also be implemented with M PMOS pull-up transistors in parallel, a series PMOS evaluate FET, and a single NMOS precharge pull-down.

As in complementary-CMOS design, series-parallel combinations of PMOS transistors must be the dual of parallel-series combinations of NMOS transistors to perform the same logic operation. NMOS transistors in parallel and PMOS FETs in series perform the NOR operation, as shown in Figs. 7.13 and 7.15. By the same token, NMOS transistors in series perform a NAND function, while PMOS devices in parallel perform a NAND operation, as shown in Figs. 7.14 and 7.16. The general structures for precharge high (low) and evaluate low (high) are shown in Fig. 7.17.

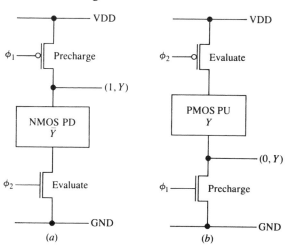

FIGURE 7.17
A general structure of (*a*) a precharge-high, evaluate-low, and (*b*) a precharge-low, evaluate-high circuit.

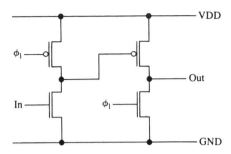

FIGURE 7.18
A circuit with noise-margin problems.

Precharge logic gives a very fast circuit, but circuit designers must beware of noise problems associated with circuits such as the one shown in Fig. 7.18. When ϕ_1 is low, the output of the first inverter is precharged high, but when ϕ_1 is high and the input is low, the first inverter is tristated, its output floats, and power-supply noise can change it. There is little noise margin left for either pull-down device.

Mostly NMOS gates can drive or be driven by mostly PMOS gates as shown in Fig. 7.19, but one must keep in mind that precharge-low circuits are slower to pull up than equivalent precharge-high circuits are to pull-down unless the channel widths of the PMOS FETs are increased. Active high gate inputs are required for unclocked, mostly PMOS gates during the precharge phase so that the evaluation circuitry of the mostly PMOS gate will be off. Active-high inputs are available if the gate is driven by mostly NMOS gate outputs which are precharged high. The precharged-low gate in turn can drive a mostly NMOS gate.

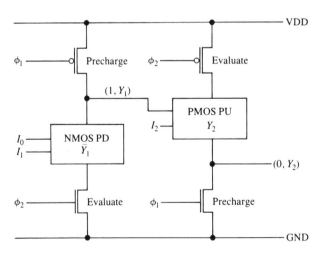

FIGURE 7.19
A precharged-high gate driving a precharged-low gate.

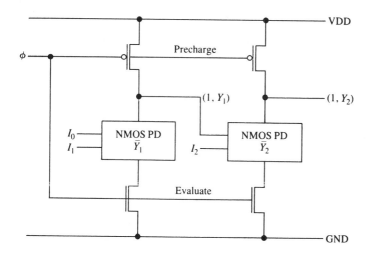

FIGURE 7.20
A precharged high mostly NMOS gate driving an identical load gate.

Precharged, mostly NMOS gates cannot drive similar gates as shown in Fig. 7.20 due to the fact that their outputs are precharged high, and become inputs to driven gates, causing them to evaluate during the precharge cycle. This is avoided in domino logic by buffering each gate with an output inverter as shown in Fig. 7.21.

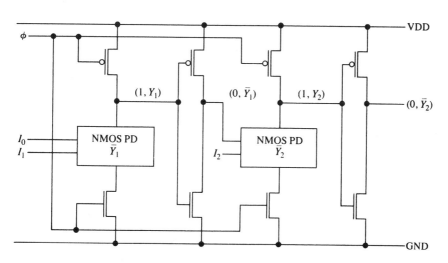

FIGURE 7.21
A buffered mostly NMOS gate driving an identical load. This is domino logic.

7.6 DOMINO CMOS STRUCTURES

A string of unclocked gates of alternating types can be precharged during one phase and the logic signals can ripple through the circuitry in an asynchronous manner during the other phase. Addition of an evaluation device to each gate gives a synchronous circuit, and domino output buffers allow all the gates to be either mostly NMOS or mostly PMOS, mostly NMOS being the faster.

The outputs of precharged networks are very sensitive to *noise* or *glitch* (any undesired transient spike) as was shown in Fig. 7.18, and require output buffering. A domino CMOS AND/OR gate is shown in Fig. 7.22. It is seen that when the clock is low, P_1 is on and N_1 is off. The inverter at the output keeps Y low, and negligible power is dissipated. When the clock goes high, P_1 is turned off and N_1 is turned on, allowing the output to respond to or evaluate the logic of the circuit.

Domino CMOS gates are noninverting due to the inverting output buffer. An AND gate consists of a precharged NAND gate followed by a standard inverter. The output of the dynamic gate goes only to the static buffer, whose output is fed to other gates of the circuit. During precharge, the dynamic gate has a high output and the buffer output is low, thus all circuit nodes which connect the output of one gate to the input of another are low, and the transistors they drive are off.

During evaluation, the output of the buffered mostly NMOS gate can make only a single transition from low to high and all nodes are latched until the next precharge. As a result, there can be no glitches at any nodes in this circuit, and

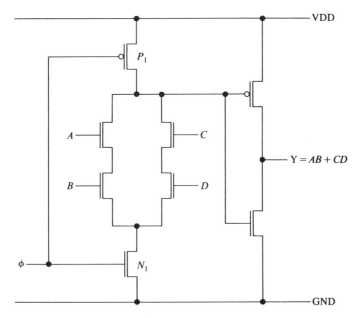

FIGURE 7.22
A domino CMOS AND-OR gate.

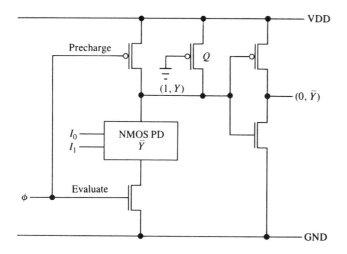

FIGURE 7.23
A static, mostly NMOS domino gate.

race conditions are eliminated. Logic signals cascade from stage to stage much like a series of dominos, each toppling the next, hence the name.

All gates must be switched from precharge to evaluate with the same clock edge. The output inverter ensures that the gating path, which is all NMOS, is buffered. This makes it possible to build complex structures, including long chains of series NMOS transistors, with a minimal loss in performance. Finally, input loading is minimized because each input consists of only one NMOS transistor.

Dynamic domino circuits are fast and draw no quiescent power, but they require a reasonable clock rate. Very low frequency operation is excluded due to the effects of leakage current. Dynamic circuits are also susceptible to noise from other signal lines.

Output-protected precharge circuits are shown in Figs. 7.23 and 7.24. Figure 7.23 shows a static mostly NMOS domino logic circuit. A weak current source labeled Q, with an aspect ratio of 20 or 25 to 1, is added to the output inverter to balance charge leakage at the output without overwhelming the pull-down devices. A modification of the mostly NMOS domino logic with output current source is shown in Fig. 7.24. The output is now fed back to drive the weak pull-up transistor which latches the output.

A static CMOS PLA structure that can operate from almost direct current to over 80 MHz has been reported in the literature (3). The basic gate is shown in Fig. 7.25, and the operation is as follows: When clock ϕ is low, transistor Q_3 is on and transistor Q_5 is off. Transistor Q_3 pulls line a-b high, while Q_5 prevents the input transistors from opposing Q_3 and pulling line a-b low. When line a-b rises above one threshold voltage, Q_4 turns on and pulls output Y low. When Y falls below the threshold voltage of Q_1, Q_1 turns on and pulls Y-BAR to the positive rail.

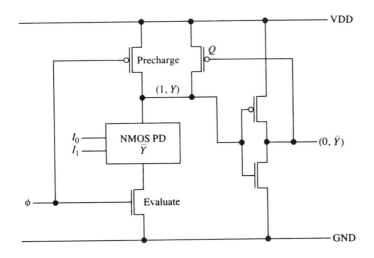

FIGURE 7.24
A latching version of a mostly NMOS domino circuit.

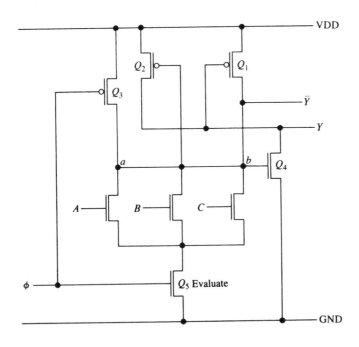

FIGURE 7.25
A high-speed CMOS OR/NOR gate.

When the clock is high, Q_5 is on, allowing the inputs A, B, and C, to evaluate. At the same time, Q_3 is turned off. If $A = B = C = 0$, there is no pull-down path to discharge line a-b, and it stays high, keeping Q_4 on, and Y low. Line a-b keeps Q_2 off, while Y keeps Q_1 on, holding Y-BAR high.

If at least one input is high when the clock goes high, line a-b is pulled low, turning Q_4 off. When line a-b is lower than the threshold voltage of Q_2, Q_2 turns on and pulls Y high. With Y high, Q_1 turns off and Y-BAR is pulled down by the inputs transistors that are on.

If the outputs are as marked in Fig. 7.25 the gate performs the OR function. If the outputs are swapped, the gate becomes a NOR gate. Two-level logic designed with these gates can be used to create a PLA. The NMOS input devices are in parallel for speed, and there are no CMOS devices in series. Transistor Q_3 precharges node b high, which then precharges the output low, and transistor Q_5 allows the inputs to conditionally pull the output high.

7.7 CHARGE SHARING

Charge sharing problems occur when two capacitive nodes charged to different voltages are connected through a pass transistor. When the pass transistor is turned on, it connects the two nodes, resulting in a redistribution of the charge on both nodes. Charge sharing is a serious problem in precharge circuits and must be carefully guarded against. One solution is to make any charge holding capacitor much larger than any capacitors it shares charge with.

A simple example of charge sharing is shown in Fig. 7.26. Capacitors C_1 and C_2 are in parallel when pass transistor P is conducting. This forces the voltages across C_1 and C_2 to be equal. If the two capacitors are charged to different initial voltages, charge sharing will occur when P turns on. Let the initial voltage and charge on C_1 be V_1 and Q_1, and the initial voltage and charge on C_2 be V_2 and Q_2. After the pass transistor turns on, the final charges on C_1 and C_2 are Q_{1f} and Q_{2f}, respectively, and both capacitors are charged to voltage V_f. The initial charge balance equation is

$$Q_1 + Q_2 = C_1 V_1 + C_2 V_2 \tag{7.1}$$

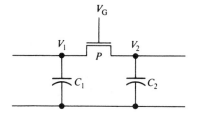

FIGURE 7.26
A simple charge sharing situation.

The final charge balance equation is

$$Q_{1f} + Q_{2f} = (C_1 + C_2)V_f \tag{7.2}$$

To find the final charge distribution, equate the charge before and after P turns on

$$C_1 V_1 + C_2 V_2 = (C_1 + C_2)V_f$$

Solve for V_f, then Q_{1f}

$$V_f = \frac{C_1 V_1 + C_2 V_2}{C_1 + C_2} \tag{7.3}$$

$$Q_{1f} = C_1 V_f = (C_1 V_1 + C_2 V_2)\left(\frac{C_1}{C_1 + C_2}\right) \tag{7.4}$$

Example 7.2. Determine the charge on each capacitor of Fig. 7.26 before and after P turns on, if $C_1 = 20$ fF, $C_2 = 20$ fF, $V_1 = 1$ V, and $V_2 = 5$ V.

Solution. Initially, $Q_1 = C_1 V_1 = 20$ fC, and $Q_2 = C_2 V_2 = 100$ fC. After P turns on

$$V_f = \frac{20(1) + 20(5)}{20 + 20} = 3 \text{ V}$$

$$Q_{1f} = Q_{2f} = C_1 V_f = 20(3) = 60 \text{ fC}$$

Example 7.3. Determine the charge on each capacitor of Fig. 7.26 before and after P turns on, if $C_1 = 10$ fF, $C_2 = 50$ fF, $V_1 = 0$ V, $V_2 = 5$ V, and $V_G = 6$ V.

Solution. Initially, $Q_1 = C_1 V_1 = 0$, and $Q_2 = C_2 V_2 = 250$ fC. After P turns on

$$V_f = \frac{10(0) + 50(5)}{10 + 50} = 4.17 \text{ V}$$

$$Q_{1f} = C_1 V_f = 10(4.17) = 41.7 \text{ fC}$$

and

$$Q_{2f} = C_2 V_f = 50(4.17) = 208.3 \text{ fC}$$

In Fig. 7.27, charge is stored on the intermediate node capacitance, C_A, during precharge. If input A goes high when B is low, then the charge is shared between capacitances C_A and C_B, and the precharge level is lowered.

A static variation of domino CMOS solves the charge-sharing problem while also eliminating dynamic decay. A grounded-gate PMOS transistor, shown in Fig. 7.28, acts as a current source providing a static holding current with no threshold voltage drop. Again an aspect ratio of 20 or 25 to 1 ensures that the current supplied by this FET is small compared to what a minimum-geometry pull-down can sink, and allows the output to be conditionally discharged.

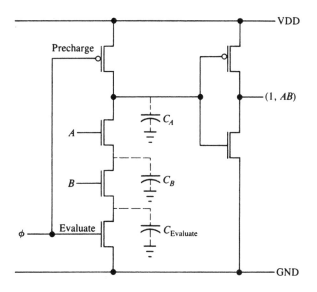

FIGURE 7.27
Charge sharing in a domino CMOS AND gate.

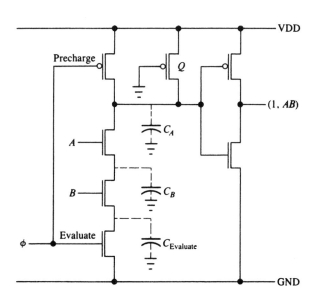

FIGURE 7.28
Addition of a PMOS current source, Q, to eliminate charge sharing.

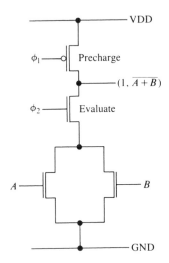

FIGURE 7.29
A mostly NMOS NOR gate enabled with an NMOS transistor in the middle of the stack.

The circuit shown in Fig. 7.29 also requires a large pull-up capacitance in order to minimize charge-sharing. During precharge, the output is pulled high. When the gate is enabled, and the inputs are such that the gate output stays high, charge is taken from the precharge capacitance and dumped on the evaluate capacitance.

To design circuits that do not suffer from charge-sharing, consider the timing diagram shown in Fig. 7.30. The bottom two signals are labeled "stable phase 1." A signal is said to be stable phase 1 if the signal is stable over the time interval phase 1, and also stable for a setup time during phase 2. This setup time allows internal nodes to be precharged during phase 1. For input signals to be stable phase 1, it is sufficient for them to be clocked on the rising edge of phase 2 (2).

To avoid charge-sharing problems in precharge circuits (2): (1) a pull-down chain of transistors can have only one gated clock or phase 1 clock input, and

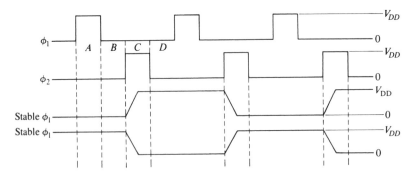

FIGURE 7.30
Timing that avoids charge-sharing problems.

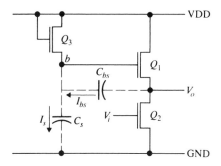

FIGURE 7.31
A bootstrap circuit that utilizes charge sharing to
pull the output signal high.

it must be the bottom transistor, (2) all other inputs must be stable phase 1, and
(3) precharged outputs can drive other gate inputs or can go through a stable
phase 1 latch to other gate inputs.

Consider the circuit of Fig. 7.27 and assume that all nodes are initially low.
Let the output be precharged high on phase 2. If A goes high and B goes low on
phase 1, charge is shared by the capacitors C_A and C_B, and the output may be
indeterminate. However, if A and B are stable phase 1, capacitances C_B and
$C_{Evaluate}$ can charge while C_A is charging. On phase 1, the evaluation capacitor is
discharged. If $AB = 10$, capacitors C_A and C_B remain charged on phase 1 and the
output is high. If $AB = 11$, then capacitors C_A, C_B, and $C_{Evaluate}$ discharge on
phase 1 and the output goes low. The above is a sufficient but not necessary
condition for correct clocking.

There are times when charge sharing is deliberately designed into a circuit.
The bootstrap circuit shown in Fig. 7.31 is one such special case. The stray
capacitance from node b to ground, labeled C_s, and the capacitance from node b
to the output, labeled C_{bs}, form an *ac* voltage divider between V_o and GND. C_{bs} is
referred to as the bootstrap capacitance and is the gate-to-source capacitance of
FET Q_1. C_{bs} is designed such that V_o can be pulled up to the plus rail.

To see how the circuit works, assume that $V_i = V_{DD}$ initially, and let
subscripts 1 and 2 refer to transistors Q_1 and Q_2, respectively. Then $V_o = V_{oL}$ and
Q_2 is in the linear region, and its drain current is

$$I_{D2} = \frac{k_2}{2}[2(V_{DD} - V_{TH2})V_{oL} - V_{oL}^2] \tag{7.5}$$

The voltage at node b is $V_{DD} - V_{TH3}$ and Q_1 is in saturation. The gate-to-source
voltage of Q_1 is $V_b - V_{oL}$, and

$$I_{D1} = \frac{k_1}{2}[V_b - V_{oL} - V_{TH1}]^2 \tag{7.6}$$

When the input voltage switches from V_{DD} to V_{oL}, Q_2 turns off and the
transient currents through C_{bs} and C_s are

$$I_{bs} = C_{bs}\frac{d(V_o - V_b)}{dt} \quad \text{and} \quad I_s = C_s\frac{dV_b}{dt}$$

Upon equating the two currents, one obtains

$$C_{bs} \frac{d(V_o - V_b)}{dt} = C_s \frac{dV_b}{dt}$$

$$C_{bs} \frac{dV_o}{dt} = (C_{bs} + C_s) \frac{dV_b}{dt}$$

$$\frac{dV_b}{dt} = \left(\frac{C_{bs}}{C_{bs} + C_s}\right) \frac{dV_o}{dt} \tag{7.7}$$

The maximum voltage at node b is obtained by integrating Eq. (7.7) to get

$$\int_{V_{DD} - V_{TH3}}^{V_{b\,max}} dV_b = \left(\frac{C_{bs}}{C_{bs} + C_s}\right) \int_{V_{oL}}^{V_{DD}} dV_o. \tag{7.8}$$

$$V_{b\,max} = V_{DD} - V_{TH3} + \left(\frac{C_{bs}}{C_{bs} + C_s}\right)(V_{DD} - V_{oL}) \tag{7.9}$$

The final value of V_b depends upon the ratio of C_{bs} to C_s. For $C_{bs} \gg C_s$, $V_{DD} = 5$ V, $V_{TH3} = 1.5$ V, and $V_{oL} = 0.4$ V

$$V_{b\,max} = 2V_{DD} - V_{TH3} - V_{oL} = 10 - 1.5 - 0.4 = 8.1 \text{ V}$$

With the gate potential of Q_1 3.1 V above its drain potential, hot-electron effects can pose a severe problem. It is not necessary to allow V_b to rise this high. The minimum value of V_b needed to pull V_o up to V_{DD} is

$$V_{b\,min} = V_{DD} + V_{TH1} = V_{DD} + V_{TH3}$$

Integrate Eq. (7.7) again to obtain

$$\int_{V_{DD} - V_{TH3}}^{V_{DD} + V_{TH3}} dV_b = \left(\frac{C_{bs}}{C_{bs} + C_s}\right) \int_{V_{oL}}^{V_{DD}} dV_o \tag{7.10}$$

Solve Eq. (7.10) for $V_{b\,min}$

$$2V_{TH3} = \left(\frac{C_{bs}}{C_{bs} + C_s}\right)(V_{DD} - V_{oL})$$

$$\frac{C_{bs} + C_s}{C_{bs}} = 1 + \frac{C_s}{C_{bs}} = \frac{V_{DD} - V_{oL}}{2V_{TH3}}$$

$$\frac{C_s}{C_{bs}} = \frac{V_{DD} - V_{oL}}{2V_{TH3}} - 1 = \frac{V_{DD} - V_{oL} - 2V_{TH3}}{2V_{TH3}}$$

$$\frac{C_s}{C_{bs}} = \frac{5 - 0.4 - 3}{3} = 0.533 \quad \text{and} \quad C_{bs} = 1.88C_s$$

The maximum voltage at node b is now the minimum value to raise the output to V_{DD}.

$$V_{b\,min} = V_{DD} - V_{TH3} + \frac{1.88}{2.88}(V_{DD} - V_{oL}) = 5 - 1.5 + 0.65(5 - 0.4) = 6.5 \text{ V}$$

With the voltage at the gate of Q_1 1.5 V higher than the voltage at the drain of Q_1, hot electron effects are much less severe.

7.8   CLOCKING

Two-phase, nonoverlapping clocking has no timing errors due to races or hazards. Furthermore, if the intervals during which both clock phases are low (i.e., time intervals B and D in Fig. 7.30 are sufficiently wide), there are no timing errors due to clock skew. Two-phase clocking is very popular due to its simplicity and reliability, and it will be employed in this text whenever possible. The signals are shown as switching between GND and VDD, implying that the clock outputs both strong 1's and strong 0's. Both clock phases must also maintain the same period, T, with no appreciable skewing.

Absolute clock skew is defined as the difference in arrival of the edge of a clock phase at a destination in the circuit, with respect to the clock edge at the source of the clock signal, whereas *relative clock skew* is the difference in local phase lag. Clock skew is measured from the time the first waveform reaches 50 percent of its maximum value to the time the second waveform reaches 50 percent of its maximum value. In Fig. 7.32a the absolute skew of ϕ_1 with respect to the primary clock, P, is t_1, the absolute skew of ϕ_2 with respect to P is $t_1 + t_2$, and the relative clock skew of phase 2 with respect to phase 1 is t_2.

Clock skew for rising and falling clock signals need not be the same. In Fig. 7.32b the falling clock signal skew is t_2, while the rising clock signal skew is t_1. Clock skew must be an acceptably small fraction of the system clock period. If the clock skew is too great, setup and hold times may be violated.

Clocks must be laid out in such a manner that the delays from the source of each clock to clocked bistable elements are identical. Since clock delay is directly proportional to the square of the length of the clock bus line, signals that travel different routes to arrive at any given point may arrive at different times, and events that are designed to occur simultaneously may not. Careful layout is required to avoid these skew problems. In practice, no matter how each clock path is chosen, any two clock paths are likely to be at different temperatures or voltage levels, and clock skew can still occur.

Clock delays can be treated as any bus delay problem, and the fastest clocking is accomplished by using suitable superbuffers to drive the clock bus, or by scaling the clock-driver loads by a factor between 2.7 and 4. The bus must be kept as short as possible, and in metal as much as possible.

The duty cycle of each clock phase in Fig. 7.30 is 25 percent. This keeps rise time and fall time from affecting the clocking. The clock signals must never both be high at the same time, or data will ripple through the circuit. This means that a clock failure must be such that the faulty phase fails low, not high.

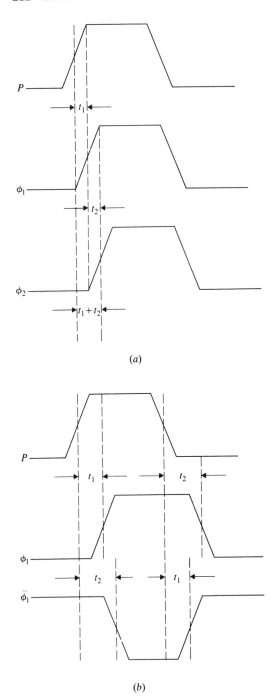

(a)

(b)

FIGURE 7.32
An example of (a) absolute and relative clock skew, and (b) rising- and falling-edge clock skew.

The basic system building blocks consist of clocked registers for sequential control of data transfer, and ripple combinational-logic circuitry between registers. Both the combinational logic and the registers can be implemented with pass transistors and inverters, using a 2-phase nonoverlapping clocking scheme. If the two clock phases are identical they are interchangeable, and this can simplify design.

In a dynamic circuit design, capacitances can be used to store charges representing logic ones and zeros for a brief period of time. The charge stored as logic information must either be updated or refreshed before significant charge leakage at the node occurs. This requires a minimum clock frequency.

Static memory devices require more power dissipation than dynamic devices, but can hold their charge as long as the system is powered up. Dynamic devices are sensitive to power-supply noise, external electric and magnetic fields, and background radiation.

The simplest memory element consists of an inverter clocked by a pass transistor. The process of latching consists of enabling the pass transistor with a clock pulse, while the data input to the clocked pass transistor must be held constant for one setup time, to allow the gate capacitance of the inverter driver to respond to the data input. The falling edge of the clock pulse can occur any time after the setup time.

After the clock signal goes low, the data cannot change for one hold time, to allow for possible differences between the falling edge of the master clock and the falling edge of the local clock line (clock skew). The inverter output voltage level will respond to the data after a propagation delay through the inverter.

7.8.1 Clock Generation

In a *synchronous machine*, all clock signals can be derived from a system clock signal, which is often a square-wave (a rectangular pulse train with a 50 percent duty cycle). System clocks can be generated from a voltage-controlled oscillator or from a crystal oscillator, both of which produce a sinusoidal signal which can be converted to a square wave. Multiphase clocks can be generated from a single-phase square-wave input with two toggle flip-flops and two AND gates as shown in Fig. 7.33.

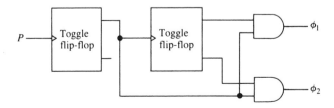

FIGURE 7.33
Generation of 2-phase clocking from a primary clock.

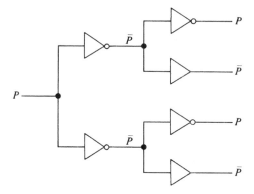

FIGURE 7.34
A simple clock tree for distributing clock signal P and its complement.

7.8.2 Clock Distribution

Clock-powering trees, as shown in Fig. 7.34, are a source of clock skew. The tree is used to generate multiple copies of the primary clock, P, and/or its complement, P-BAR. Each gate of the tree has some uncertainty associated with its delay. This is referred to as gate skew. Clock skew can be minimized by placing all gates of a tree on the same chip.

The physical layout of the clock network must conform to design rules that ensure the integrity of the clock signal by minimizing electrical coupling, switching currents, and impedance mismatches. Equalizing path delays and maintaining a sharp signal quality help reduce skew.

Buffers drive a very wide metal line, designed to minimize power loss and voltage drops while maximizing the signal speed. The wide metal line branches into groups of narrower lines, which in turn may branch into still narrower lines. Nonmetal segments such as polysilicon have higher resistance and distort the clock signal due to impedance mismatches. This should be avoided.

Clock signals can cross under power lines using a diffusion as shown in Fig. 7.35a. A lower resistance crossunder using a polysilicide is shown in Fig. 7.35b. Crossunders should be minimized, subject to the constraint that the number of crossunders should be equalized for the two clock phases, in order to equalize signal delays. Multiple metal processes are necessary to maintain low clock skew for very high speed systems.

7.8.3 Clocked Storage Elements

A capacitor, usually a gate-to-substrate capacitor, is used to dynamically store data for several seconds at room temperature, or several milliseconds at 70°C. A pair of inverters forming a loop with an enable pass transistor can be used to convert dynamic storage into static storage, but it still requires a periodic refresh signal, which can be other than the enable signal.

A two-phase clocking scheme with combinational logic inserted between

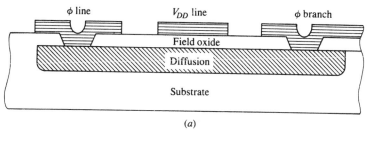

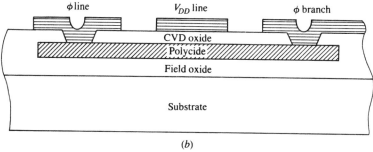

FIGURE 7.35
Clock-line crossing under a power line (*a*) using diffusion, and (*b*) using polycide.

every pair of registers yields a simple pipeline structure, as was shown in Fig. 1.2. Precharging can be done on phase 1 while the inputs are changing. The feedback loop can be opened and arbitrary combinational logic (C/L) can be inserted in the feedback path between the pass transistors clocked on phase 1 and phase 2.

Feedback paths can be added around every combinational-logic block, as long as they are clocked through two registers on the two clock phases. It is possible to cascade registers by running a feedback path from one output register to another input register clocked on the same phase, as shown in Fig. 7.36. The only timing requirement is that the combinational logic respond quickly enough with respect to the clock period.

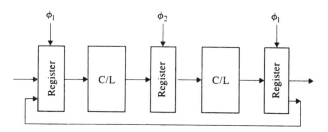

FIGURE 7.36
Feedback path around a cascade of two combinational-logic blocks.

CMOS circuits can be designed using two-phase or complementary single-phase clocking. Complementary single-phase clocking is a special case of two-phase clocking, which uses ϕ and ϕ-BAR as two nonoverlapping signals. Since there is no dead time between ϕ and ϕ-BAR signals, complementary single-phase clocking is more susceptible to clock skew than regular two-phase clocking is.

Example 7.4. Calculate the clocking frequency of a two-phase system consisting of pass transistors, inverters, and superbuffers. The propagation delay high-to-low, t_p, of each inverter is 0.30 ns, the string of pass transistors is designed to match the propagation delay of an inverter, and superbuffers are needed to drive a fan-out load of 27 inverter gates.

Solution. NMOS inverters driven by pass transistors have an inverter ratio of 8 to 1, which gives a maximum inverter delay of $8t_p$. Since the combinational logic uses only pass FETs with delays matched to the inverters the total delay is twice that of a simple 8-to-1 inverter, or $16t_p$. Three superbuffers scaled 3 to 1, will drive a fan-out of 27, with a delay of $3(3t_p) = 9t_p$, bringing the total delay to $25t_p$.

In most designs, the stray parasitic capacitance is at least as large as the capacitance designed into the circuit. This doubles the total delay to at least $50t_p$ for one clock phase, and a minimum clock period of about $100t_p$ for the two-phase clocking system. If t_p is 0.30 ns, one can expect a clocking period of at least 30 ns, corresponding to a maximum clock frequency of 33 MHz.

7.9 SUMMARY

CMOS is the only technology that offers a cost-effective solution to the power-density problem, and it is the technology of choice for future digital applications, where the power dissipation of NMOS would be too great.

Much CMOS is designed to be TTL compatible. Future scaling will require smaller supply voltages to limit substrate current and hot-electron effects. CMOS is better suited to low supply-voltage operation, because it is ratioless and has better noise tolerance than NMOS.

One major disadvantage of CMOS/bulk is that the layout which best reflects the functional topology of the circuit must often be sacrificed in order to locate transistors of the same polarity closer together, so that like devices can be put into the same well. This requires rearranging the surface layout of a circuit.

Circuit speed can be improved by using precharging. With two-phase nonoverlapping clocking, the logic can have outputs precharged during phase 1, and evaluated during phase 2. This avoids some rise-time and fall-time problems, but requires busing both phases throughout the circuit. In some applications, it may be possible to use two complementary phases in which case only one clock line need be bused throughout the chip, and locally inverted.

NMOS logic is always precharged high, but CMOS can be precharged both low and high. Precharged-high (precharged-low) gates require only one pull-up (pull-down), regardless of the number of inputs, and this type logic uses less space than conventional CMOS requires.

Clocked logic can be divided into two groups, ripple circuitry without evaluation devices, and synchronous, or gated, circuitry with evaluation devices.

Standard CMOS gates should not be designed for more than three or four inputs because the self-loading and the series transistor stack make the structure inefficient in speed and area. Precharge-high NOR gates and precharge-low NAND gates avoid transistor stacks.

Dynamic systems have three components of power: active, standby, and refresh. At TTL input levels, CMOS reduces the active and standby current, relative to NMOS, by a factor of 2. The lower active current reduces power-supply voltage transients, and allows smaller decoupling-capacitors. Refresh current increases with increased refresh frequency.

Dynamic data must be refreshed about every 2 ms. CMOS memory designs can reduce this dissipation also, with respect to NMOS, giving CMOS the edge in two of the three components of power. Smaller voltage swing and reduced load capacitance give NMOS the edge in dynamic power dissipation. For constant-voltage scaling, power dissipation increases by the same factor that line widths are scaled down.

Buried contacts between polysilicon and diffusion are common in NMOS layouts, but are seldom used in CMOS because the contact is limited to *n*-type devices, and metal contacts are still needed for *p*-type devices.

CMOS/bulk devices must be grouped by type and placed in wells. This gives rise to design layouts that are not always grouped according to function, and are also less suited to automated layout implementation.

CMOS/SOS has several drawbacks, such as low channel mobility, high source-to-drain leakage current, and floating substrate effects on both static and dynamic characteristics. However, for many VLSI applications these parameters can be designed into the circuit provided they are reasonably constant and are adequately incorporated into circuit models.

SOS films used to be of low quality and quite expensive, but these disadvantages are diminishing. SOS technology has higher radiation tolerance than CMOS/bulk and is preferred for military applications.

Two-phase clocking eliminates race and hazard problems, and gives more reliable results with less design effort, but doubles the number of clock bus lines and uses more real estate than single-phase clocking. As pointed out by Noice et al., proper operation of two-phase clocking eliminates skew (2). Any nonoverlapping clocking which is sufficiently slow can be made reliable, but the speed penalty is often too great.

Capacitance contributes electrical inertia in the sense that a finite time is required to change a node voltage. This inertia helps to stabilize circuits against noise spikes or static hazards. If the energy of a noise pulse is too low, the capacitance of the node prevents the node from responding to the voltage spike.

Complementary clock inputs on flip-flops can simplify the logic, but they also increase the loading of the clock lines. Each master-slave flip-flop loads the clock line with four transmission gates. If one superbuffer can drive a fan-out of eight transmission gates, it can only drive two flip-flops. To drive more flip-flops requires a more powerful driver, either larger superbuffers that can source and sink more current, or two or more buffers in parallel. Shift registers can also be sensitive to propagation delays on the clock line, because each flip-flop must be clocked before the flip-flop driving it can change state.

A finite-state machine realizes sequential logic functions due to feedback. An FSM with two latches clocked on two phases supports SCAN-PATH testing, since it can use level sensitive scan device latch pairs which are hazard-free master-slave latches with a scan input port.

REFERENCES

1. R. H. Krambeck, C. M. Lee, and H. S. Law, "High-Speed Compact Circuits with CMOS," *IEEE Journal of Solid-State Circuits*, vol. SC-17, no. 3, 1982, pp. 614–619.
2. D. C. Noice, R. Mathews, and J. Newkirk, "A Clocking Discipline for Two-Phase Digital Systems," *Proceedings of the IEEE International Conference on Circuits and Computers*, September –October, 1982.
3. W. E. Engeler, M. Lowy, J. Pedicone, J. Bloomer, J. Richotte, and D. Chan, "A High Speed Static CMOS PLA Architecture," *IEEE International Conference on Computer Design, ICCD'* 88, Rye Brook, N.Y., 3–5 Oct., 1988, pp. 348–351.

PROBLEMS

7.1. (*a*) Repeat Example 7.3 with $V_G = 5$ V.
   (*b*) Repeat part *a* if the device parasitic capacitance shunting C_1 is 2.6 fF, and that shunting C_2 is 4 fF.

7.2. For the bootstrap circuit shown in Fig. 7.31, $V_{oL} = 0.40$ V, $V_{TH3} = 1.5$ V, and $V_{DD} = 5$ V. Neglect any capacitive loading of the output, and calculate the maximum voltage at node *b* if:
   (*a*) $C_{bs} = 2C_s$.
   (*b*) $C_{bs} = 5C_s$.

7.3. NMOS, 2-phase, internal clocking can be obtained from a single-phase master clock as shown in Fig. P7.3. Sketch the waveforms of the two phases derived from the single phase. Estimate the relative values of timing intervals *A*, *B*, *C*, and *D* of Fig. 7.30 if each NOR gate rising (falling) propagation delay is 10 percent (5 percent) of the clock period.

7.4. Local generation of CMOS 2-phase clocking is more complex in that the complements of the two clock phases must not overlap. A circuit to generate suitable two-phase clocking is shown in Fig. P7.4. Sketch the waveforms of the two derived phases with respect to the master phase. Assume $t_{pHL} = t_{pLH} = 0.1$ T, where T is the period of the master clock.

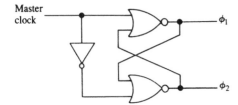

Master clock

ϕ_1

ϕ_2

FIGURE P7.3
A circuit for generating local NMOS clocking from a master clock.

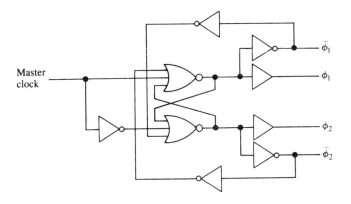

FIGURE P7.4
A circuit for generating local CMOS clocking from a master clock.

7.5. Realize a CMOS 3-input (A, B, C) majority function with all four possible combinations of SOP and POS gates. The majority function is true if more than one input is true. The functions are: $SOP = AB + AC + BC$, $SOP\text{-}BAR = (\bar{A} + \bar{B})(\bar{A} + \bar{C})(\bar{B} + \bar{C})$, $POS = (A + B)(A + C)(B + C)$, and $POS\text{-}BAR = \bar{A}\bar{B} + \bar{A}\bar{C} + \bar{B}\bar{C}$.

7.6. A CMOS clock driver is shown in Fig. P7.6. Explain the purpose of the transmission gate. How should this gate be scaled?

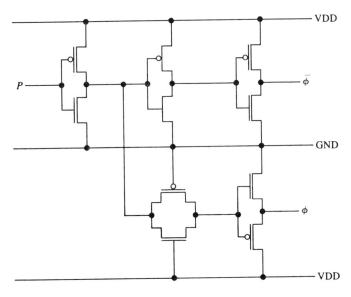

FIGURE P7.6
A CMOS clock driver circuit which generates ϕ and $\bar{\phi}$.

Problems 7.7 through 7.13

Do SPICE simulations of the circuits of Probs. 7.7 through 7.13. Use the previous SPICE transistor models. Drive a load C_L of 31 fF, use a square-wave input voltage signal of period 6 ns, and assume minimum geometry for all devices, unless otherwise specified.

7.7. Simulate the CMOS inverter circuit of Fig. 7.1a, if
   (a)   both transistors are minimum geometry, and
   (b)   the pull-up aspect ratio is 0.5.

7.8. Simulate the circuit of Fig. 7.22. Let the inputs all be high, and plot V_o. Measure the rise times and fall times of the two outputs.

7.9. Simulate the circuit of Fig. 7.25. The inputs are all high. Plot the voltages at Y and $\bar{Y}$ if both outputs drive loads of 31 fF.

7.10. Simulate the circuit of Fig. 7.26 after pass transistor P turns on. Plot the voltages across each capacitor from $t = 0$ to ≥ 6 ns, if $V_1 = 0$ V, $V_2 = 5$ V, $V_G = 5$ V, and:
   (a) $C_1 = 100$ fF and $C_2 = 500$ fF;
   (b) $C_1 = 10$ fF and $C_2 = 50$ fF.
   Explain the differences between answers a and b.

7.11. (a)   Simulate and explain the circuit of Fig. 7.27. if ϕ is a 5 V step at $t = 0$, and V_A is a 5 V step at $t = 1$ ns. Plot the voltage across C_A from $t = 0$ to $t = 4$ ns.
   (b)   Repeat part a if ϕ is a 5 V step at $t = 1$ ns, and V_A is a 5 V step at $t = 0$.

7.12. Simulate the bootstrap circuit of Figure 7.31 and plot the voltages V_b and V_o for
   (a) $C_{bs} = 20$ fF and $C_s = 1$ fF, and
   (b) $C_{bs} = 100$ fF and $C_s = 1$ fF.

7.13. Simulate the circuit of Fig. P7.6, under no-load conditions if the primary clock has a period of 3 ns. Plot ϕ and $\bar{\phi}$. Does the circuit perform satisfactorily?

CHAPTER
8

SPECIAL
CIRCUIT
LAYOUTS
AND
TECHNOLOGY
MAPPING

8.1 INTRODUCTION

While highly complex logic is often best implemented with symmetric, repeatable, and expandable structures such as PLAs and ROMs, many simple logic problems can be solved with special circuit approaches. There are a number of circuits for which unique, clever layouts have been devised, some of which will be investigated in this chapter.

The tally circuit is a special application of pass-transistor logic, and will be studied first. Two-level logic will be examined next; NAND-NAND, NOR-NOR, and AND-OR-INVERT (AOI) will be compared. The AND-OR-INVERT circuit will perform two-level logic at almost the speed of one-level logic.

The exclusive-OR (EOR) gate is functionally equivalent to an AOI structure, as is the exclusive-NOR (ENOR), and all three are topologically identical. The exclusive-OR circuit is obtained from the exclusive-NOR circuit by interchanging one pair of inputs, and both are special cases of AND-OR-INVERT logic.

NMOS and CMOS multiplexing (MUX) circuits will be examined also. The CMOS MUX with clocked precharge is structurally equivalent to an NMOS MUX, except for the n well required by the pull-up circuitry. The general-purpose function block discussed in Sec. 6.8 is structurally related to the MUX also. The Mead-Conway barrel shifter will also be studied.

Layout and routing problems and techniques will be studied next. The problem of interconnecting a large number of nodes on a chip is increasingly taking more design time and chip area and many designs are limited by the metallization routing. A large effort is being invested in solutions to routing problems at present. Two-metal and multimetal designs are being investigated in attempts to ease routing limitations.

The goal of wire routing is to maximize metal width while minimizing the total wire length, the number of crossovers, and the number of interconnects. The basic tradeoff is between chip area and routability. If sufficient wiring space is not available, the chip cannot be wired as is, and the layout must be redone. If too much area is allocated for wiring, the chip cost is too high.

The success of any algorithm is measured by its completion rate and computation time. Acceptable solutions must guarantee completion. Most algorithms do well for small layouts, but many fail to complete complex routing layouts. When the computer is unable to finish the routing, a good designer may be better off to ignore the routing attempt, and start over.

Power and clocking should be routed first. When laying out an array of alternating VDD and GND grids, channels must be laid out in such a way as to allow routing nets through them. Module placement on the chip is related to routing success, and some routing algorithms allow the designer to adjust placement interactively in order to assist the router.

8.2 TALLY CIRCUITS

A *tally circuit* counts the number of inputs that are high and outputs the answer. If there are N inputs there are $N + 1$ possible outputs, corresponding to 0, 1, 2, ..., N inputs that are high. Output S_i is the sum of the number of inputs that are high. A 4-input, 5-output tally circuit is shown in Fig. 8.1.

There are several conceptual approaches to laying out the circuit. The first method that comes to mind might be to write a minimum sum-of-products solution for each of the $N + 1$ output functions. For the 4-input tally circuit shown in Fig. 8.1, the output sum-of-products solutions are:

S_0 is true if no inputs are high: 1 term
S_1 is true if only one input is high: 4 terms
S_2 is true if any two inputs are high: 6 terms
S_3 is true if all the inputs but one are high: 4 terms
S_4 is true if all the inputs are high: 1 term

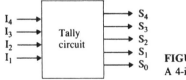

FIGURE 8.1
A 4-input, 5-output tally circuit.

The sum-of-products solutions consist of the binomial expansions of N items taken M at a time, as M ranges from 0 to N. In the above example there are a total of sixteen product terms, requiring sixteen 4-input AND gates. One 6-input and two 4-input OR gates are also required to obtain the desired outputs.

This approach yields a total of 19 gates and 78 inputs, with the 5 outputs in a canonical sum-of-products form. This is a worst-case, or upper-bound, solution to the problem.

Another convenient approach would be to use a ROM look-up table. For a 4-input tally circuit, this requires 4 inputs, 16 words of 5 bits each, and 5 outputs. This is also quite uneconomical. A PLA design will be smaller than an equivalent ROM layout, but it is still not an ideal solution.

A third approach might consist of an iterative network such as a chain of simple adders. Parity checkers are often designed this way.

A fourth approach would be a hierarchy of small tally circuits. For 4 inputs, this could be done with two 2-input tally circuits, with their outputs combined in a third 2-input tally circuit, and run through a decoder to yield the correct output.

A fifth attempt might be a tree network, which would have the layout shown in Fig. 8.2. Each node requires a yes/no circuit to steer the signal to an output branch according to whether the number of high inputs is greater than a given amount or not. In Fig. 8.2, if the input is 4 highs (logic 1's), the signal flow is from node a to d to S_4. For an input of 3, the signal path is from node a to d to S_3. An input of 2 sends the signal from node a to b to S_2, etc.

What is desired is a circuit that can be easily laid out in a regular and expandable manner, with a minimum number of pull-up devices and a minimum area requirement.

Charge-steering (pass-transistor) logic is ideally suited to this type network, and the basic layout of a 3-input, 4-output tree network is shown in Fig. 8.3. Each tree branch requires two choices, depending upon the inputs. Two pass transistors can be gated to accomplish each branching operation. The circuit must be readily expandable to any reasonable size.

A stick-diagram of a 3-input tally circuit designed with pass transistors and only one pull-up load device is shown in Fig. 8.4 (1). This circuit is highly

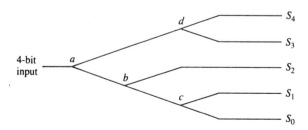

FIGURE 8.2
A tree network realization of a 4-input tally circuit.

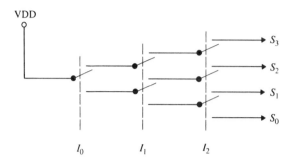

FIGURE 8.3
A conceptual layout of a 3-input tally circuit.

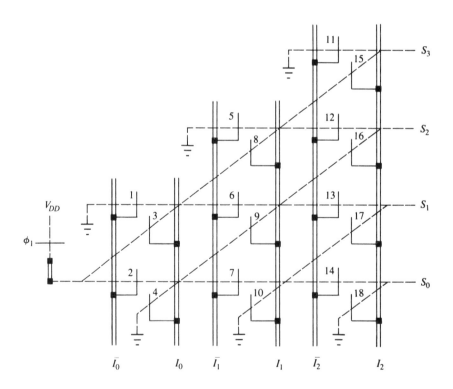

FIGURE 8.4
A stick-diagram of a 3-input tally circuit designed with pass transistors.

TABLE 8.1

Input			Enabled path	High
I_0	I_1	I_2	PU to output	output
0	0	0	2, 7, 14	S_0
0	0	1	2, 7, 17	S_1
0	1	0	2, 9, 13	S_1
0	1	1	2, 9, 16	S_2
1	0	0	3, 6, 13	S_1
1	0	1	3, 6, 16	S_2
1	1	0	3, 8, 12	S_2
1	1	1	3, 8, 15	S_3

repetitive, easily expandable to any number of inputs, and requires no additional pull-ups. Since all the pull-down devices are pass transistors, they can be minimum geometry also.

The circuit allows a shift right, or a shift up and right. When I_0 is false, I_0-BAR shifts the signal to the right, and when I_0 is true, it shifts the data up one row and to the right. Each input that is true causes the input to shift up and to the right, each input that is complemented causes the input to shift right only.

Label the inputs I_0, I_1, I_2, plus their complements, as shown in Fig. 8.4. When the input is 0, 0, 0, the only path from the pull-up to an output is through transistors 2, 7, and 14. The pull-up is now connected to S_0, which goes high, for a tally of 0. When the input is 1, 0, 0, the only path from the pull-up to an output is through transistors 3, 6, and 13. The output is S_1 high for a tally of 1.

All eight combinations of inputs and the paths they activate are shown in Table 8.1, and the length of each pass-transistor string is equal to the number of inputs. The tree structure is ideally suited to small or slow circuits where propagation delays are not important. However, the circuit can be expanded to larger size by allowing for the insertion of restoring inverters at suitable intervals.

8.3 NAND-NAND, NOR-NOR, AND AOI LOGIC

All boolean functions can be represented in a canonical sum-of-products form (AND-OR), as well as in a canonical product-of-sums form (OR-AND). AND-OR logic converts directly to NAND-NAND logic and OR-AND logic converts directly to NOR-NOR logic.

A typical dynamic CMOS NAND-NAND implementation of a simple sum-of-products function is shown in stick form in Fig. 8.5, and a stick-form dynamic CMOS NOR-NOR implementation of a product-of-sums solution is shown in Fig. 8.6. These circuits can be converted to NMOS by replacing the pull-up with a depletion-mode NMOS FET, and deleting the *n* well. The *AND-OR-INVERT*

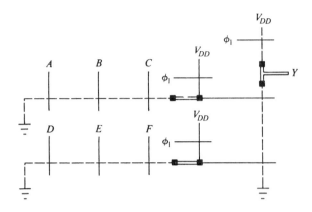

FIGURE 8.5
A NAND-NAND implementation of $Y = ABC + DEF$.

structure often will simplify the circuit, giving two levels of logic for the speed of one level (if the added input capacitance is negligible), and requiring a minimum number of pull-up load devices. For these reasons, the AOI implementation of two-level logic should always be kept in mind. The NAND-NAND and NOR-NOR circuits both require three pull-ups and dissipate three times the power of an equivalent AOI circuit. A typical clocked CMOS AOI structure is shown in

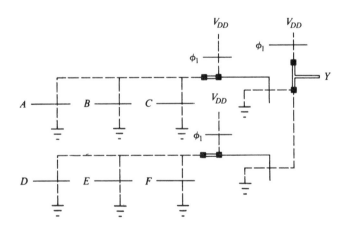

FIGURE 8.6
A NOR-NOR implementation of $Y = (A + B + C)(D + E + F)$.

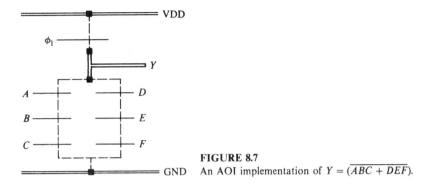

FIGURE 8.7
An AOI implementation of $Y = \overline{(ABC + DEF)}$.

Fig. 8.7. Figure 8.8 shows an NMOS and a CMOS static AND-OR-INVERT circuit.

Dynamic logic dominates VLSI design due to its much lower power dissipation. Dynamic NMOS circuitry suffers from both circuit complications and loss of packing density with respect to static NMOS. These are the main reasons for choosing NMOS in the first place. Dynamic precharge-high evaluate-low NMOS and CMOS AOI circuits are shown in Fig. 8.9.

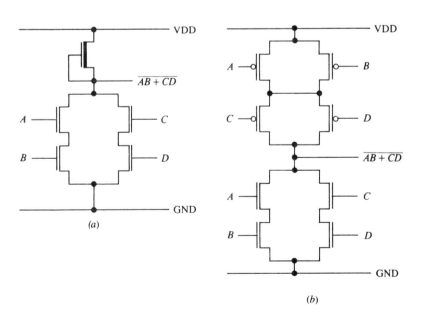

FIGURE 8.8
Static AOI gates to realize $Y = \overline{(AB + CD)}$ in (a) NMOS, and (b) CMOS technology.

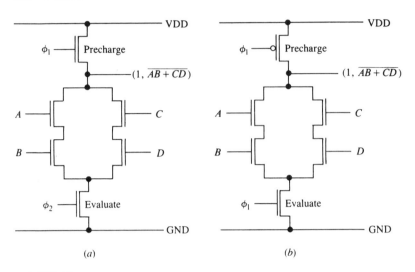

FIGURE 8.9
Dynamic AOI gates in (a) NMOS, and (b) CMOS technology.

Memory design is still largely done in NMOS because it is faster than CMOS, and because the savings in real estate due to the utilization of dynamic logic more than offset the increased clocking circuitry needed. This allows the designer time that can be applied to the more complicated clocking circuitry and substrate pump design. Often, a satisfactory compromise is to use CMOS peripheral circuitry with standard NMOS memory matrices (the mostly NMOS approach), in order to maintain the low standby power dissipation of CMOS, while approaching the speed of NMOS.

8.4 EXCLUSIVE-OR STRUCTURES

Since $\overline{A \oplus B} = \overline{A\bar{B} + \bar{A}B} = \bar{A}\bar{B} + AB = \bar{A} \oplus B = A \oplus \bar{B}$, the exclusive-NOR (ENOR) circuit can be implemented with the same circuit as the exclusive-OR (EOR) by simply interchanging two inputs. They are topologically identical. The exclusive-OR (exclusive-NOR) circuit, shown in Fig. 8.10, is identical to the AOI structure and is simple and easy to implement. Modified EOR/ENOR structures are shown in Figs. 8.11 and 8.12.

The circuits shown in Figs. 8.10 and 8.11 are NMOS. They are structurally similar to precharged CMOS circuits, and can be converted to CMOS by replacing the pull-up by a clocked PMOS device and adding an *n* well. A CMOS EOR equivalent of the NMOS circuit of Fig. 8.12 is shown in Fig. 8.13. It consists of one conventional inverter, one transmission gate, and one "floating" inverter whose pull-up is input *A* and whose pull-down is the output of the other inverter.

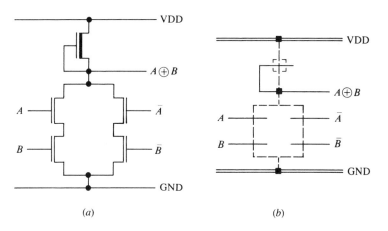

FIGURE 8.10
The NMOS EOR/ENOR structure, with inputs for $A \oplus B$. (a) Circuit diagram; (b) stick drawing.

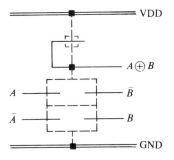

FIGURE 8.11
A modified NMOS EOR/ENOR circuit.

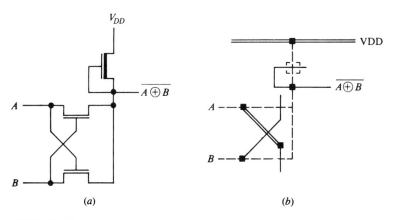

FIGURE 8.12
An EOR/ENOR gate which requires no complemented inputs. (a) Layout; (b) stick drawing.

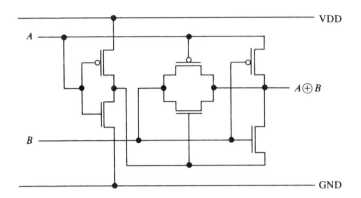

FIGURE 8.13
A static CMOS EOR circuit.

8.5 MULTIPLEXER STRUCTURES

The basic symbol of a 4-to-1 *multiplexer* (MUX) and an equivalent circuit for it are shown in Fig. 8.14. The goal is to implement a simple, cost-effective multiplexer circuit. The MUX can be seen to consist of switched paths, as did the tally circuit. It is thus ideally suited to pass-transistor logic, and can be easily implemented in NAND form or NOR form.

8.5.1 NMOS Multiplexers

A NOR implementation requires eight enhancement-mode transistors and eight contacts, not counting any driving inverters which are external to the circuit. The circuit is shown in Fig. 8.15. The NOR approach is preferred for large multiplexers.

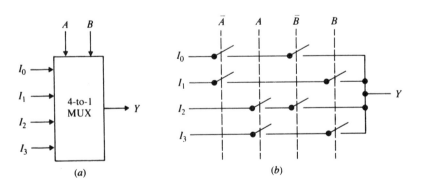

FIGURE 8.14
(a) Symbol and (b) equivalent circuit of a 4-to-1 MUX.

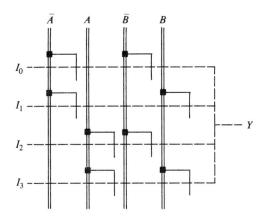

FIGURE 8.15
The NOR implementation of an NMOS 4-to-1 MUX.

An alternative approach to multiplexer design consists of a NAND structure, using depletion-mode devices to short circuit the undesired connections, while using enhancement-mode devices to form the switches that exert control. The MUX is defined by the locations of the ion implants required to form the depletion-mode transistors, as shown in Fig. 8.16. If a large NAND multiplexer is required, restoring inverters must be incorporated in the layout.

8.5.2 CMOS Multiplexers

A CMOS multiplexer is shown in Fig. 8.17. The structure is the same as for the NMOS NOR multiplexer, except that the NMOS pass transistors have been

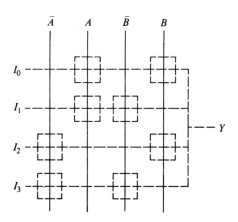

FIGURE 8.16
The NAND implementation of an NMOS 4-to-1 MUX.

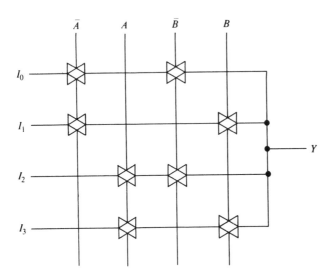

FIGURE 8.17
The CMOS implementation of a 4-to-1 MUX.

replaced by CMOS transmission gates. The NMOS 4-to-1 multiplexer has a faster fall time, and the CMOS MUX has the faster rise time.

To lay out a CMOS MUX, the first step is to redraw the circuit with all the NMOS pull-down devices in the bottom half of the layout, and all the PMOS pull-up transistors in the top half of the layout, as shown in Fig. 8.18. This allows one to put all the PMOS devices in a single isolation well and all the NMOS devices in another single isolation region.

While simple to lay out, conventional CMOS multiplexers take lots of real estate. The pull-down part of the circuit is an NMOS multiplexer, and pass-transistor logic must supply both pull-up and pull-down paths. A static pull-up can be obtained by running the output, Y, through an inverter and feeding the inverted signal, Y-BAR, to the gate of a PMOS pull-up transistor. Whenever Y is low the pull-up device will be off, and whenever Y is high the pull-up transistor is on. This circuit is shown in Fig. 8.19, and has negligible dc power dissipation.

A dynamic CMOS pull-up circuit can be realized by precharging the pull-up on phase 1 of the clock as shown in the circuit of Fig. 8.20. The dynamic circuit is comparable in speed to the all-NMOS multiplexer. Compare the layout of the CMOS MUX in Fig. 8.20 with the CMOS function blocks in Fig. 6.31.

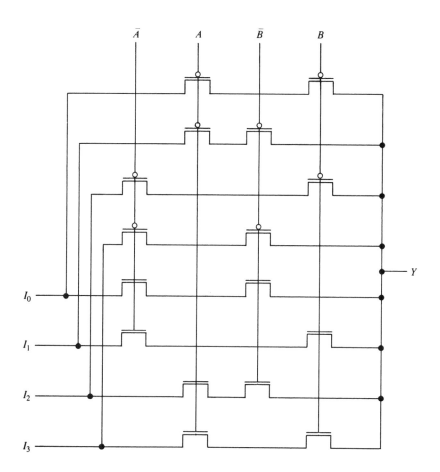

FIGURE 8.18
A CMOS 4-to-1 MUX with full pull-up and pull-down circuitry.

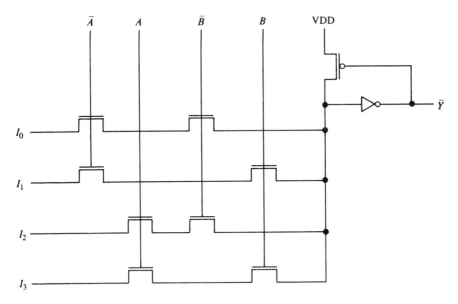

FIGURE 8.19
A CMOS 4-to-1 MUX, with a static pull-up driven by Y-BAR.

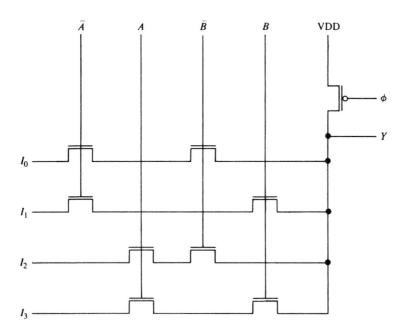

FIGURE 8.20
A dynamic CMOS 4-to-1 MUX, using a clocked precharge pull-up.

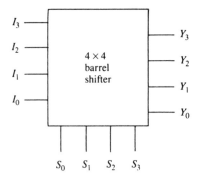

FIGURE 8.21
Block diagram of a 4-bit barrel shifter.

8.6 THE BARREL SHIFTER

Another specific design is the barrel shifter. A *barrel shifter* is a wraparound or endaround shifter that is a very useful switch array. It uses only combinational logic, and can be easily implemented in silicon (1). The basic layout is shown in Fig. 8.21. The inputs are labeled I_i, the shift controls S_i, and the outputs Y_i. If a shift of one or two is desired, then the outputs will be as indicated in Fig. 8.22.

The barrel shifter will be laid out with two 4-bit buses running horizontally through it, and the data paths running vertically through it. A way of connecting any bus with any output bit is needed, and the 4×4 *crossbar switch* is a simple circuit from which to start.

The switching is done with transistors labeled S_{ij}, where switch ij connects bus i to output j. All sorts of shifting and interchanging of data can be done with this structure, but it requires N^2 control lines which limits the design to reasonably small values of N.

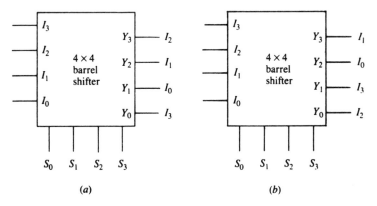

FIGURE 8.22
Conceptual picture of (a) a SHIFT-1 and (b) a SHIFT-2 operation.

To convert the crossbar shifter to a barrel shifter, one must add a third horizontal bus line to handle the shift signals. Next, add all the FET switches to connect bus i to output i as shown in Fig. 8.23, and connect the gates of all these transistors together with a line labeled SHIFT-0.

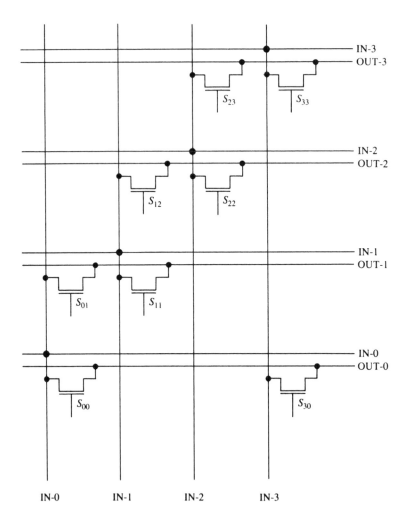

FIGURE 8.23
Starting layout for a 4 × 4 crossbar shifter with SHIFT-0 and SHIFT-1 transistors in place.

Add the FET switches to connect bus i to output $i + 1$, and connect the gates of all these transistors together with a line labeled SHIFT-1. The 4×4 barrel shifter at this point is shown in Fig. 8.24. Continue in this manner until finished. Only one of the shift lines may be high at any one time. The finished circuit is shown in Fig. 8.25.

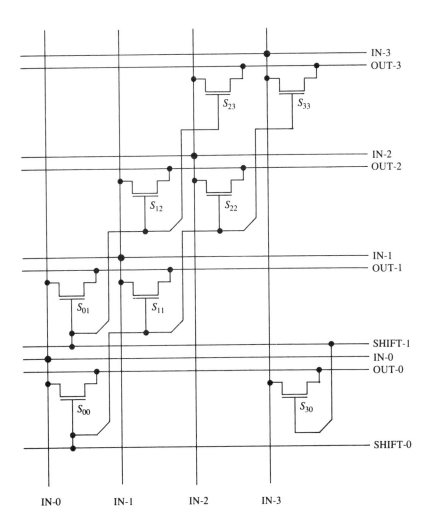

FIGURE 8.24
The crossbar shifter with SHIFT-0 and SHIFT-1 control lines added.

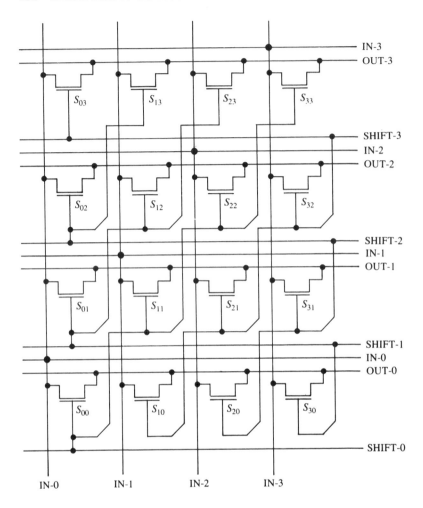

FIGURE 8.25
The completed 4 × 4 shifter.

The barrel shifter is now ready to be laid out. The buses can run horizontally through the shifter in polysilicon, the output lines can run through horizontally in diffusion, and the control lines for shifting can run vertically in metal. The lines connecting the shift signal to the gates of the switching transistors can then run horizontally in polysilicon also. This will be left for a design problem.

8.7 CHIP ARCHITECTURE

After the algebraic simplification is determined and a network is decided upon, it must be implemented in silicon. The first step in laying out a floorplan is the routing of supply rails and clock rails. In doing this, sufficient space must be left between the power rails to allow for data buses and combinational logic cells. Once this is accomplished, the floor plan can be laid out.

Starting with chip planning, the relative positions and interconnectivity of all major function blocks must be outlined. To avoid topological impossibilities, routing must be worked out and a detailed layout of all data paths, clock phases, power buses, and control signals must be done before layouts of any subsystem can be done. Once it is chosen, the busing must be rigidly adhered to during subsequent design.

A good *routing algorithm* will attempt to minimize the total routing area. A *net* consists of one or more interconnecting wires, which are to be routed. From a performance viewpoint, the critical nets should be routed first to guarantee them a shorter, straighter path. The penalty for this is a slightly larger chip area (2, 3, 4). This can be done by determining clock skews and data-path delay between clocked elements. The required inputs are the clock signals, their waveforms, and the desired operating frequency. Weights for signals on a clock path are determined from the skew that the delay of that path introduces in the clock signal. If the clock goes through gating logic, those gates that introduce a large skew are also weighted.

Power and ground must be available to all parts of the system, must be routed in metal due to the high currents required, and they should only cross when absolutely necessary. One approach is a set of interdigitated comb structures as shown in Fig. 8.26.

All pull-up current must pass through the V_{DD} pin to the V_{DD} line and all pull-down current must pass through the GND line to the GND pin. To avoid metal migration caused by excessive current, power lines must be wide enough to handle large capacitive loads while maintaining current densities below one milliampere per square micron of cross-sectional area.

Sometimes it is physically impossible to increase a power line to the required width. In this case, other alternatives must be investigated, such as

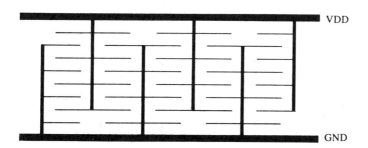

FIGURE 8.26
VDD and GND interdigitated structure.

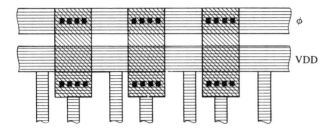

FIGURE 8.27
Metal clock line crossing under a power line.

adding more power supply pins to distribute the current, or reducing the capacitive load requirements of the chip.

Most chip layouts are metal limited, and careful planning is needed to decide whether metal should run horizontally or vertically in any particular block. One can start by choosing a predominant direction for the metal lines, or, in a two-metal process, decide which metal layer will run vertically and which will run horizontally. Which signals should be in metal must next be decided.

Metal power lines and clock lines often run in parallel, and crossings are unavoidable, as there are now two sets of interdigitated combs. *Crossunders* must be used for the clocking lines as shown in Fig. 8.27 since they carry less current than the power lines. To obtain low-resistance contacts, crossunders should be made as wide as possible, with multiple contact cuts as shown in Fig. 8.28.

The *multiple-contact structure* is superior to a large contact hole because the process engineer has adjusted the etching processes to be optimum for small contact cuts. This usually means that large contact cuts will tend to etch faster on the sides, causing the holes to be barrel-shaped, rather than rectangular. Also,

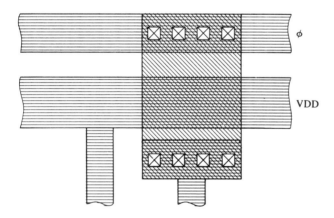

FIGURE 8.28
A wide crossunder structure, with multiple contacts.

current tends to crowd to the periphery of a contact, and multiple contacts force the current to distribute itself more evenly.

The resistance of the metal supply lines can result in significant voltage drops, causing V_{oL} to rise and V_{oH} to drop. This decreases noise margins for both high and low outputs. In CMOS applications at frequencies less than about 1 MHz, current densities are not of much concern, but noise immunity problems can be important.

Regular structures simplify design layout and design-rule checking by visual inspection. A common layout scheme is the *Manhattan layout* which uses vertical and horizontal lines only. In such a layout the power lines, VDD and GND, could run horizontally as could two clock phases, with one phase crossing under VDD and the other phase crossing under GND.

If data is in diffusion and control is in polysilicon one must avoid cross-overs of data and control as they form parasitic transistors. Either data or control signals must be run in metal where the lines cross. This gives the designer two choices, either to run metal parallel to control or parallel to data. It is often easier to visualize the layout if the data buses run horizontally and the control signals run vertically.

When designing with two metal layers, there are two common layout possibilities of the two-metal floor plan, either metal 1 running vertically and metal 2 running horizontally, or vice versa. The data and power can be run in metal 2, with control lines in metal 1. If data and power buses run horizontally in metal 2, control buses must run vertically in metal 1.

Polysilicon can be used for local busing, provided the interconnects are kept to short paths. Polysilicide buses have lower resistance, and can be used for medium length bus lines. Diffusion should only be used as a very short intercon-nect, due to its high resistivity.

A tristate bus driver that can drive both up and down requires large sourcing and sinking transistors, and a method of disabling both. This scheme is satisfactory except that it wastes space. A precharged bus circuit is often a better solution, as shown in Fig. 8.29. Allow only one evaluate or enable signal (EV) to

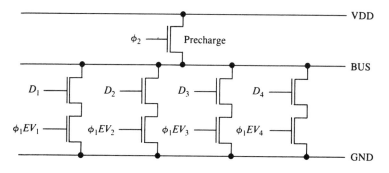

FIGURE 8.29
A 2-phase, precharged bus circuit. EV_i is the evaluate signal for data signal, D_i.

go high during any single phase-1 clock period and the bus can be driven from as many sources as necessary. The bus performance is only limited by the pull-down capability of the two series transistors. This yields a fast circuit that is simple to lay out.

8.8 WIRE ROUTING

Two-layer metallization allows the designer to lay out metal both vertically and horizontally on the floor plan. In this approach, if a metal wire must change direction, a via is used to connect the two metal layers at the change point.

Due to the complexity of the problem, many authors treat module placement and the routing between modules as two separate problems, even though they are logically related because routing is critically dependent upon placement. Placement adjustment can alter the paths taken during global routing, creating intercell spacing problems that did not previously exist. This could lead to another placement adjustment, and the approach may not converge (5).

The first consideration in routing is the determination of the shortest path between two nodes. More advanced schemes often find a "minimum cost," or "best cost" path, where cost may be defined to include an estimate of the congestion, number of available wire tracks in a local area, individual or overall wire length, etc.

One strategy is to split the problem into *global* (*loose*) *wiring* and *local* (*detailed*) *wiring*. Global routing is the preliminary step, and requires a routing plan in which each net is assigned to a particular region of routing area. The goal is to make 100 percent assignment of nets to routing regions, while minimizing the total wire length. This is followed by local routing.

Define the number of wiring tracks at the boundary between two adjacent cells as the *channel capacity*. Global wiring then ensures that all wires are routed without exceeding the capacities of individual channels. Local wiring then determines the fine track routes within the global route.

8.8.1 Global Routing

Initial global routing is often done using a wire-length criterion, since it can be implemented more efficiently than an area criterion, and because all timing-critical nets must be routed with minimum wire length. The clock is a major time-critical signal and the phases must be routed to maintain equal skew.

Since modules are in general of irregular shape and size, the routing region should be divided into manageable pieces once placement is completed. This is a critical step in global routing. The routing area can be divided into disjoint rectangular areas, which can be classified by their topology. A two-sided channel is a *rectangular routing area* with no obstruction inside, with pins on two parallel sides and with signals entering and leaving through the other two sides. A *switch box* is a rectangular routing area with no obstructions inside and with signals entering from and leaving in all four directions (6).

Some more advanced routing algorithms can deal with routing areas containing obstructions. Obstacle avoidance capability allows designers to pre-wire special nets such as power and clock lines, either by hand or with special-purpose routers. The general router then works around these obstructions.

Figure 8.30 shows a layout consisting of six modules. The modules and the periphery, both of which are the sources and sinks of nets, are shown hatched. There are eight vertical channel regions and nine horizontal channel regions. Switch boxes occur where channels intersect. The twelve switch boxes are labeled SB, the eight vertical channel regions are labeled VC, and the nine horizontal channel regions are labeled HC in Fig. 8.30.

A potential region of congestion is referred to as a *bottleneck*. A normal bottleneck exists between the opposite edges of two neighboring modules, and a diagonal-type bottleneck exists between opposite corners of two neighboring modules. As a rule, if two bottlenecks overlap, keep the one with the smaller number of tracks (choices). Prior to routing, one should generate a *bottleneck graph*, calculate the routing density in each bottleneck and adjust the placement of modules.

A common approach is to route one net at a time, choosing the shortest possible path. The problem can then be represented by a routing graph that depicts relationships between routing regions and nets to be connected. It is usually impossible to route all the nets with shortest connection paths because

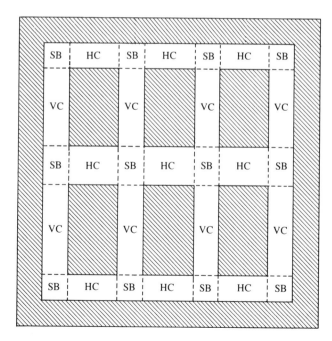

FIGURE 8.30
Routing channels and switch boxes for a placement of six modules.

they compete for paths to be used. One can route all nets independently, rerouting nets which cause congestion, or route nets sequentially and update the information about routing regions after completing each net.

After global routing, the layout should be compacted as much as possible. Normal bottlenecks are routed by the channel router, and other regions are routed by the switch-box router. The routing order for switch-box regions starts from one corner of the chip, usually the lower left corner, and proceeds to the diagonal corner. Each channel region must be routed before its neighboring switch-box regions are routed. The switch-box problem is more difficult than the two-sided channel-routing problem (7).

8.8.2 Local Routing

Detailed (local) routing is usually done by either a *maze-search algorithm* or a *line-search algorithm*. In the channel-routing approach a number between 0 and N can be assigned to each terminal, with unused terminals assigned the number 0. Terminals with the same number, other than 0, are to be interconnected.

A minimum of two levels of connect must be assumed. In a single-metal technology, one layer is in polysilicon or polysilicide and the other layer is in metal. Two metal layers can also be used, in which case polysilicon can be used for additional crossunders. A set of routes must be obtained, usually in a Manhattan geometry. The constraints are that different nets do not intersect on the same layer, that critical routing is of minimum length, and that the width of the channel is minimized. The Manhattan geometry assumes that vertical and horizontal tracks are on different metal layers.

The maximum number of possible interconnections of a system of N nodes increases as

$$\frac{N!}{2!(N-2)!} = \frac{N(N-1)}{2}$$

which is the number of combinations of N items taken two at a time. For N large, the maximum possible number of interconnects increases as the square of the number of nodes. This is the reason why large systems become limited by routing problems.

One of the earliest routing schemes is the Lee-Moore *maze-running algorithm* (8, 9), which finds the shortest path between any two points. This is done by dividing the layout into a grid of nodes, and weighting each node by its distance from the source of the wire to be routed.

The end points of a bus line are identified, after which the distance from the node at one end of a bus line to the node at the other end of the bus line is counted in a Manhattan manner, to give a path which consists of horizontal and vertical line segments. The correct answer is the route that requires the smallest number of squares. This method is easily programmed for a computer layout of the routing maze.

If a solution exists, the Lee-Moore routing algorithm will find it, but it requires an excessive amount of storage, since large designs may contain millions of grid points. Another disadvantage to this approach is that the wavefront extends in all directions, and computation is very slow. The speed of the algorithm can be greatly enhanced by propagating wavefronts from both the source and the target. This can reduce computation time by up to 50 percent.

In Fig. 8.31, bus lines *A-B* and *C-D* have already been chosen, and the

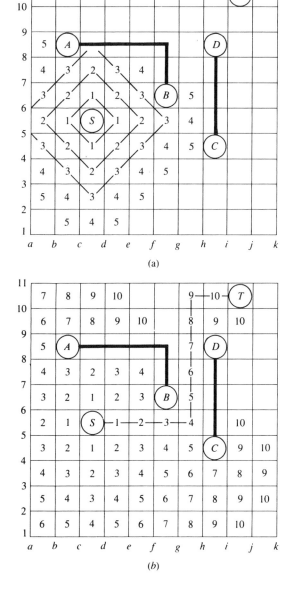

(a)

(b)

FIGURE 8.31
The maze-running approach with a wavefront propagating from the source *S*. (*a*) Partially completed routing; (*b*) completed routing.

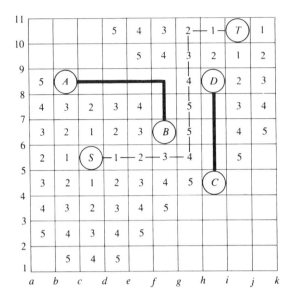

FIGURE 8.32
The maze-running approach with a wavefront propagating from both the source and the target.

shortest path from the source point, S, to the target point, T, is desired. The squares are numbered in relation to their distance from node S. The wavefront fans out in a diamond shape from the point of origin as shown in Fig. 8.31a, stopping when it encounters an obstacle in its path. From Fig. 8.31b it is seen that a path of length 11 squares between S and T is the shortest route.

With waves fanning out from S and T both, as shown in Fig. 8.32, the wavefronts intersect on the count of 5, which is much less computation time than was required when only one wavefront was being computed from S, as shown in Fig. 8.31.

To further reduce computation time, algorithms which assign penalties to moves away from the target have also been proposed. The Lee-Moore approach can be extended to two-metal levels by assigning penalties for deviation from the preferred direction of metal run, and penalties for vias connecting the two levels.

In the *line-search approach*, vertical and horizontal lines are drawn from the source, S, and the target, T, followed by horizontal or vertical lines that intersect the original lines, but go further. This step is repeated until nodes S and T are connected.

An example is shown in Fig. 8.33, where lines connecting A to B and C to D are already laid out, and it is again desired to connect node S to node T. Horizontal and vertical lines are drawn through the source and target points until they meet. The algorithm would first find paths S-G and S-J, as well as paths T-K and T-L, followed by paths G-L, J-H, and H-K. Line segments H-K and J-H intersect, as do segments G-L and T-L. There are two solutions: S-G-L-T, consisting of three line segments and seventeen squares long; and S-J-H-K-T, consisting of four line segments and thirteen squares long. In this example the path with more line segments is the shorter one. In general, the program must calculate all path lengths to determine the preferred solution.

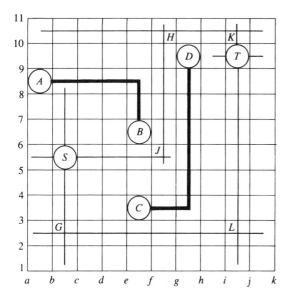

FIGURE 8.33
The line-search approach to connect two nodes.

8.8.3 Refinements on Maze-Routing

After the channels are routed in metal and polysilicon, it would be convenient to conclude with a routine to maximize the metal runs. Since many routers route metal horizontally wherever possible, this step would replace vertical wiring in polysilicon with vertical wiring in metal, subject to the usual constraints imposed by wire crossings and obstacles in the channel. This will have little effect upon the routing of dense channels where many polysilicon-metal crossings exist, but could be quite useful in less densely packed channels.

Two examples of metal maximization are shown in Fig. 8.34. Two metal wires connected by a polysilicon line are shown in Fig. 8.34a. In a single or double metallization process, there is no reason not to connect them as shown in Fig. 8.34b. In Fig. 8.34c two metal lines meet a polysilicon line which forms a FET. The device must remain but the metal can come closer to the transistor as

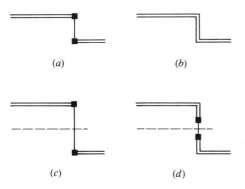

FIGURE 8.34
Layouts (a) and (c) before, and (b) and (d) after metal maximization.

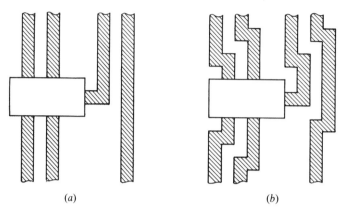

FIGURE 8.35
An example of plowing. (*a*) Before, and (*b*) after relocation of a module.

shown in Fig. 8.34*d*. In a double-metal process with one metal vertical and the other metal horizontal, vias will be required to connect the two levels. In this case, an approach which minimizes the number of vias after routing would also be useful.

The Berkeley software program *Magic* incorporates a feature called *plowing* (10). When a module is relocated, or another line must be squeezed in, it is extremely advantageous to maintain the net interconnections. Plowing allows relocation while maintaining the integrity of routed nets. An example is shown in Fig. 8.35, where a module and its interconnects are moved to the right. Plowing can also be used to compact a design once it is laid out.

Most layouts have terminals that are fixed, and cannot easily be interchanged. In routing a horizontal channel, this may result in a large number of horizontal tracks. PLAs, PROMs, PALs, and function blocks, have interchangeable terminals since their geometries are programmable. This allows the designer to minimize the number of horizontal tracks required, which in turn reduces the channel width while shortening line lengths. Figure 8.36 shows terminal

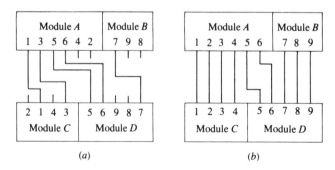

FIGURE 8.36
Modules with two rows of terminals. (*a*) Unaligned; (*b*) aligned.

placements of four modules before and after interchanging terminals. In Fig. 8.36*a* the channel must be widened before completing the routing, and many crossovers exist, while in Fig. 8.36*b* the channel width can be reduced and there are no crossovers.

8.9 MODULE LAYOUT

Functional modules have a predesigned layout, usually with rectangular boundaries. Modules are selected from a library database, and placed on the layout, with the object of obtaining a minimum-area design. Most systems do placement first, then routing. This requires starting with excess routing channel width, which can be reduced later by compacting the design.

Good functional block placement is essential in order to obtain a minimum-area layout. Automatic compaction algorithms usually adopt a separate *x*-compaction and *y*-compaction strategy, and cannot obtain a minimum geometry when faced with simple schemes that can be compacted diagonally by shrinking both *x* and *y* directions simultaneously.

A good interactive compaction router allows the designer to move functional blocks or wire segments without having to keep track of the wire interconnections. The software performs the tedious work, allowing the designer to concentrate on placement and achieve a compact layout. Such an interactive tool has been designed by Mori (11). To reduce computation time, only one functional block is allowed to move at a time, but several connected functional blocks can be moved as a single unit if necessary.

8.10 CLOCK DISTRIBUTION AND FLOOR PLAN

The large buffers needed to drive the clock lines are connected to the clock pad, and should be placed near the pad. The clock lines should be in metal, except for where they must cross a power line. The metal clock line can cross under a metal power line in diffusion or in polysilicon. The main requirements are speed and freedom from hazards and skewing. Local clocks can be generated from master clocks, but their delays must match the delay of the master clock.

The clocks must be distributed in such a manner that skew from one part of the chip to another is minimal. To accomplish this, the series resistances in different clock paths must be equal, and the clock driver must be tuned to the capacitive load on each clock. The main contributions to clock line resistance are from crossunders, and they must be designed to equalize the resistances of different clock lines. Buffers can be used immediately after each crossunder to minimize delay.

Power supplies must be laid out carefully at this point also. The main problem in the power supplies is to ensure that power bus voltage noise spikes are small enough to have no significant effect on chip operation. PLAs generally are designed to precharge on the same clock phase. This can lead to large voltage spikes on the power lines. Connecting a separate power pad to the PLA supply lines can help greatly. When more than two clock phases are available, another solution is to precharge the PLA AND-plane and OR-plane on different clock phases.

I/O switching is another major source of power-line noise, and it can be reduced by using numerous power supply pads. Output pads should be designed with just enough drive capability to meet external requirements, since excess drive capability tends to exacerbate noise problems.

In laying out the cells and nets, mirroring cells vertically allows vertically adjacent cells to share positive and negative rails. This is even more important in CMOS than in NMOS, due to the isolation wells required. The positive rail must connect the *n*-well structure, therefore it will be close to the PMOS devices. The negative rail will then be near the NMOS devices and will connect to the *p* well. Figure 8.37*a* shows the arrangement of *n* wells and *p* wells, and an example of two stages of a two-bit shift register layout is shown in Fig. 8.37*b*.

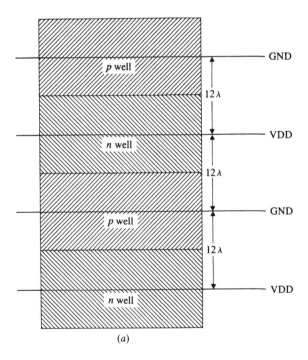

(a)

FIGURE 8.37
Floorplan for layout of wells with alternating positive and negative rails. (a) Well layout.

(Continued)

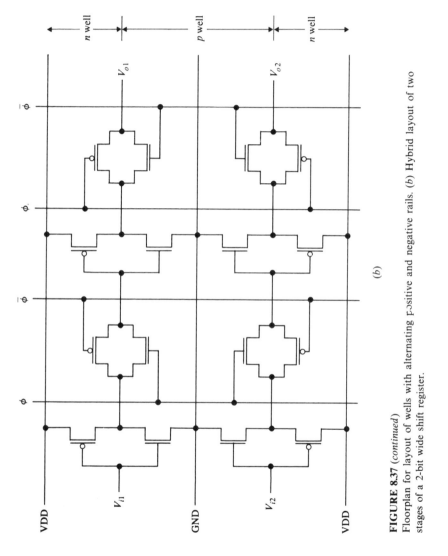

FIGURE 8.37 (*continued*)
Floorplan for layout of wells with alternating positive and negative rails. (*b*) Hybrid layout of two stages of a 2-bit wide shift register.

251

8.11 PACKAGING

Large systems must be partitioned onto multiple chips. Pads are large capacitive loads, and separate chips means increased power dissipation or loss of speed, due to the added number of I/O pads required. Negative package considerations include unreliability of sockets and wiring, limited pinouts, discrepancies between on-chip and off-chip speed, and packaging costs.

The package must have sufficient pins and the chip must fit into the cavity of the package. To avoid wire sagging, bonding wires must be limited to reasonable lengths, typically 5 mm or so. Bonding wires must never cross, or they can short circuit. The pads should be spread as evenly as possible around the perimeter. A reasonable rule of thumb would be to limit the pads per side of a chip to 30 percent of the total number of pads.

Three contacts are always needed for NMOS: substrate, VDD, and GND. CMOS requires at least one well contact in addition to the above three contacts. One must also consider multiple VDD and GND connections both for noise reduction and for current handling capability, especially if currents of more than 100 mA are involved.

8.12 SUMMARY

Special NMOS and CMOS circuits have been investigated. Clever designs can greatly facilitate VLSI layout. The Mead-Conway tally circuit and barrel shifter were examined with this in mind.

NAND-NAND and NOR-NOR logic were examined. The NMOS and CMOS AND-OR-INVERT and exclusive-OR/exclusive-NOR circuits were shown to be the same topologically, and to be superior in performance to NAND-NAND and NOR-NOR logic.

It is desirable to postpone the final details of a circuit as long as possible, and designing with multiplexers aids in doing this. Multiplexers are closely related to logic function blocks. Both can be implemented in NOR logic with enhancement-mode devices, or in NAND logic with both depletion-mode and enhancement-mode pass transistors.

Routing can be partitioned into global and detailed or local routing. Placement of modules or cells is critical in optimizing wire routing. When laying out routing, the goal is to minimize crossovers, interconnects, total length, and line resistance. The possible tradeoffs are area, speed, power, and testability. Power lines are especially susceptible to current crowding and noise problems. Clock line delays are critical in reducing clock skew.

As component density increases, wire routing becomes a more serious bottleneck. The interconnections of nodes are made through one or more metallization layers, with routing channels generally running horizontally and vertically on alternate metal layers. In this approach, a wire changes direction by means of a via connecting the two metallization layers.

The possible number of interconnections increases as the square of the number of devices. Wiring often occupies more chip area than devices do, and as geometries continue to shrink, wiring requirements continue to increase. In general, component positioning on a chip must be done with wire routing requirements in mind. This has led to new techniques in routing. The grid of wire channels on a chip contains many blockages due to internal wiring of components. Via placement is also a problem, as design rules require minimum spacing between vias, and between vias and active devices.

Several of the more basic routing algorithms were discussed and examples given. For a more detailed discussion of routing, the reader is referred to the text by Mukherjee (12).

REFERENCES

1. C. A. Mead and L. A. Conway, *Introduction to VLSI Systems*, Addison-Wesley Publishing Company, Reading, Mass., 1980.
2. V. D. Agrawal, "Synchronous Path Delay Analysis in a MOS Circuit Simulator," *Proceedings of the 19th Design Automation Conference*, Las Vegas, Nevada, June 14–16, 1982, pp. 629–635.
3. J. K. Ousterhout, "Crystal: A Timing Analyzer for *n*MOS VLSI Circuits," *Third Caltech Conference on Very Large Scale Integration*, 1983, pp. 57–69.
4. A. E. Dunlop, V. D. Agrawal, D. N. Deutsch, M. F. Jukl, P. Kozak, and M. Wiesel, "Chip Layout Optimization Using Critical Path Weighting," *Proceedings of the 21st Design Automation Conference*, Albuquerque, New Mexico, 1984, pp. 133–136.
5. G. W. Clow, "A Global Routing Algorithm for General Cells," *Proceedings of the 21st Design Automation Conference*, Albuquerque, New Mexico, 1984, pp. 45–50.
6. G. Dupenloup, "A Wire Routing Scheme for Double-Layer Cell Arrays," *Proceedings of the 21st Design Automation Conference*, Albuquerque, New Mexico, 1984, pp. 32–35.
7. J. Soukup, "Circuit Layout," *Proceedings of the IEEE*, vol. 69, 1981, pp. 1281–1304.
8. E. F. Moore, "The Shortest Path Through a Maze," *Proceedings of the International Symposium on Switching Theory*, Harvard University Press, vol. 1, 1959, pp. 285–292.
9. C. Y. Lee, "An Algorithm for Path Connection and its Applications," *IRE Transactions on Electronic Computers*, September 1961, pp. 346–365.
10. J. K. Ousterhout, G. T. Hamachi, R. N. Mayo, W. S. Scott, and G. S. Taylor, "Magic: A VLSI Layout System," *Proceedings of the 21st Design Automation Conference*, Albuquerque, New Mexico, 1984, pp. 152–159.
11. H. Mori, "Interactive Compaction Router for VLSI Layout," *Proceedings of the 21st Design Automation Conference*, Albuquerque, New Mexico, 1984, pp. 137–143.
12. A. Mukherjee, *Introduction to nMOS & CMOS VLSI Systems Design*, Prentice-Hall, Englewood Cliffs, New Jersey, 1986, pp. 306–332.

PROBLEMS

8.1. Draw a stick diagram of the NMOS *R-S* flip-flop shown in Fig. P8.1. Lay the circuit out with VDD running horizontally through the center and GND buses at the top and bottom. Make the circuit simple, symmetric, and without crossovers.

8.2. Draw a stick-diagram of the circuit in Fig. P8.2 directly, and in AOI form. Use clocked PMOS pull-ups. Estimate the relative power consumption and speed of both circuits.

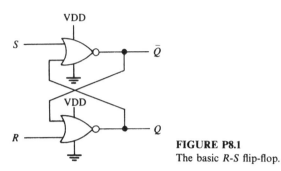

FIGURE P8.1
The basic *R-S* flip-flop.

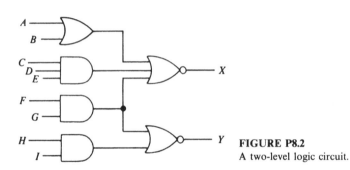

FIGURE P8.2
A two-level logic circuit.

8.3. Minimize the number of contacts to the NOR MUX of Fig. 8.15. The number of contacts can be significantly reduced by sacrificing some of the symmetry of the layout. Rearrange the circuit and obtain a layout requiring the least number of contacts. Is the result desirable?

DESIGN PROBLEMS

8.4. Lay out one cell of the tally circuit shown in Fig. 8.4 and save it in the cell library. Once the basic cell is laid out, use vertical and horizontal replicating to interface the cell with its nearest neighbors. The stick drawing of a possible Manhattan layout is shown in Fig. P8.4.

8.5. Lay out an NMOS 4-to-1 MUX as shown in Fig. 8.16. The control lines are to run vertically in polysilicon and the data lines horizontally in diffusion. Save this as a cell in the library.

8.6. Lay out a typical cell of a 4 × 4 barrel shifter as shown in Fig. 8.25. Follow the suggestions given in Sec. 8.6. The stick drawing of a possible Manhattan layout is shown in Fig. P8.6.

8.7. Lay out a 2-dimensional array of identical cells using a 3-phase clocking scheme. Every cell has two unidirectional data wires to its six nearest neighbors, one for sending data to the neighbor, and one for receiving data from the neighbor, as shown in Fig. P8.7. VDD, GND, and one clock phase must run through every cell, with the three clock phases alternating, and the cells must stack tightly. *Hint:* Visualize a brick wall.

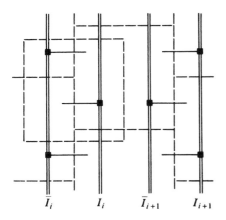

FIGURE P8.4
Stick drawing of one cell of a tally circuit.

$\overline{I}_i$ I_i $\overline{I}_{i+1}$ I_{i+1}

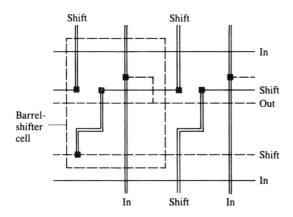

FIGURE P8.6
Stick drawing of one cell of a barrel shifter.

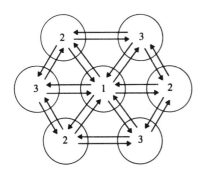

FIGURE P8.7
A brick-wall layout design. Numbers 1, 2, and 3 refer to clock phases.

CHAPTER
9

REGULAR
ARRAYS
OF LOGIC

9.1 INTRODUCTION

Shift registers are the basic structures for moving data, and data can be stored statically, pseudodynamically, or dynamically, as charge on nodes in the registers. Each method of charge storage will be examined, and a shift-right/shift-left register will be laid out in a Weinberger array.

Pipelined machines will be studied, followed by distributed-input gate structures. A 2-line to 4-line decoder and a 3-line to 8-line decoder will be examined as typical distributed-input structures. Programmable read-only memories (PROMs) and programmable logic arrays (PLAs) will be discussed next. The PROM and the PLA are special cases of programmable logic devices (PLDs), which also include programmable array logic (PALs), and dynamic logic arrays (DLAs). All four PLDs will be examined briefly.

Adding feedback to a PLD converts it to a finite-state machine (FSM). The Mead-Conway approach to finite-state machine design is a structured approach which does not allow arbitrary connections between logic gates, but requires synchronous systems, with data moving between registers that are alternately clocked on a 2-phase scheme. All inputs to the system must be synchronized, so there will be no races.

The result of this approach is a finite-state machine that is simple and easy to lay out using established design rules. It is easy to test each FSM module, and there is less chance of error in designing the system. This FSM is the basic pipeline structure, or register-to-register transfer of data, with local feedback added.

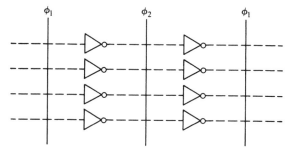

FIGURE 9.1
A mixed-mode stick drawing of a clocked 4-wide parallel shift register circuit.

9.2 BASIC MEMORY ELEMENTS

The *shift register* is a simple, elementary structure for moving a sequence of data bits, and is the basic structure of register-to-register transfer. To move a sequence of words from register stage to register stage, stack together several shift registers in parallel. One is now moving data on a conveyor belt. This is shown in Fig. 9.1.

Switching logic, also referred to as *combinational logic* (C/L), or *boolean logic* (B/L), must be inserted between the register stages to control the data movement. A simple example of switching logic added to the conveyor belt structure of Fig. 9.1 is shown in Fig. 9.2.

There are two choices for the circuit of Fig. 9.2 on phase 2 of the clock: one can shift the data to the right or up and to the right (SHUP). If ϕ_2 SHUP-BAR is high, the pass transistors labeled Q_A pass the data, while the transistors labeled

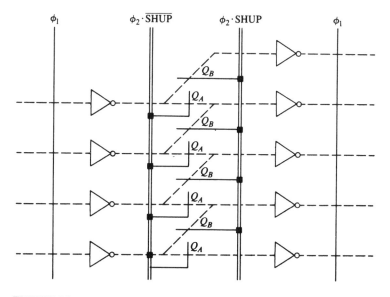

FIGURE 9.2
A mixed-mode stick diagram of shift-registers with combinational logic added.

Q_B are off. When ϕ_2SHUP is high, transistors Q_A are off, and transistors Q_B are on. This causes the entire word to be shifted up and to the right.

Data is stored in registers in the form of logic ones and zeros, depending upon whether certain nodes are charged or not. Charge may be stored in a dynamic or static manner, or by a combination of these two methods, which could be referred to as pseudostatic storage.

9.2.1   Dynamic Charge Storage

Dynamic charge storage is simpler and requires less space than static charge storage, but it requires clocking the data at a sufficiently high rate that the charge on the various nodes does not leak off. Typically, this requires a minimum refresh rate of 500 Hz to 1 kHz, corresponding to a charge storage time of about 1 or 2 ms.

A simple *dynamic charge storage circuit* consists of a clocked inverter with the charge stored on the gate-to-substrate capacitance, C_{gb}, of the pull-down device, as shown in Fig. 9.3. As the input, DATA, is clocked through the pass-transistor into the inverter by the write-enable signal, WRITE, the complement of the input data, DATA-BAR, is presented to the output.

9.2.2   Static Charge Storage

The basic *static charge storage device* is the SR flip-flop, composed of two cross-coupled NOR gates, as shown in Fig. 9.4. Due to positive feedback, the flip-flop is extremely stable and will hold the charge until power is removed. Another advantage of this circuit is that both the output, Q, and its complement, Q-BAR, are available.

The main disadvantage of the dynamic storage element is the need for refresh circuitry. The main disadvantages of the flip-flop, as compared to the dynamic storage element, are that it requires two inverters, takes more chip area, and dissipates more standby power.

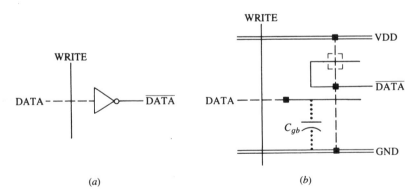

(a)   *(b)*

FIGURE 9.3
A dynamic charge-storage memory element. (*a*) Mixed-mode drawing; (*b*) stick drawing.

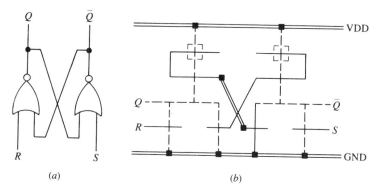

FIGURE 9.4
The basic NMOS RS flip-flop. (*a*) Equivalent circuit; (*b*) stick drawing.

9.2.3 Pseudostatic Charge Storage

Charge can also be stored in a *pseudostatic* manner, by means of a circuit with a clocked feedback path, as shown in Fig. 9.5. The complement of the data LOAD signal is the data HOLD signal. When data is loaded into the storage element, the feedback path is opened by the pass transistor clocked on HOLD and the charge on the first inverter is determined by the input signal on the DATA line. (The datum is loaded into the register.) When the LOAD signal is low, the HOLD signal is high, the feedback path is closed, and the two inverters latch the data. Again, both Q and Q-BAR are available as output.

9.3 SHIFT REGISTERS

A string of clocked inverters forms a *dynamic shift register* as shown in Fig. 9.6. This is the same basic circuit as in Fig. 9.3, with the single clocked inverter replaced by a clocked register of four inverters handling a four-bit wide data bus.

In a similar manner, a string of SR flip-flops can be clocked to form a *static*

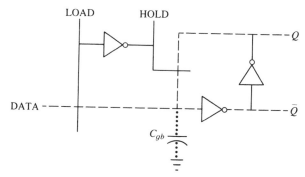

FIGURE 9.5
A mixed-mode drawing of a pseudostatic storage element.

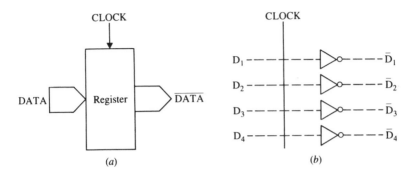

FIGURE 9.6
A dynamic shift register. (*a*) Symbol; (*b*) mixed-mode stick drawing.

shift register. A string of cross-coupled inverters, with a clocked input and a clocked feedback path, forms a pseudostatic shift register as shown in Fig. 9.7. Note that both LOAD and HOLD are clocked on phase 1 of a 2-phase clock.

This is the same basic circuit as in Fig. 9.5, with the single clocked inverter again replaced by a clocked register of N inverters handling an N-bit wide data bus. The D_i are the states of the N pseudostatic storage elements. An N-bit wide data line D is input, and both D and D-BAR are available as output.

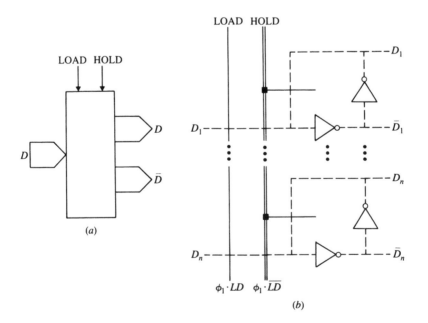

FIGURE 9.7
A pseudostatic shift register. (*a*) Symbol; (*b*) mixed-mode drawing.

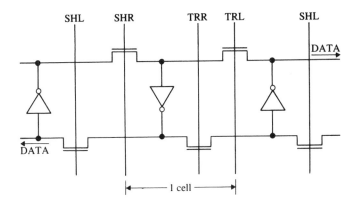

FIGURE 9.8
A circuit diagram of a clocked, 2-phase, shift-right/shift-left register.

A simple, clocked, 2-phase shift-right/shift-left register can be designed as shown in Fig. 9.8, and laid out as shown in Fig. 9.9. The behavior of the circuit is as follows (1):

To circulate the data in place, assert the TRanslate-Left, TRL, control signal during clock phase 1, and the TRanslate-Right, TRR, control signal during clock phase 2. This causes the data to shift left through one pass transistor in the upper data path during phase 1, and to shift right through one pass transistor in the lower data path during phase 2, resulting in no net change in the data location.

To shift data to the right, assert the SHift-Right signal, SHR, during clock phase 1, and the TRanslate-Right signal, TRR, during clock phase 2. This causes the data to shift right along the upper data line during phase 1, and to shift right

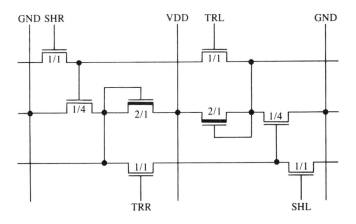

FIGURE 9.9
A Weinberger layout of a shift-left/shift-right register.

along the lower data line during phase 2, resulting in a net shift of one cell to the right.

To shift data to the left, assert the TRanslate-Left control signal, TRL, during clock phase 1, and the SHift-Left signal, SHL, during clock phase 2. This causes the data to shift left along the upper data line during phase 1, and to shift left along the lower data line during phase 2.

One control signal is sufficient to operate the shift register. If the control signal is labeled CNTRL, then the three basic operations can be achieved with one control signal as follows: To circulate the data in place, assert CNTRL-BAR during both clock phases. To shift the data one cell to the right, assert CNTRL during phase 2 and CNTRL-BAR during phase 1 of the clock. To shift the data one cell to the left, assert CNTRL during phase 1 and CNTRL-BAR during phase 2 of the clock.

9.4 PIPELINED MACHINES

A *serial shift register* is constructed by clocking inverters with alternate phases of a two-phase system as shown in Fig. 9.10. One stage consists of two inverters and both clock phases.

If the inverters of an *N*-wide string of the serial shift registers of Fig. 9.10 are replaced by boolean-logic blocks, the resulting structure is known as a pipelined machine. A mixed-mode stick drawing is shown in Fig. 9.11.

Pass transistors are required for both logic steering and the clocking of data into registers; but conceptually, it is desirable to separate these two functions. Let a combination of pass transistors and logic elements be treated as a register clocked on the phase during which the input pass transistors are turned on. Treat

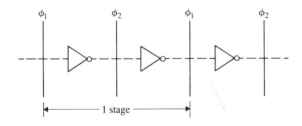

FIGURE 9.10
A mixed-mode drawing of a serial shift register.

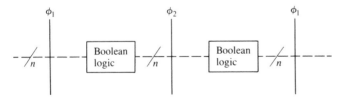

FIGURE 9.11
A mixed-mode drawing of the basic pipeline structure.

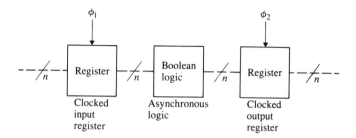

FIGURE 9.12
Clocked registers driving combinational logic blocks in a pipeline structure.

any logic functions associated with the input pass transistors as part of the preceding combinational-logic module. The circuit can then be symbolically diagrammed as shown in Fig. 9.12, with clocked registers controlling the shifting of data.

As seen from Fig. 9.12, data inputs are stored in the input register during phase 1 of the clock, from which they propagate into and through the combinational-logic block, and are presented as inputs to the output register. On phase 2 of the clock, the output register loads the data from the combinational-logic block. If the output register is driving a second logic block, the process repeats. A sequence of registers and combinational-logic blocks becomes a pipelined machine.

9.5 DISTRIBUTED-INPUT GATE STRUCTURES

The use of transistor gate inputs arranged on parallel data paths yields a more structured approach to combinational logic and decoder design. A significant advantage of this topology is that changes in logic may be made without requiring major changes in layout.

An enhancement-mode transistor NOR layout of a two-line to four-line decoder is shown in Fig. 9.13, along with the decoder truth table. This is structurally similar to the general function blocks studied in Sec. 6.8.

A simple, regular way to implement a combinational logic function of N inputs of width M bits is to use a memory of 2^N words of M bits each. This requires an N-input address to the *read only memory* or ROM, and utilizes the full truth table for the output functions. Frequently, only a small fraction of the 2^N minterms available for a canonical sum-of-products implementation is required, and the ROM is often very wasteful of chip area.

Programmed logic arrays (PLAs) are usually far more compact than ROMs because only the minterms required need be implemented. This is the major advantage of the PLA structure over an equivalent ROM implementation. Schemes that will be discussed in Chap. 10 can achieve even more compaction.

Inputs		Output			
A	B	Y_0	Y_1	Y_2	Y_3
0	0	1	0	0	0
0	1	0	1	0	0
1	0	0	0	1	0
1	1	0	0	0	1

(a)

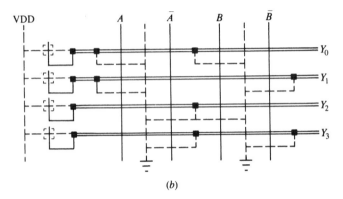

(b)

FIGURE 9.13
A NOR pass-transistor realization of a 2-line to 4-line decoder. (a) Truth table; (b) stick drawing.

9.6 NMOS PLAs

The basic *PLA structure* consists of an *AND plane* driving an *OR plane*, as shown in Fig. 9.14. The terminology corresponds to a sum-of-products (SOP) realization of the desired function, and bears no correspondence to the actual implementation. The SOP realization converts directly into a NAND-NAND implementation. When a product-of-sums (POS) solution is desired, it can be implemented in OR-AND or NOR-NOR logic. In either case, the first array is referred to as the AND plane, and the second array as the OR plane. The lines connecting the AND plane to the OR plane are called the product lines, in keeping with the AND-OR terminology.

Physically, the OR plane matrix is identical in form to the AND plane matrix, but its layout is rotated 90 degrees with respect to the AND plane. The input and output registers need not be identical, but they are also repetitive structures.

The overall size of a PLA is a function of the number of inputs, the number of product terms, the number of outputs, and the value of lambda. The PLA must be programmed by appropriately locating transistors on the array.

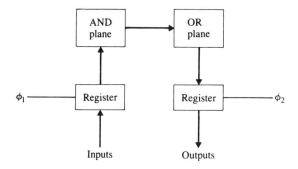

FIGURE 9.14
The basic floor plan of a PLA structure.

9.6.1 NMOS PLA Layouts

The NMOS PLA can be realized in either NAND-NAND logic or NOR-NOR logic. For any but the smallest PLAs, the NAND implementation is much smaller because it needs no metal contacts in the matrix of the AND or OR plane and is more compact. The NAND structure is much slower than the NOR implementation due to the series pass transistor structure. A NAND PLA with N control transistors in series is about $N \times N$ times slower than the NOR realization, while the NAND implementation is typically smaller in area than the NOR realization by a factor of about three to one.

A NOR-NOR realization of an NMOS PLA with enhancement-mode pull-down devices is shown in Fig. 9.15, including input and output buffers and two-phase clocking. The PLA has 3 inputs and has been programmed to realize four product lines with three output lines. The product lines realized by this PLA are:

$$P_0 = \bar{I}_0 \bar{I}_1 \qquad P_1 = \bar{I}_0 I_1 \qquad P_2 = I_0 I_1 \bar{I}_2 \qquad P_3 = I_0 I_2 \qquad (9.1)$$

The outputs realized by the PLA of Fig. 9.15 are

$$Y_0 = P_1 \qquad Y_1 = P_0 + P_2 + P_3 \qquad Y_2 = P_1 + P_2 \qquad (9.2)$$

A NAND-NAND realization of the NMOS PLA shown in Fig. 9.15 is given in Fig. 9.16. The pull-ups in Figs. 9.15 and 9.16 are shown as depletion-mode NMOS devices. Dynamic CMOS PLAs with PMOS pull-ups could be laid out in a similar manner.

9.6.2 Programming the NMOS PLA

The *personality matrix*, Q, of a PLA is defined as follows (2). In the AND plane, element $q_{ij} = 0$ if a FET is to connect product line p_i to input line I_j, $q_{ij} = 1$ if a FET is to connect product line p_i to input line I_j-BAR, and q_{ij} is a don't care ($\times$) if neither input is to be connected to product line p_i. In the OR plane, $q_{ij} = 1$ if product line p_i connects to output Y_j, and 0 otherwise. The personality matrix of

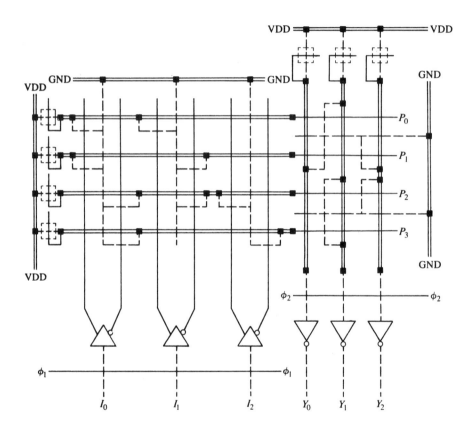

FIGURE 9.15
A stick drawing of an NMOS NOR-NOR PLA realization.

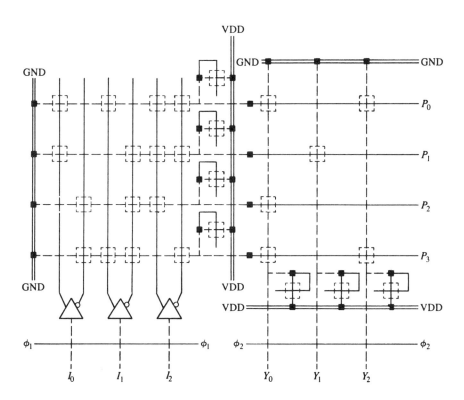

FIGURE 9.16
A stick drawing of an NMOS NAND-NAND PLA realization.

the PLA shown in Figs. 9.15 and 9.16 is

$$Q = \begin{bmatrix} 1 & 1 & \times & 0 & 1 & 0 \\ 1 & 0 & \times & 1 & 0 & 1 \\ 0 & 0 & 1 & 0 & 1 & 1 \\ 0 & \times & 0 & 0 & 1 & 0 \end{bmatrix}$$

The procedure for laying out a NOR-NOR PLA is as follows:

For each logic 1 in the input columns of the personality matrix, run a diffusion path from the appropriate product-term line, under the corresponding inverted input line in the PLA AND plane to ground. The transistor thus created is controlled by the inverted input line. Whenever that controlling line crossing the AND plane is high, the product-term line will be low.

For each logic 0 in the input columns of the personality matrix, run a diffusion path from the appropriate product-term line, under the corresponding noninverted input or state line in the PLA AND plane, to ground. The transistor thus created is controlled by the noninverted input line. Whenever that controlling line crossing the AND plane is high, the product term line will be low. Don't care terms are connected to neither the true nor the complemented input lines.

For each logic 1 in the output columns of the personality matrix, run a diffusion path from the next-state output line in the PLA OR plane, under the corresponding product term line, to ground. This creates a transistor controlled by the product-term line. Then, if that controlling product-term line is high, the path to the output inverter will be low, and the output will be high. The output is low unless at least one product line controlling it is high.

The procedure for laying out a NAND-NAND PLA is similar.

For each logic 1 in the input columns of the personality matrix, place an ion implant under the appropriate product line where it intersects the noninverted input line in the PLA AND plane. The transistor thus created is always on and the noninverted input line has no control over that product line. Whenever all the controlling input lines in the AND plane are high, the product line will be low.

For each logic 0 in the input columns of the personality matrix, place an ion implant under the appropriate product line where it intersects the inverted-input line in the PLA AND plane. The transistor thus created is always on and the inverted input line has no control over that product line. Whenever all the controlling input lines are high, the product line will be low. A don't care requires ion implants for both the true and complemented input signals.

For each logic 0 in the output columns of the personality matrix, place an ion implant under that product line where it intersects the output line in the PLA OR plane. The transistor thus created is always on and that product line has no control over the output line. Whenever the controlling product lines are high the noninverted output will be low.

Figures 9.17 and 9.18 show possible layouts of the NAND-NAND and NOR-NOR PLA structures given in Figs. 9.15 and 9.16, augmented with clock lines for precharging and evaluating the PLAs.

9.6.3 The Precharged NMOS PLA

Depletion-mode pull-up devices are slow, but they are just along an edge of each plane. Precharging the output lines of both the AND plane and the OR plane avoids the slow depletion-mode pull-up. During phase 1 each product line and each output line can be precharged to VDD, while phase 2 isolates the ground and prevents the PLA from evaluating the logic. During phase 2 the PLA will determine which input lines remain charged and which input lines will be discharged, while the product lines determine which output lines will be pulled low.

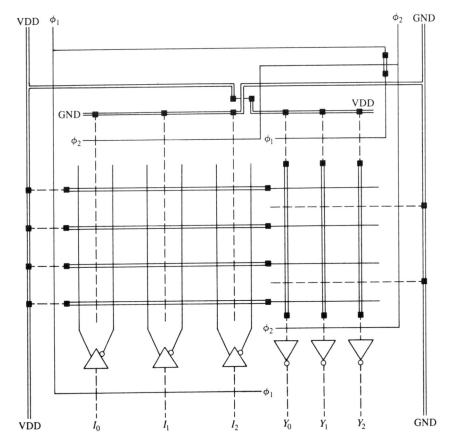

FIGURE 9.17
A precharged NMOS NOR-NOR PLA.

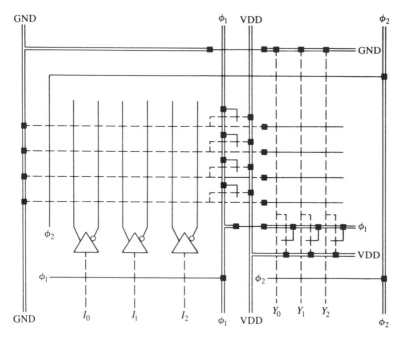

FIGURE 9.18
A precharged NMOS NAND-NAND PLA.

9.6.4 The CMOS PLA

The basic CMOS PLA is obtained by providing an *n* well and replacing the pull-up devices in the NAND-NAND array or in the NOR-NOR array with enhancement-mode PMOS devices as shown in Plate 7. The CMOS array can be precharged or not, and can be clocked with the same two-phase clocking scheme as used above for the NMOS PLA. CMOS PLA design offers many more varieties of layout than does NMOS. These will be discussed in more detail in the next chapter.

9.7 PROGRAMMABLE LOGIC DEVICES

There are several close relatives of the basic PLA. A digital, application-specific IC family, widely used in VLSI design, is the *programmable logic device* or PLD. The AND-OR structure of the PLA is the core of all PLDs, since this structure can be used to implement any two-level boolean function. Multilevel logic can be realized with Weinberger arrays or gate matrices, as discussed in Sec. 11.2.

9.7.1 The Field-Programmable Logic Array

The *field-programmable logic array* (FPLA), shown in Fig. 9.19, has an address decoder (the AND array) and a data matrix (the OR array). In the FPLA, both

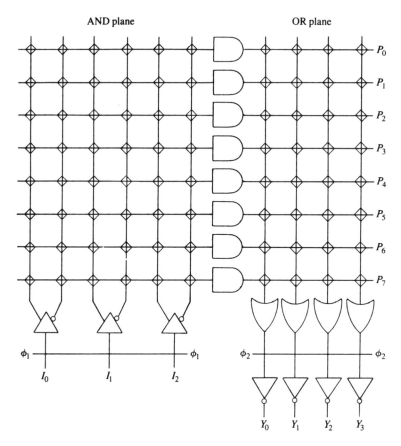

FIGURE 9.19
The clocked FPLA structure.

the address decoder and the data matrix are programmable. This is shown by placing hollow diamonds at all the *crosspoint sites*. A crosspoint is the intersection of a row and a column of the PLA. When programming the PLA, the appropriate crosspoints can be filled in to indicate connections.

Each AND gate can have don't-care inputs, which implies that multiple inputs can select the same word. Also, since multiple AND outputs can be on simultaneously, multiple words in the OR array can be selected at the same time, thus allowing a function to be divided among multiple FPLAs.

There are two special cases of FPLA: the *programmed read-only memory* or PROM, wherein the OR matrix is programmable and the AND matrix is fixed, and the *programmed array logic* or PAL, wherein the AND matrix is programmable and the OR matrix is fixed. (PAL is a registered trademark of Monolithic Memories, Inc.)

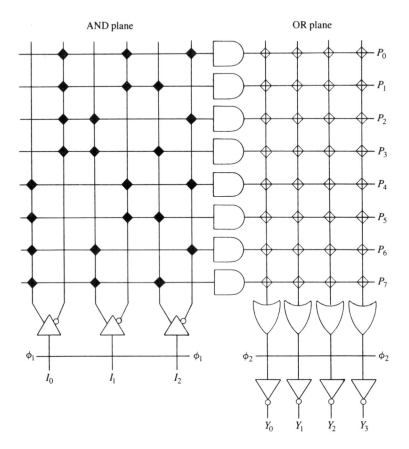

FIGURE 9.20
The clocked PROM structure.

The PROM configuration is shown in Fig. 9.20, with the AND-plane crosspoint connections darkened. A PROM is useful for creating simple logic devices such as memory-address decoders, but the fixed AND array limits its use in more complex applications where multiple addresses might be needed for the same word.

9.7.2 Programmable-Array Logic

The PAL structure is the mirror image of the PROM structure, as can be seen in Fig. 9.21, where the OR plane has been preprogrammed. Since it has a programmable AND array, multiple addresses can select the same word, and multiple words in the array can be selected simultaneously.

PALs and FPLAs overcome one of the major inefficiencies of PROMs by allowing only as many inputs as necessary for a specific implementation. Since

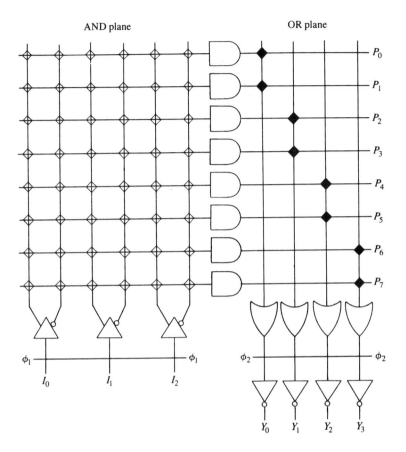

FIGURE 9.21
The clocked PAL structure.

PALs do not have the fuses or the programming and testing circuitry required by the OR arrays of FPLAs, they are typically about 15 percent faster than FPLAs for the same power consumption. PALs used to be limited to control logic and I/O applications but recent improvements in performance make PALs suitable for data-path logic also.

The PAL shown in Fig. 9.21 has 2-input OR gates in the OR plane. Commercial devices typically have 8-input OR gates, and realize an 8-wide AND-OR structure.

9.7.3 Dynamic Logic Arrays

The *dynamic logic array* (DLA) resembles a PLA with the AND and OR planes merged such that the OR logic is performed in the AND plane. The DLA is ideally suited to implementations with few crosspoint connections in the OR

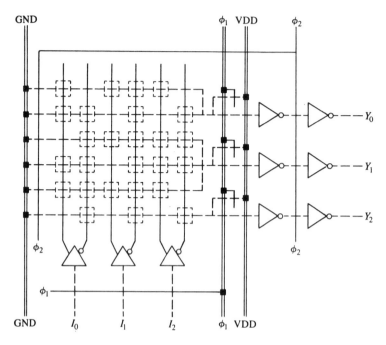

FIGURE 9.22
A clocked DLA realization of the three functions in Eq. (9.3).

plane. It can realize a sum-of-products solution with less area than a PLA and can be clocked and precharged the same as a PLA structure. The DLA is less programmable than an equivalent PLA, but it combines the speed, simplicity and small size of dynamic logic with the programmability of a PLA.

An example of a NAND DLA is shown in Fig. 9.22. It realizes three output functions. The first output function consists of the OR of two product terms, whereas the second output function is the OR of three product terms, and the third output function consists of only one product term. The outputs are:

$$Y_0 = \bar{I}_0 \bar{I}_2 + I_1 I_2 \qquad Y_1 = I_0 + I_1 + \bar{I}_2 \qquad Y_2 = I_0 I_1 I_2 \qquad (9.3)$$

and the personality matrix of the DLA is:

$$Q = \begin{bmatrix} 1 & \times & 1 & 1 & 0 & 0 \\ \times & 0 & 0 & 1 & 0 & 0 \\ 0 & \times & \times & 0 & 1 & 0 \\ \times & 0 & \times & 0 & 1 & 0 \\ \times & \times & 1 & 0 & 1 & 0 \\ 0 & 0 & 0 & 0 & 0 & 1 \end{bmatrix}$$

The above four basic architectures of PLDs can be augmented by additional logic functions such as registers, latches, and feedback paths to achieve specific applications. Many different PLD configurations have been developed that incorporate a variety of these features.

9.8 THE FINITE-STATE MACHINE AS A PLA STRUCTURE

The PLA can be used to store information related to the past history of its inputs. This is memory and causes the same inputs to combine with different feedback signals to produce different outputs. When feedback is added to the AND OR PLA structure, the PLA becomes a *finite state machine* (FSM). If input and output buffers and two-phase clocking are added, the structure is as shown in Fig. 9.23.

Hierarchically, the design procedure is as follows:

1. Plan the digital processing systems as combinations of register-to-register data transfer paths, controlled by finite-state machines.
2. Plan geometric shapes, relative sizes, and interconnection topologies of all subsystem modules so that all modules merge together snugly with a minimum of space and time wasted by random interconnecting wiring.
3. Dynamic storage registers are constructed using charge stored on input gates of inverting logic.
4. Combinational logic in the data paths is implemented with steering logic composed of regular structures of pass transistors.
5. Most of the combinational logic in finite-state machines is implemented with PLAs.
6. All functioning is sequenced using a two-phase nonoverlapping clock scheme.

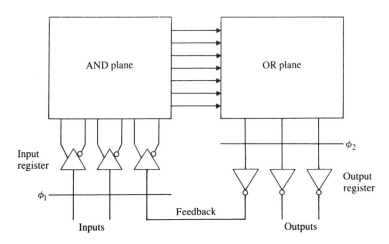

FIGURE 9.23
A clocked finite-state machine.

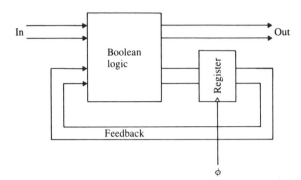

FIGURE 9.24
A Mealy machine; some outputs are asynchronous.

A finite-state machine can be designed as a Mealy machine or a Moore machine. The *Mealy machine*, shown in Fig. 9.24, has outputs which may change with input changes in an asynchronous manner and cause erroneous behavior. Hence, the Mealy machine should be avoided whenever possible.

The *Moore machine*, shown in Fig. 9.25, has outputs which depend upon and change only with state changes, since all the outputs of the boolean-logic block go through a state register, and are synchronously clocked.

The importance of the PLA/FSM in VLSI is due to its:

1. Regularity; it has a standard easily expandable layout
2. Convenience; little design effort is required
3. Compactness; it is efficient for small circuits
4. Modularity, which makes it possible to design hierarchical PLAs and FSMs into large sequential systems
5. Suitability to being computer generated

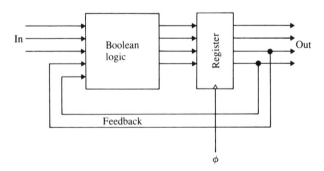

FIGURE 9.25
A Moore machine; all outputs are clocked.

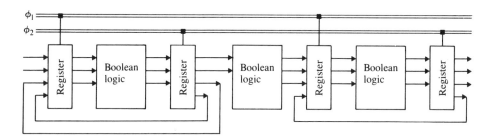

FIGURE 9.26
A sequential system, consisting of a series of combinational-logic modules with feedback.

In designing PLAs, one should always be able to RESET from any state. For N feedback loops there are 2^N states. To avoid lockout, design for all 2^N states.

Any large sequential system can be constructed from a series of finite-state machines as shown in Fig. 9.26. If Moore machines are used, everything goes through only one combinational-logic block between clock pulses, whereas Mealy machine outputs can ripple downstream.

There is still the basic clocking problem which led to the design of master-slave flip-flops; the clock pulses must be very short to avoid rippling in a Moore machine. This can be more easily accomplished by using at least two clock phases.

9.9 FEEDBACK IN PROGRAMMABLE LOGIC DEVICES

In general, feedback must include flip-flops and shift registers in the loop, which can gate outputs back to the AND plane. To avoid races the feedback loops will be clocked by two phases as a Moore machine.

There are four flip-flop choices, S-R, J-K, T, and D. When faced with two or more design layouts, the usual criteria is size. The larger the PLA layout, the more costly in chip real estate, and the more capacitance the drivers face. Size directly affects performance as well as cost.

The PLA size is determined by the number of inputs, including fed back signals, the number of outputs, and the number of product terms. A simple criterion of PLA size is the total number of crosspoints required. The number of crosspoints is the product of the number of rows and the number of columns of both the AND plane and the OR plane. A transistor placed at a crosspoint can short circuit that row to that column, in which case the crosspoint becomes an electrical node. It will be convenient to use "node" as a synonym for crosspoint.

Let R, C, and N represent *rows*, *columns*, and *crosspoints*, respectively. Then a PLA with four inputs, eight product terms, and five outputs requires an AND plane of $8R \times 4C = 32N$, and an OR plane of $8R \times 5C = 40N$. The total size of the PLA is thus $8R \times 9C = 72N$. In general, R rows by C columns produce N crosspoints (potential nodes).

Example 9.1. Find the personality matrix, Q, for a four-bit modulo-10 counter with delay flip-flops in the feedback loop. Give an implementation of the finite-state machine.

Solution. Let $n + 1$ refer to the next state of a variable, whose present state has no superscript. The minimum sum-of-products functions required as flip-flop inputs are

$$W^{n+1} = XYZ + W\bar{Z} \qquad \text{(most significant bit)}$$

$$X^{n+1} = X\bar{Y} + X\bar{Z} + \bar{X}YZ$$

$$Y^{n+1} = \bar{W}\bar{Y}Z + Y\bar{Z}$$

$$Z^{n+1} = \bar{Z}$$

The OR-plane matrix drives the four flip-flops, and the outputs are fed back to the AND plane. As with other inputs to the AND plane, both true and complemented flip-flop outputs are fed back. The PLA outputs could be taken directly from the four flip-flops. This gives a PLA of dimensions $8R \times 12C = 96N$, but this loads the flip-flop outputs. If it is desired to obtain the outputs directly from the OR matrix, the PLA is shown in Fig. 9.27, and in Plate 8, and has dimensions of $12R \times 16C = 196N$, which doubles the size of the PLA.

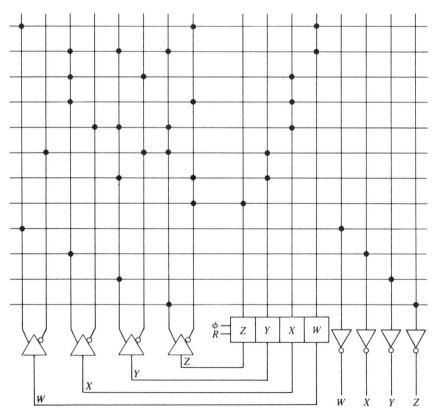

FIGURE 9.27
A modulo-10 counter implemented with D-type flip-flops.

The personality matrix for the counter is given below. The inputs are taken to be I_0, I_1, I_2, and $I_3 = W$, X, Y, Z, respectively. The outputs are taken in reverse order, Y_0, Y_1, Y_2, $Y_3 = Z$, W, Y, X, respectively.

$$Q = \begin{bmatrix} 0 & \times & \times & 1 & 0 & 0 & 0 & 1 \\ \times & 0 & 0 & 0 & 0 & 0 & 0 & 1 \\ \times & 0 & 1 & \times & 0 & 0 & 1 & 0 \\ \times & 0 & \times & 1 & 0 & 0 & 1 & 0 \\ \times & 1 & 0 & 0 & 0 & 0 & 1 & 0 \\ 1 & \times & 1 & 0 & 0 & 1 & 0 & 0 \\ \times & \times & 0 & 1 & 0 & 1 & 0 & 0 \\ \times & \times & \times & 1 & 1 & 0 & 0 & 0 \end{bmatrix}$$

Conventional counters whose modulo, M, is not an integral power of 2, require a gate that detects the state $M - 1$ and resets all the flip-flops prior to the next count. A PLA can implement a variety of fixed- or variable-modulo counters. The AND plane is used to sense the present state by serving as a coincidence detector for SET or RESET levels to control the flip-flop array and determine the next state of the system.

Inputs to the AND plane may include external control lines to provide any desired counting sequence, or to interrupt the normal counting sequence at any time and SET the AND plane to any predetermined state. The sequencing of the flip-flops requires two control functions, the normal binary incrementing function and the external inputs which determine the modulo. The inputs to each flip-flop are obtained from the OR plane of the PLA. The inputs to the AND plane are the external controls and the outputs of the flip-flops. In general, one should check various designs to determine the PLA with the least number of nodes.

The number of crosspoints that are occupied by transistors is the number of nodes actually needed, and the ratio of crosspoints used to the total number of crosspoints is a measure of the sparseness of the PLA. Methods of reducing the number of unused crosspoints will be considered in Chap. 10.

An excellent discussion of PLA design with flip-flops in the feedback path can be found in Carr and Mize (3).

9.10 MULTIOUTPUT LOGIC MINIMIZATION

The number of input lines and output lines of a PLA is determined by the system requirements. This fixes the number of columns of the PLA, and the design engineer can only reduce the number of product lines or rows. Thus, to create the smallest possible PLA for any specific application, the designer must be able to minimize the number of product lines needed. This is an exercise in multioutput gate minimization, and the Quine-McCluskey technique can be modified to accomplish this (4,5).

To apply the *Quine-McCluskey tabular method* to more than one output function, each minterm must be labeled to identify the function or functions to which it belongs. The standard tabular reduction method for single functions is then augmented by three new rules (6).

1. Two implicants can only be combined if they have at least one label (output function) in common.
2. The label of combined products only contains letters common to the labels of both original implicants.
3. The products whose entire label is contained in the label of the larger implicant are checked off.

The procedure is best explained by an example as follows.

Example 9.2. Three functions X, Y, and Z are to be implemented with a minimum-sized PLA. The procedure is to determine which minterms can be combined to obtain prime implicants, followed by a determination of which prime implicants are essential, necessary, and redundant.

$$X(A, B, C, D) = \Sigma m(2, 4, 10, 11, 12, 13) \tag{9.4}$$

$$Y(A, B, C, D) = \Sigma m(4, 5, 10, 11, 13) \tag{9.5}$$

$$Z(A, B, C, D) = \Sigma m(2, 10, 11, 12) + d(3) \tag{9.6}$$

Solution. The minterms are ordered by the number of 1's in each minterm, as in the standard Quine-McCluskey approach; with appended labels specifying the function which contains that minterm. The reduction procedure follows the above three additional rules, viz.

TABLE 9.1

Minterm		Label		
0010	(2)	XZ		
0100	(4)	XY	*	(a)
0011	(3)	Z		
0101	(5)	Y		
1010	(10)	XYZ		
1100	(12)	XZ	*	(b)
1011	(11)	XYZ		
1101	(13)	XY	*	(c)

Minterms 2 and 5 cannot be combined because they occur in different functions (rule 1). Minterms 2 and 3 can combine because they both belong to function Z (rule 1), and the label of the combined pair is Z since both minterms occur only in function Z (rule 2). When minterms 2 and 3 are combined to form a new implicant, only minterm 3 can be checked off, since minterm 2 also belongs to function X, and must still be accounted for in the cover of X (rule 3).

Proceeding in this manner, all the minterms except 4, 12, and 13 combine into larger implicants. Minterms 4, 12, and 13 are prime implicants. They are flagged with an asterisk, and are labeled a, b, c in Table 9.1. The remaining minterms are combined and arranged in Table 9.2.

TABLE 9.2

Minterm pairs		New label		
001×	(2, 3)	Z		
×010	(2, 10)	XZ	*	(d)
010×	(4, 5)	Y	*	(e)
×100	(4, 12)	X	*	(f)
×101	(5, 13)	Y	*	(g)
101×	(10, 11)	XYZ	*	(h)
110×	(12, 13)	X	*	(i)

TABLE 9.3

Implicant		Label		
×01×	(2, 3, 10, 11)	Z	*	(j)

All ten prime implicants are now determined. The prime implicant table must next be set up to determine essential and necessary prime implicants. This is Table 9.4.

TABLE 9.4

Prime implicant		X						Y					Z			
		2	4	10	11	12	13	4	5	10	11	13	2	10	11	12
a	4		✓					✓								
b	12					✓										✓
c	13						✓					✓				
d	2,10	✓		✓									✓	✓		
e	4,5							✓	✓							
f	4,12		✓			✓										
g	5,13								✓			✓				
h	10,11			✓	✓					✓	✓			✓	✓	
i	12,13					✓	✓									
j	2,3,10,11												✓	✓	✓	

From Table 9.4 it can be seen that the following prime implicants are essential: b is essential for minterm 12 in Z, d is essential for minterm 2 in X, and h is essential for minterm 11 in X and minterms 10 and 11 in Y. The remaining prime implicants are all optional, and must be examined for necessary prime implicants. Prime implicant b also covers minterm 12 in X, d covers minterm 10 in X, as well as minterms 2 and 10 in Z, and minterm h covers 10 in X, as well as minterms 10 and 11 in functions Y and Z.

Minterm j is seen to be redundant because function Z is already covered. Minterms 4 and 13 must be covered in X, and minterms 4, 5, and 13 must be covered in Y. The prime implicants that must be examined further are shown in Table 9.5, along with the minterms they cover.

TABLE 9.5

Prime implicant		X 4	X 13	Y 4	Y 5	Y 13
a	4	✓		✓		
c	13		✓			✓
e	4,5			✓	✓	
f	4,12	✓				
g	5,13				✓	✓
i	12,13		✓			

There are no clear-cut choices in Table 9.5. To examine all the possibilities, form the function H, which contains all possible permutations of cover sets for the remaining prime implicants. From Table 9.5, H is

$$H = (a + f)(c + i)(a + e)(e + g)(c + g) = (a + ef)(g + ce)(c + i)$$
$$= acg + ace + cef + agi + efgi$$

The last term consists of four prime implicants and is not a minimal solution. This still leaves four possible sets of solutions, namely,

$$a + c + g = \bar{A}B\bar{C}\bar{D} + AB\bar{C}D + B\bar{C}D$$
$$a + c + e = \bar{A}B\bar{C}\bar{D} + AB\bar{C}D + \bar{A}B\bar{C}$$
$$c + e + f = AB\bar{C}D + \bar{A}B\bar{C} + B\bar{C}\bar{D}$$
$$a + g + i = \bar{A}B\bar{C}\bar{D} + B\bar{C}D + AB\bar{C}$$

The first two choices have eleven literals each, and are not minimal. The last two possibilities have ten literals each, and require the same number of inverters. Prime implicants c, e, and f are arbitrarily chosen as necessary, making the other prime implicants redundant. Table 9.6 lists all the essential and necessary prime implicants, and which functions are covered by each.

TABLE 9.6

Prime implicant		Output
EPI	$b = AB\bar{C}\bar{D}$	X, Z
NPI	$c = AB\bar{C}D$	X, Y
EPI	$d = \bar{B}C\bar{D}$	X, Z
NPI	$e = \bar{A}B\bar{C}$	Y
NPI	$f = B\bar{C}\bar{D}$	X
EPI	$h = A\bar{B}C$	X, Y, Z

The individual functions must now be examined to see if prime implicants that are essential to one function are also essential or necessary to other functions. Examination of Table 9.6 shows that prime implicant $b = AB\bar{C}\bar{D}$ is contained in $f = B\bar{C}\bar{D}$, and is redundant in output X while essential to output Z. The three functions are found to be

$$X = AB\bar{C}D + \bar{B}C\bar{D} + B\bar{C}\bar{D} + A\bar{B}C \tag{9.7}$$

$$Y = AB\bar{C}D + \bar{A}B\bar{C} + A\bar{B}C \tag{9.8}$$

$$Z = AB\bar{C}\bar{D} + \bar{B}C\bar{D} + A\bar{B}C \tag{9.9}$$

The minimized PLA is shown in Fig. 9.28. It consists of 6 rows, 11 columns, 66 crosspoints, and 30 connected crosspoints.

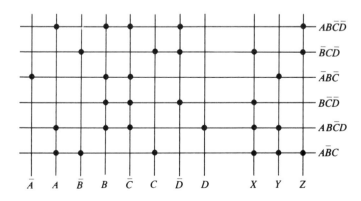

FIGURE 9.28
The optimized PLA of Example 9.2.

9.11 SUMMARY

Three basic memory charge-storar , approaches were examined: static, pseudo-static, and dynamic. Basic shift registers, shift-right/shift-left registers, and distributed-input structures were investigated.

Four categories of programmable logic devices (PLDs) were investigated: the field-programmable logic array (FPLA), the programmable read-only memory (PROM), the programmable array logic (PAL), and the dynamic logic array (DLA).

Both clocked and unclocked NMOS NAND-NAND and NOR-NOR PLAs were designed, after which PALs and PROMs were studied. PLDs have typical delays, including external buffers, of 2 to 3 ns per gate, and power dissipations of the order of 0.5 to 1.5 mW per equivalent gate. Speed-power products of this magnitude are competitive in today's market. PLDs can also be programmed very quickly as compared to gate-array prototypes which have rework cycles of 8 to 10 weeks.

Another benefit of PLDs is that the devices can be tested quickly in situ. Both ac and dc timing-analysis programs for semicustom IC designs are being continuously improved; but critical-path delays, switching noise, and line reflections still cannot be predicted accurately until the chip is tested in the system.

Once a design has been converted into a suitable boolean expression, a computer program can accept an input file and assemble the data into an output mask file for a PLD. A good program allows designers to input test vectors to simulate and debug the PLD, and to test the finished device.

Adding feedback to a PLD gives one a finite-state machine (FSM). Mealy and Moore FSMs were discussed and compared. Two-phase clocked Moore machines are the preferred FSM. When flip-flops and/or shift registers are included in the feedback path, the FSM becomes a very effective sequential-machine design tool.

A measure of the effective use of chip area by a PLA is the ratio of crosspoints containing switching devices to the total number of crosspoints required. When this ratio is low, the PLA is said to be sparse, and it does not utilize its chip area efficiently.

REFERENCES

1. C. A. Mead and L. A. Conway, *Introduction to VLSI Systems*, Addison-Wesley Publishing Co., Reading, Mass., 1980, pp. 72–75.
2. M. M. Ligthart, E. H. L. Aarts, and F. P. M. Beenker, "Design-for-Testability of PLAs Using Statistical Cooling," *Proceedings of the 23d Design Automation Conference*, June 29–July 2, 1986, pp. 339–345.
3. W. N. Carr and J. P. Mize, *MOS/LSI Design and Application*, Texas Instruments Electronics Series, McGraw-Hill Book Company, New York, N.Y., 1972, pp. 232–258.
4. W. V. Quine, "The Problem of Simplifying Truth Functions," *American Mathematical Monthly*, vol. 59, no. 8, October 1952, pp. 521–531.

5. E. J. McCluskey, "Minimization of Boolean Functions," *Bell System Technical Journal*, vol. 35, no. 5, November 1956, pp. 1417–1444.
6. F. J. Hill and G. R. Peterson, *Introduction to Switching Theory and Logical Design*, John Wiley & Sons, New York, N.Y., 2d ed., 1974, pp. 159–167.

PROBLEMS

9.1. Make a stick drawing of one cell of a horizontal LIFO stack.

Use Truth Table P9.2 for Probs. 9.2, 9.3, and 9.4.

9.2. Design a minimum-size (minimum N) PLA to convert Gray code to weighted BCD. How much larger would the PLA be if both true and complemented output lines are available? If only one output per variable is provided, does it matter whether it is the true or complemented output?

9.3. Repeat Prob. 9.2 for a minimum-size PLA to convert Gray to weighted BCD and Gray to decimal simultaneously.

9.4. Repeat Prob. 9.2 for a minimum-size PLA to convert a weighted BCD to a Johnson BCD code.

TABLE P9.2
Truth tables

Decimal	Gray				8-4-2-1 BCD				Johnson BCD				
	A	B	C	D	W	X	Y	Z	R	S	T	U	V
0	1	1	1	1	0	0	0	0	0	0	0	0	0
1	0	1	1	1	0	0	0	1	0	0	0	0	1
2	0	0	1	1	0	0	1	0	0	0	0	1	1
3	1	0	1	1	0	0	1	1	0	0	1	1	1
4	1	0	0	1	0	1	0	0	0	1	1	1	1
5	0	0	0	1	0	1	0	1	1	1	1	1	1
6	0	1	0	1	0	1	1	0	1	1	1	1	0
7	1	1	0	1	0	1	1	1	1	1	1	0	0
8	1	1	0	0	1	0	0	0	1	1	0	0	0
9	0	1	0	0	1	0	0	1	1	0	0	0	0

9.5. Design a PLA to realize the function $Y^{n+1} = A\bar{B} + \bar{A}B + CY$. Use a delay flip-flop to provide the feedback. Find the sparseness factor S.

9.6. Minimize the four functions W, X, Y, and Z, and realize a minimum-sized PLA to implement them. The d_i are don't care minterms.

$$W = \Sigma m(4, 5, 8, 14) + d(15) \qquad X = \Sigma m(1, 8, 14, 15) + d(5)$$

$$Y = \Sigma m(4, 5, 8, 14, 15) \qquad Z = \Sigma m(1, 3, 5, 11, 15) + d(14).$$

9.7. Map the functions given in Eqs. (9.7), (9.8), and (9.9), and compare the result to that given in Fig. 9.28.

DESIGN PROBLEMS

9.8. Lay out one cell of the horizontal LIFO stack of Prob. 9.1.

9.9. A CMOS minority gate is configured as an AND-OR-INVERT structure shown in Fig. P9.9a and a stick diagram of the gate is shown in Fig. P9.9b. Lay out the CMOS minority gate.

9.10. Design a 4-bit binary counter as a dynamic CMOS DLA structure. Represent the next state of the counter by the superscript $n + 1$, and the present state by the variable. Then the counter can be represented by the following equations:

$$A^{n+1} = \bar{A} \qquad B^{n+1} = A \oplus B \qquad C^{n+1} = A \oplus C \qquad D^{n+1} = ABC \oplus D$$

The counter is to be realized with a four-column DLA, with control lines running vertically in polysilicon over output/product lines running horizontally in diffusion, with undesired transistors short circuited by depletion implants. During phase 1, all output lines are to be precharged. During phase 2, control transistors discharge appropriate output lines to ground. Two inverters on each output line produce a one-cycle delay of the data that are fed back to control the DLA.

Hint: Break down the problem into two parts, the precharge circuitry and the AND/OR plane. A stick drawing with horizontal data paths and vertical clocking and power line is shown in Fig. P9.10. Decide how to lay this out before laying out the entire counter.

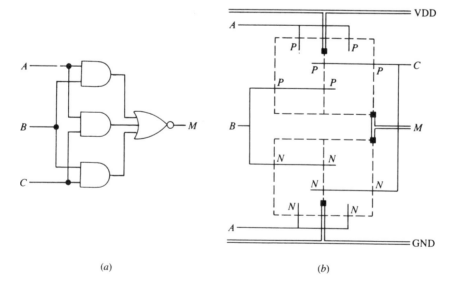

(a)   (b)

FIGURE P9.9
A CMOS minority gate. (a) Circuit; (b) stick drawing.

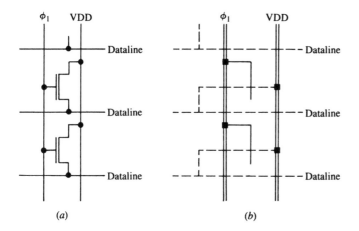

(a)   (b)

FIGURE P9.10
Counter precharge circuitry. (a) Circuit; (b) stick drawing.

CHAPTER
10

ADVANCED PROGRAMMABLE LOGIC TECHNIQUES

10.1 INTRODUCTION

Due to the time, cost, and complexity of VLSI design an orderly, structured form of logic implementation is necessary for handling combinational sequential logic functions. PLAs are increasingly popular choices which offer designers flexibility because logic implementation can be delayed until other details such as routing have been finalized, and because last-minute changes can be made easily and quickly. The PLA is the most general form of programmable device; the PROM, PAL, and DLA being subsets of the PLA. In this chapter, the generic term "PLA" will be assumed to include all four categories.

PLAs are also attractive to the VLSI designer because their regular structure requires a minimum number of separate cell designs, and allows for ease in testing while offering the opportunity for simple, rapid expandability. Complementary CMOS PLAs tend to be very slow due to the need for series transistor chains, and they often require complicated clocking schemes of three or more phases. Complementary CMOS static PLA layouts are also topologically more complex than static NMOS PLAs, and newer techniques of dynamic CMOS such as domino CMOS are replacing them.

CMOS has a better output-voltage logic swing and better noise margins than equivalent NMOS devices operating with the same supply rails, and NMOS speed advantages over CMOS are disappearing as device geometries continue to shrink. Circuit speed is already limited by interconnect delays, and future scaling will further limit performance due to drift-velocity saturation at very short channel lengths. Increased source/drain resistance, contact resistance, and channel on-resistance will further degrade the speed response of both n-channel and p-channel devices, reducing the advantage of NMOS over CMOS even more.

The negligible standby power dissipation of CMOS allows the use of large push-pull transistors to minimize switching speed. These large transistors have greater input loading, but interconnect capacitance often dominates, and increasing the channel widths of superbuffers and totem-pole output stages can make the circuit run faster without significantly increasing the overall power consumption.

The CMOS PLA has several alternative layout possibilities, which will be considered in detail. The discussion will be limited to one-phase and two-phase clocking schemes.

10.2 GENERAL PLA CONSIDERATIONS

A detailed structure of a PLA is shown in Fig. 10.1. The inputs are temporarily stored by input latches on phase 1. If evaluation transistors are omitted, the

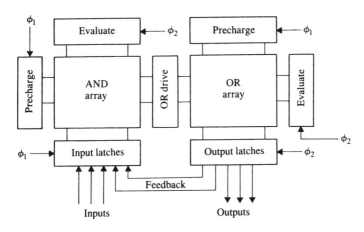

FIGURE 10.1
A completely general PLA block with feedback.

inputs ripple through the AND plane forming product terms which then ripple through the OR plane to produce the desired outputs, which are stored in output latches on phase 2. If evaluation transistors are used, the signals are gated through the AND and OR planes on phase 2.

NMOS PLAs are faster than CMOS PLAs and require less area, but for large PLA layouts the power dissipation is excessive, forcing the design engineer to go to CMOS. Static CMOS PLAs have lower power dissipation and require slightly less area than their dynamic counterparts, but don't have the speed of dynamic CMOS.

PLA area and performance are related in a linear manner to the total device count (1). For a given temperature and supply voltage, a PLA performs best when only a single input and output switch. The device performance degrades monotonically as the number of devices that are switching increases. Worst-case performance occurs when all the inputs and outputs switch simultaneously, and it can be measured under this condition.

For small PLAs, the minimum propagation delay is the delay of the input and output latches, plus the delay of a single AND-plane input and single OR-plane output transistor.

Area, speed, and power are all critical parameters as PLA size increases. Larger PLAs are slower due to the higher capacitances of the fan-in and fan-out devices, plus the increased capacitance of longer input lines, product lines, and output lines.

Typical values of sheet resistance, specific capacitance, and line length are given in Table 10.1. The maximum line length is calculated on the assumption that the delay of the line must be much less than the delay of a gate, so that the line may be considered an electrical node, at a unique voltage level. (See Prob. 10.1.)

Diffusion should never be used for long lines, as it typically has larger sheet resistivity than polysilicon. Polysilicon lines have excessive resistance and capacitance, and their length must be minimized. The resistance of polysilicon lines is as critical as its capacitance. Purely capacitive lines can be driven by sufficiently large superbuffers, but resistance still degrades circuit performance. Long polysilicon lines in the PLA AND plane develop large voltage drops and require

TABLE 10.1
Typical values

Layer	Resistance, Ω/sq	Capacitance to FOX, (fF/μm^2)	Maximum length, λ
Metal	0.02–0.08	0.01–0.04	10,000
Silicide	0.05–6.00	0.05–0.10	1,000
Polysilicon	10–100	0.04–0.06	100
Diffusion	15–200	0.08–0.10	50

interface pull-ups with large ratios to handle the weak ones that are input to the OR plane. This adds additional delay to the overall structure.

Two processes have been developed to reduce polysilicon line resistance. The *refractory-polysilicon process* places a thin layer of refractory metal on top of the polysilicon, reducing the line resistance by an order of magnitude or better. In the *double-metal process*, the polysilicon gate line can be run underneath one metal layer on the other metal layer, with frequent contacts to the polysilicon line. This adds little to the capacitance while greatly reducing the resistance of the polysilicon gate lines, and superbuffers can easily drive the capacitance.

Gate capacitance can also be reduced by terminating polysilicon lines at the last gate contact in the row or column, thus keeping rows and columns as short as possible. OR planes are usually smaller than AND planes, but in the event of a large number of output lines, the outputs of the AND planes may have to be driven by superbuffers also.

Power and/or ground lines should never be run in polysilicon or diffusion, as large currents and resistances lead to excessive potential drops. If poly or diffusion must be used, frequent metal-to-power and metal-to-ground connections will minimize this problem. To avoid metal migration, large PLAs require power and ground lines that are wider than the minimum metal line widths.

Large PLAs also require both inverting and noninverting input superbuffers to drive the capacitance of the AND array. If the AND plane is large or dense, sense amplifiers may be required between the AND plane and the OR plane, and the output may require superbuffers if a large capacitive load is being driven by the PLA.

Large PLAs have large fan-ins and should be designed with parallel devices, since series-connected FETs are slow. Also, it is desirable to design as much of the circuitry as possible with NMOS devices which are faster than PMOS devices. To realize a PLA with parallel logic structures requires NMOS devices for the NOR/OR logic-evaluating circuitry and PMOS FETs for the NAND/ AND logic-evaluating circuitry.

NAND gates are preferred in complementary-CMOS design, because the series-connected transistors are higher-speed NMOS. However, for a fan-in larger than 4 or 5, a cascade of several low fan-in gates might be preferable. For small PLAs, the NAND arrangement is more compact and can be programmed by modifying the implant mask only. There are no contacts to metal internal to a NAND array, but there are twice as many series transistors as are required for a conventional NAND gate because each input must be present in true and complemented form.

In all arrays, *coupling noise* is a major concern because of the *coherent noise* effects of many lines changing simultaneously and in the same direction (2). In random logic these small noise sources would not pose such a problem, but they are a serious concern in tightly packed arrays. Current spikes due to precharging are also important.

In two-phase precharged CMOS PLAs, evaluate transistors can be used to keep the planes from evaluating until the inputs are stable. During phase 1, the

AND plane is precharged high. The inputs may be changing during phase 1, but the output of the AND plane is not discharged since there is no path to ground. The AND plane must be stable on phase 2 when selected lines in the AND plane conditionally discharge. This can cause noise external to the PLA due to a current surge in the GND line, while internal noise is caused by the falling lines, which capacitively pull down the inputs, and pull down the precharged AND-plane outputs.

Small, low-speed PLAs can be designed with domino logic or with series-input gates. For transistors of the same size, a 2-input parallel NMOS NOR gate is typically about four times as fast as a 2-input series NMOS NAND gate and twice as fast as a 2-input parallel PMOS NAND gate. If NMOS AND logic with fan-ins greater than three is desired, one alternative is to combine NAND and NOR gates as shown in Fig. 10.2. The outputs of the mostly PMOS NAND gates

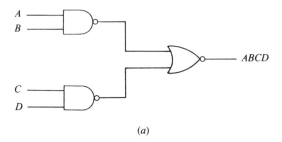

(a)

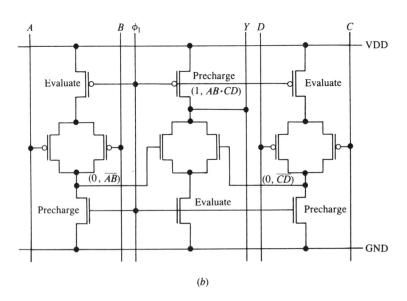

(b)

FIGURE 10.2
A 4-input AND gate constructed in NAND-NOR logic. (a) Circuit; (b) expanded circuit.

must be precharged low and conditionally charged high. The parallel NMOS NOR gate is then precharged high and conditionally discharged low.

PLA size is nominally proportional to the square of the fan-in, since the number of rows and the number of columns of the PLA are proportional to the fan-in. Let the speed of an NMOS inverter be specified by one unit of delay, t_d. The 2-input PMOS NAND gates of Fig. 10.2 then have a delay of about $4t_d$, while the NMOS NOR gate they drive is about four times as slow as an NMOS inverter. The 4-input NAND gate of Fig. 10.2 then has a worst-case delay of about $8t_d$, as compared to $16t_d$ for a conventional 4-input NAND gate.

The speed advantage is striking for large fan-in NAND gates. Three-input NMOS NAND gates and 4-input NMOS NOR gates might have the maximum acceptable fan-in. One can then synthesize a 12-input NAND gate with four 3-input NAND gates and one 4-input NOR gate. Each NAND gate has a delay of $3^2 t_d$, while the NOR gate has a delay of $4^2 t_d$. The total delay would then be $25t_d$ as opposed to 12^2 delay units or $144t_d$ for a 12-input NAND gate. The propagation delay has been reduced by a factor of $144/25 = 5.76$ to 1.

10.3 PLA AND-OR PLANES

The heart of a PLA is its AND-OR circuitry, and there are four basic parallel-logic structures that can be used to form the AND-OR or OR-AND logic of the PLA; NMOS-NOR, NMOS-AND, PMOS-NAND, and PMOS-OR gates.

The AND gate is obtained as the output of an NMOS NOR gate with complemented inputs, and the OR gate is obtained as the output of a PMOS NAND gate with complemented inputs, as shown in Fig. 10.3. The NMOS gates must have their inputs precharged low and their outputs precharged high, while the converse is true of the PMOS NAND structures.

Assume the appropriate input literals are available. Then, for two-level logic, a sum-of-products solution can be realized in AND-OR, NAND-NAND, OR-NAND (OAI), or NOR-OR logic. To be restricted to parallel-logic structures, NMOS gates must drive PMOS gates and vice versa in order to precharge properly. This eliminates NAND-NAND (both PMOS) and OR-NAND (both PMOS) structures. A product-of-sums solution can be realized in OR-AND,

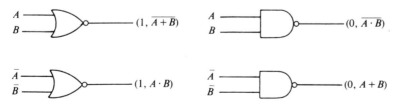

FIGURE 10.3
Four possible parallel-input logic gates for implementing AND-OR or OR-AND logic.

NOR-NOR, AND-NOR (AOI), and NAND-AND logic. Again, parallel-logic precharge requirements eliminate NOR-NOR (both NMOS) and AND-NOR (both NMOS) structures.

Of the possibilities discussed above, a parallel-logic circuit can be implemented in SOP form with AND-OR or NOR-OR logic, or in POS form with OR-AND or NAND-AND logic, since the NAND and OR gates of Fig. 10.3 are identical mostly-PMOS structures as shown in Fig. 7.16, while the NOR and AND gates of Fig. 10.3 are identical mostly-NMOS structures as shown in Fig. 7.13. If evaluation transistors are included, the logic is clocked through the PLA; otherwise, it ripples through from the input latches to the output latches.

10.4 PLA INPUT CIRCUITRY

If an NMOS PLA is driven by suitably sized superbuffers, the standard NMOS inverter ratio of 4 to 1 is satisfactory. A CMOS PLA can be designed with minimum size pull-up and pull-down devices. If electrical symmetry is desired, the PMOS channels can be made slightly wider than the NMOS channels and the NMOS devices can be put in a p well.

The inputs to the PLA need to be buffered and gated, and each input has to be available in complemented and uncomplemented form. This requires a minimum of two input buffers. A simple clocked CMOS input circuit, driven by a CMOS transmission gate, is shown in Fig. 10.4. To keep complemented and uncomplemented inputs in phase both inverting and noninverting superbuffers are employed. The term "superbuffer" can be enlarged in this discussion to include more than one stage of MOS buffers, or a bi-CMOS buffer stage with a BJT push-pull output, depending upon the drive requirements of the PLA.

The circuit of Fig. 10.4 outputs a noninverted signal which is precharged high and an inverted signal which is precharged low. Replacing the middle transistor, Q, by an NMOS device causes the evaluate and precharge transistors to trade places, and changes the precharged outputs so that the inverted output is now precharged high and the noninverted output is precharged low. If this is done the output of the latch must be taken from node b instead of a.

Frequently, two input signals occur in minterm pairs, but not independently of each other. A small additional input circuitry prior to the AND plane might reduce the number of product lines required as well as the number of devices required, thereby reducing both input capacitances and line capacitances.

For either CMOS or NMOS PLAs, two input signals can be ANDed or ORed before entering the AND plane. This is referred to as *input decoding* or *partitioning* and is used as a means of compacting the design. When input partitioning is used, either the minterms or the maxterms of the input literals drive the AND plane. There is a small cost penalty for this, since no extra inputs

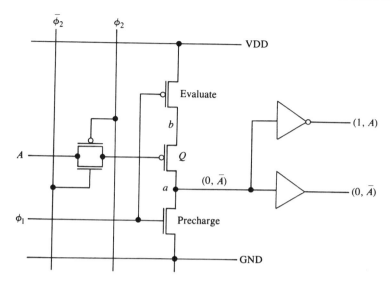

FIGURE 10.4
A gated PLA latching input circuit which outputs a precharged-low inverted input signal to both inverting and noninverting superbuffers.

are required, and the designer has the option of having either the original inputs or the partitioned inputs available at the AND-plane output.

Partitioned inputs can implement all sixteen combinations of two variables. It is not obvious what the best input partitioning is, and the designer might do well to try several combinations of input variables in order to minimize the PLA size. It is very difficult to partition more than two variables satisfactorily.

If two pairs of inputs appear ideally suited for partitioning, except that a term which requires one or the other input but not both is also required, decoding can still be used. For example, if A and B as well as C and D are suitable for partitioning, except for a term such as $AC\bar{D}$ or $\bar{B}\bar{C}D$, the terms can be obtained as follows:

$$ AC\bar{D} = (AB)(C\bar{D}) + (A\bar{B})(C\bar{D}) $$

and

$$ \bar{B}\bar{C}D = (\bar{A}\bar{B})(\bar{C}D) + (A\bar{B})(\bar{C}D) $$

Each term can now be realized with decoded input minterms, and no additional input lines are required. Two-variable input partitioning circuitry for a CMOS PLA is shown in Fig. 10.5, and a stick layout is shown in Fig. 10.6.

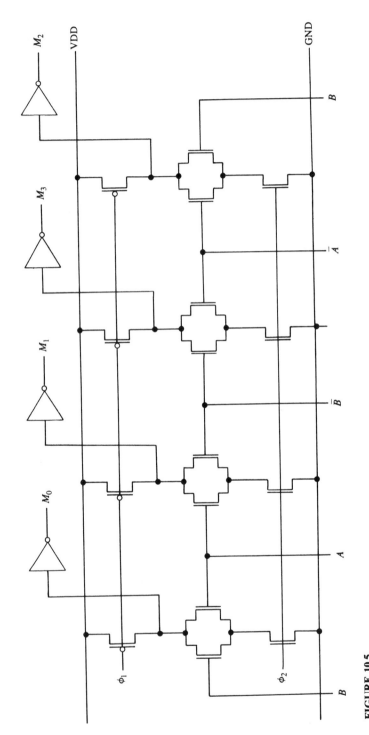

FIGURE 10.5
Partitioned or decoded inputs to a CMOS PLA.

296

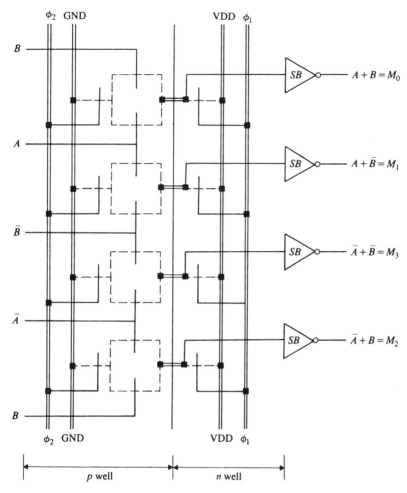

FIGURE 10.6
Stick drawing of the decoded input of the CMOS PLA.

10.5 PLA OUTPUT CIRCUITRY

A simple, dynamic CMOS output latch is shown in Fig. 10.7. The input signal to the latch is an output of the PLA, V_{out}. During phase 1, the latch output is precharged high. During evaluation the PLA OR-plane output, V_{out}, conditionally goes high, allowing the latch output, V_o, to go low. If the PLA output remains low the latch output remains high.

The output of the PLA must attain its final settled value for a minimum setup time before clock phase 2 goes high. It must remain constant during a minimum hold time to allow for possible delays between the falling edge of the master clock and the falling edge of the local clock (clock skew).

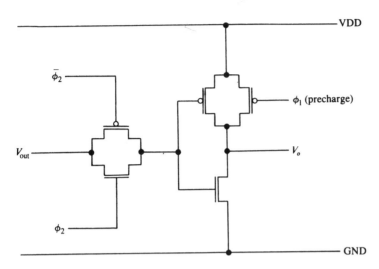

FIGURE 10.7
A CMOS dynamic PLA output latch. V_{out} is the voltage level of a PLA output line.

When designing finite-state machines, it is sometimes necessary to latch the output of a PLA with a flip-flop, and feed the flip-flop output back to the AND plane. A CMOS S-R cross-coupled NOR output latch is shown in Fig. 10.8. The two NOR gates have active-high inputs which SET or RESET the latch by pulling the appropriate NOR output low. The SET and RESET transistor inputs come from the PLA OR plane, whose output must be preset low so that the latch is in the idle state with both SET and RESET inputs low during phase 1.

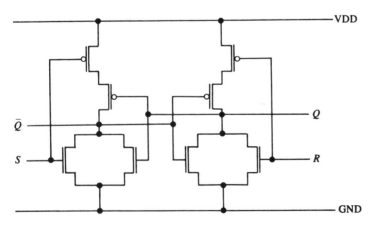

FIGURE 10.8
A CMOS NOR S-R output latch with parallel pull-down.

For setting or resetting, the appropriate input must go high during evaluation. No timing signal is required but two OR-plane outputs are necessary for each flip-flop. The S-R latch can drive a CMOS superbuffer which must be able to supply sufficient current to drive the load. If the load is very large, it may be necessary to take the PLA output directly from buffered product lines, leaving the flip-flop outputs free to drive the AND-plane lines. See Fig. 9.27.

A CMOS S-R cross-coupled NAND flip-flop is shown in Fig. 10.9. The cross-coupled NAND latch has active low-inputs and is used if the OR-plane output is precharged high, because the SET and RESET inputs come from two OR-plane outputs and must be high in the idle state.

For setting or resetting, the appropriate input must go low during evaluation. No timing signal is required but two OR-plane outputs are required for each flip-flop. The $\bar{S}$-$\bar{R}$ latch must be able to drive the AND-plane, and perhaps the PLA load.

10.6 THE AND-PLANE-OR-PLANE INTERFACE

The current supplying and sinking capability of a buffer that is driving a large capacitive load can be increased as needed. Circuits with high fan-in and large input capacitance, such as the OR plane of a PLA, require a different approach.

When charging or discharging a capacitor, the basic timing equation is: $I = C dV/dt$, or $\Delta t \approx (C/I)\Delta V$. In a PLA NOR-NOR realization, the discharge current is fixed by the maximum width of a pull-down device, which is controlled by the pitch of the OR plane. The input capacitance of the AND plane is also fixed, and the only variable left is the voltage swing, ΔV.

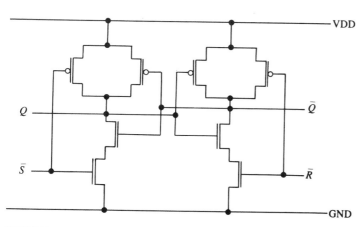

FIGURE 10.9
A CMOS NAND S-R output latch with parallel pull-up.

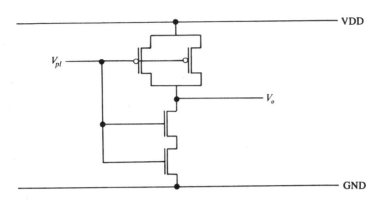

FIGURE 10.10
A single-ended sense amplifier.

An amplifier designed to operate with a small input voltage swing is referred to as a *sense amplifier*. It can be single-ended to sense an absolute voltage change, or double-ended to detect a differential voltage change. A simple sense amplifier can be constructed from a 2-input NAND gate using minimum geometry, as shown in Fig. 10.10, where the inverter noise margins have been reduced to increase sensitivity.

A *charge-sharing sense amplifier* can be constructed as shown in Fig. 10.11. This circuit also trades noise margin for sensitivity. The input line is precharged by Q, which clamps the product line to a threshold voltage below the reference voltage, V_{ref}, while capacitor C_2 is precharged high by the clock. C_1 is charged to $V_{ref} - V_{TH}$, and C_2 is charged to V_{DD}.

When the product line is pulled down, V_{pl} drops and the clamp transistor, Q, attempts to replenish the charge on C_1. If C_1 is much larger than C_2, the charge transferred from C_2 to C_1 greatly amplifies the voltage swing at node b,

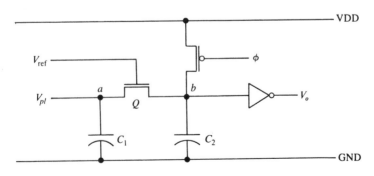

FIGURE 10.11
A charge-sharing sense amplifier.

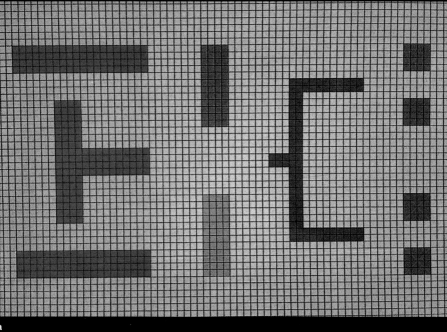

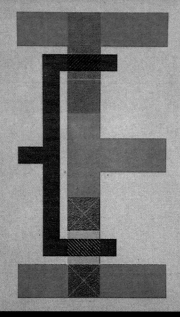

b

PLATE 1

The CMOS inverter. a) Blow-up with grid lines, and b) laid out with Magic.

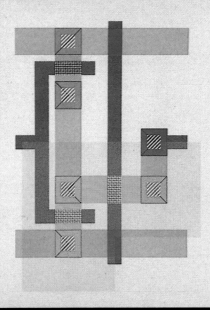

PLATE 2
The clocked CMOS inverter. a) Magic layout, and b) CIF layout with FETs and contacts highlighted.

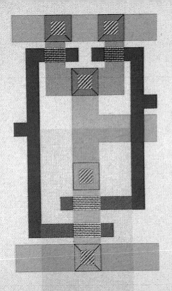

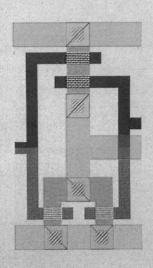

PLATE 3

CIF layouts of a) a CMOS NAND gate, and b) a CMOS NOR gate, with FETs and contacts highlighted

PLATE 4

Magic layout of a transmission gate a) with CONTROL and CONTROL_BAR aligned, and b) with CONTROL

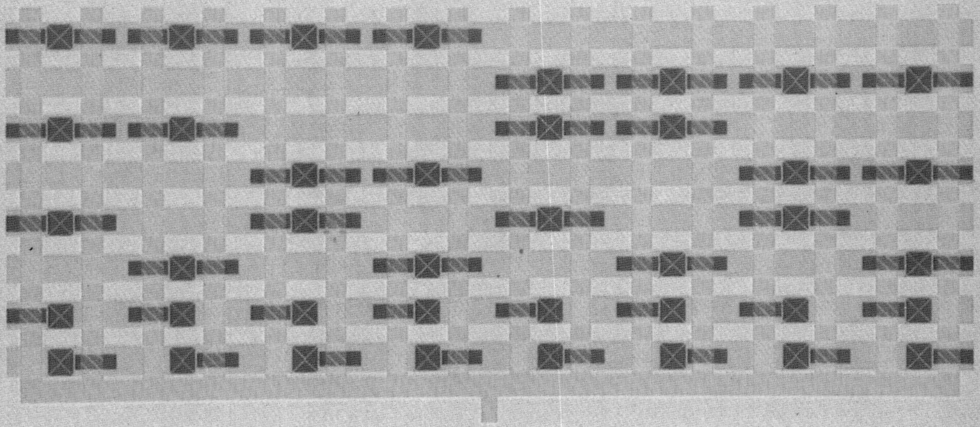

PLATE 5

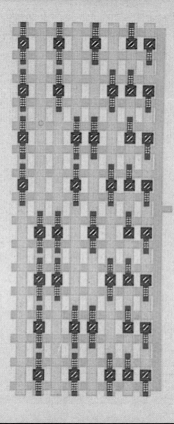

PLATE 6
CIF layout of a four-variable ULM with FETs and contacts highlighted.

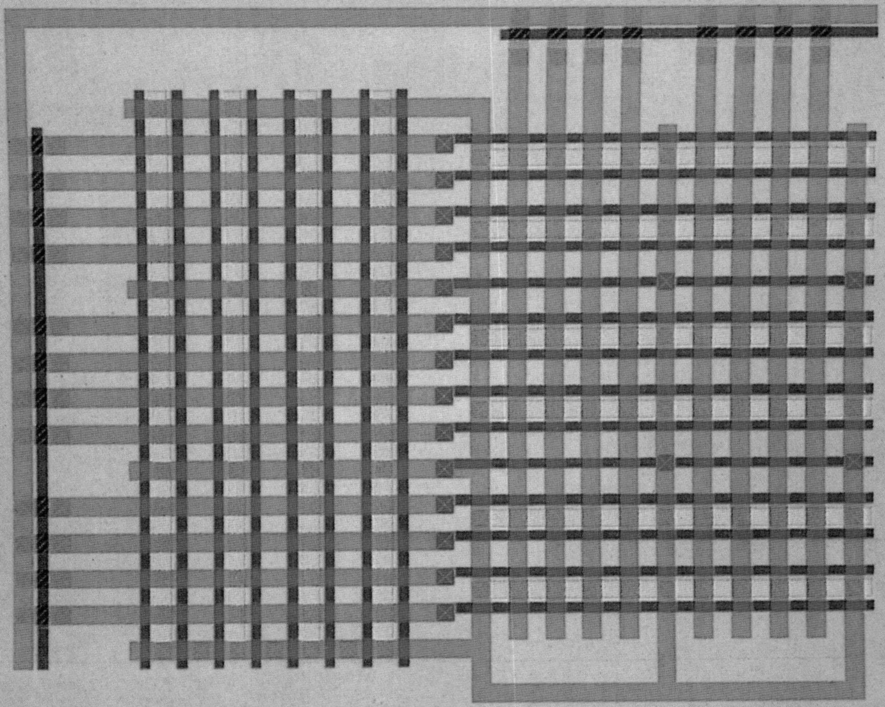

PLATE 7
Magic layout of a CMOS PLA with four inputs and eight outputs.

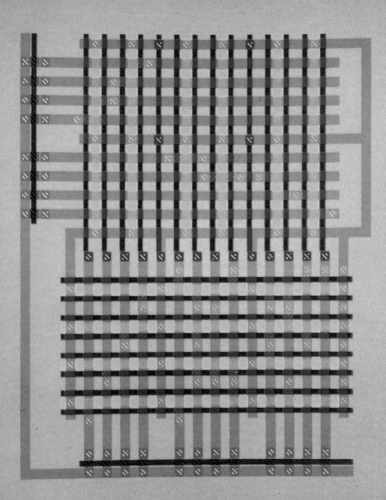

PLATE 8
CIF layout of a CMOS PLA programmed as shown in Fig. 9.27, with the contacts highlighted.

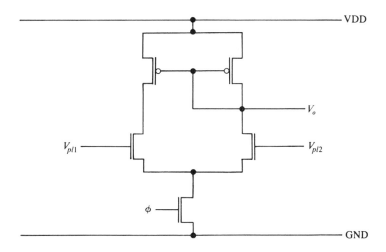

FIGURE 10.12
A differential sense amplifier.

and causes the output to switch rapidly. One must take care that node a is charged all the way to $V_{\text{ref}} - V_{TH}$. Otherwise, charge can leak from C_2 to C_1, and if the voltage at node b drops below V_{INV}, the output can switch erroneously. A static NMOS version of the circuit in Fig. 10.11 is obtained by replacing the clocked PMOS pull-up device by a depletion-mode NMOS FET.

A *differential sense amplifier*, as shown in Fig. 10.12 senses a small difference between the voltages of two input lines, V_{pl1} and V_{pl2}, and amplifies this difference. The product lines should be precharged to one-half the supply voltage for use with this type amplifier. A simple circuit for precharging the product lines to $V_{\text{INV}} = V_{DD}/2$ is shown in Fig. 10.13. An additional advantage to this approach is

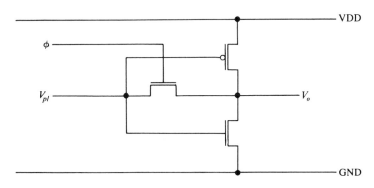

FIGURE 10.13
A CMOS inverter that precharges to $V_{DD}/2$.

that keeping the voltage swing small minimizes capacitively coupled noise also.

10.7 SMALL RIPPLE PLAs

For small ripple PLAs, or when speed is unimportant, 2-input or 3-input series NAND and NOR gates may be acceptable. A small ripple PLA can be implemented with NOR-NOR logic, using series mostly PMOS gates driving parallel mostly NMOS gates or with parallel mostly NMOS gates driving series mostly PMOS gates. In this case the SOP function can be realized with NAND-NAND logic as shown in Figs. 10.14 and 10.15, and the POS function can be realized with NOR-NOR logic as shown in Figs. 10.16 and 10.17.

The PMOS inputs must be precharged high, while the NMOS inputs must be precharged low. The inputs are clocked into the input latches during phase 1, while the rest of the PLA is in the precharge state. During phase 2, the logic is evaluated in a ripple-through manner and stored in the output latches.

The circuit realization shown in Fig. 10.14 requires the AND plane outputs to be precharged high and conditionally discharged low, and the OR plane outputs to be precharged low and conditionally charged high. The realization shown in Fig. 10.15 requires the AND-plane outputs to be precharged low on phase 1, and conditionally charged high on phase 2, while the OR-plane outputs are to be precharged high on phase 1, and conditionally discharged low on phase 2.

If precharge conditions do not determine the AND-plane gates, fan-in requirements can determine whether the AND plane or the OR plane is designed with series gates. Since NOR-NOR realizations require slow series mostly PMOS gates, either in the AND plane or in the OR plane, they are slower than small ripple NAND-NAND realizations. Both NAND-NAND approaches require series NMOS gates which must have a minimum fan-in, or be designed as multiple low fan-in gates as discussed in Sec. 10.2 and shown in Fig. 10.2.

The small ripple PLA design is convenient for dynamic logic arrays. Ripple circuitry is also desirable when designing multiple levels of logic. For instance, a particular AND-OR output can serve as input to another AND plane. The AND-OR operation can be implemented in ripple-through fashion using both NOR-NOR and NAND-NAND logic. If the OR plane output is fed back to the same AND plane that drives it, it must be clocked through both phases to avoid critical races.

There is always the possibility of charge-sharing problems with series-input circuits. Methods of avoiding charge redistribution were discussed in Sec. 7.7, and must be strictly adhered to.

Small static PLAs can be used when power dissipation is not a serious problem. They are unwieldy and difficult to lay out in CMOS/bulk, but they are easier to lay out in CMOS/SOS and easiest to lay out in NMOS. For performance reasons the NAND-NAND structure with the NMOS devices in

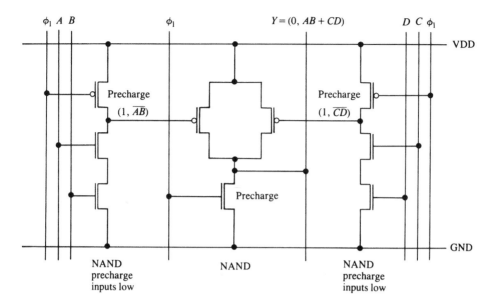

FIGURE 10.14
The SOP NAND-NAND PLA realized with series-input gates followed by parallel-input gates.

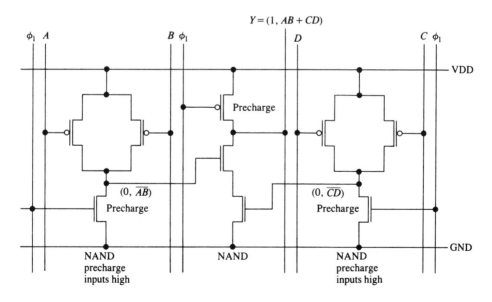

FIGURE 10.15
The SOP NAND-NAND PLA realized with parallel-input gates followed by series-input gates.

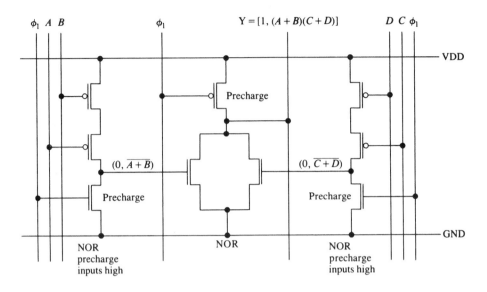

FIGURE 10.16
The POS NOR-NOR PLA realized with series-input gates followed by parallel-input gates.

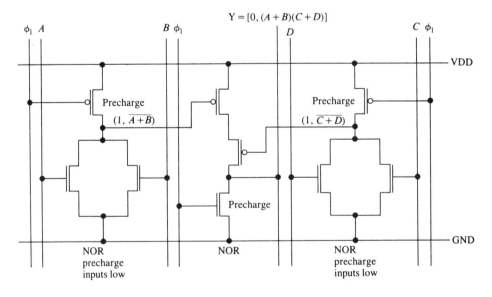

FIGURE 10.17
The POS NOR-NOR PLA realized with parallel-input gates followed by series-input gates.

series is preferred to the NOR-NOR design with series PMOS transistors since the series NMOS design is inherently faster than a comparable series PMOS design.

Small, mostly NMOS domino PLAs are both fast and dense, with low power dissipation. Because of the inverters at the output of each gate, NMOS gates can drive NMOS gates in a precharge and ripple-through manner. Domino PLAs use less area than static CMOS PLAs, and exhibit better performance due to their smaller parasitic capacitances. Glitch-free and race-free operation is also possible, and charge-sharing can be avoided by following proper timing procedures.

The major advantage of domino PLA design is that it needs only one clock. Because of the NAND-NOT design of NMOS AND-gates, large domino PLAs have many series pull-down devices, and performance degrades as the PLA becomes large.

10.8 PLA REDUCTION

Often the active devices in a PLA are sparsely distributed and require a large area, a typical sparse PLA using about 10 to 20 percent of the AND- and OR-plane nodes. This results in unnecessarily long lines which require large drivers and have poor performance. Techniques that reduce the size of a PLA will thus yield both a smaller and a faster PLA design.

One should not become so absorbed in high-powered reduction techniques as to overlook simple approaches. For example, a four-bit modulo-10 counter can be designed with J-K flip-flops. The required boolean expressions for the flip-flop inputs are

$$A_J = BCD \qquad A_K = D \qquad B_J = CD \qquad B_K = CD$$

$$C_J = \bar{A}D \qquad C_K = \bar{A}D \qquad D_J = 1 \qquad D_K = 1$$

Direct implementation yields a PLA of size $8R \times 21C = 168N$, and a sparsity factor of $S = 24/168 = 0.143$.

The PLA can be reduced, by first noting that flip-flops B, C, and D have both inputs identical. They are operating in the toggle mode, and can be replaced by toggle flip-flops, thus reducing the number of columns of the PLA by 3, giving dimensions of $8R \times 18C = 144N$, and $S = 21/144 = 0.146$.

$\bar{A}$ is the only complemented variable present in this PLA. If one can omit the inverting AND-plane drivers for inputs B, C, and D, three more columns can be deleted. The PLA now has dimensions $8R \times 15C = 120N$, and a sparsity factor of $21/120 = 0.175$. This is still a sparse PLA, but it has 71.4 percent the area of the original design. The original PLA and the reduced PLA are shown in Fig. 10.18.

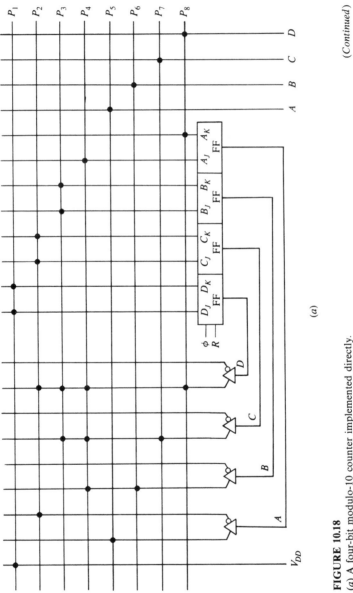

FIGURE 10.18

(a) A four-bit modulo-10 counter implemented directly.

(Continued)

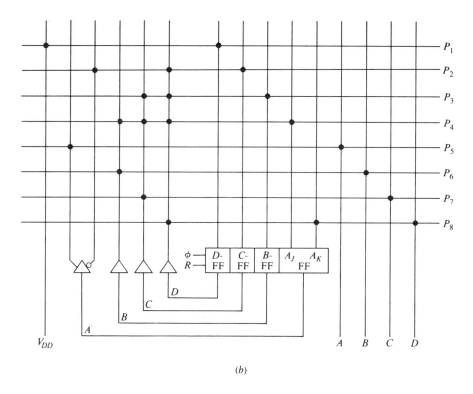

(b)

FIGURE 10.18 (*continued*)
(b) A four-bit modulo-10 counter implemented (reduced).

10.8.1 PLA Folding

Row and/or column folding is a technique for reducing the physical size of a PLA by merging rows and/or columns and reducing the sparsity of the matrix. The maximum reduction in area is achieved if individual inputs and outputs are custom-folded.

Once a boolean expression is simplified into a suitable form for PLA implementation, the AND-plane inputs and the product-lines should be ordered such that pairs of columns in the AND-plane allow for input signals from the top and bottom of the physical PLA. Pairs of columns in the OR plane can also be folded to allow output signals from the top and bottom of the PLA. This is shown in Fig. 10.19.

Row-folding can reduce the number of product lines by splitting the AND plane and inserting the OR plane between the two segments of AND plane, as shown in Fig. 10.20. If two product lines are not both required by an output, they may be folded because the two rows or product lines do not have transistors located at the same crosspoints in the OR plane.

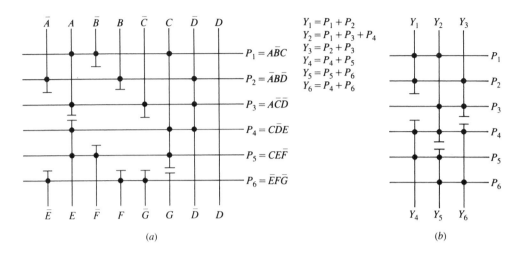

$Y_1 = P_1 + P_2$
$Y_2 = P_1 + P_3 + P_4$
$Y_3 = P_2 + P_3$
$Y_4 = P_4 + P_5$
$Y_5 = P_5 + P_6$
$Y_6 = P_4 + P_6$

(a) (b)

FIGURE 10.19
A column custom-folded PLA. (a) AND-plane column-folding; (b) OR-plane column-folding.

In order to implement the PLA without folding or partitioning, columns in the AND array are needed for each input signal and its complement. One row in the AND array is needed for each unique product term, and one column in the OR array is needed for each output signal of the PLA.

The PLA personality matrix was defined in Sec. 9.6.2. The personality matrix represented each element in the AND array by a 0 if the true input was present in the product term, by a 1 if the complemented input was present in the product term, and by an × if the signal was missing (don't care). For the purpose of folding a PLA one must keep track of the crosspoints which are connected by a transistor. To do this, the personality matrix must be expanded to list the true

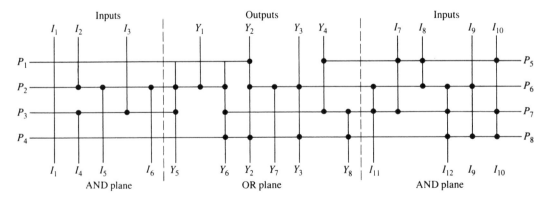

FIGURE 10.20
A row or product-line folded PLA.

and complemented columns of the AND-plane inputs separately. Call this the expanded or decoded personality matrix. In the following discussion, rows will be ordered from top to bottom and columns will be ordered from left to right. Each input line will be treated separately, so that it can be folded independently of any other column.

The function must first be reduced to a minimum sum-of-products form. In the PLA matrix, the presence of a transistor at a crosspoint site will be indicated by a 1, and the absence of a transistor will be indicated by a 0. This can be thought of as the expanded personality matrix, with each input line treated independently. The matrix so formed will consist of 1's at every crosspoint site in both the AND and OR planes for which a transistor is present. A basic criterion for folding a row or column is that the pairs of rows or columns merged must not contain 1's at the same crosspoint locations.

Next, pairs of columns of the PLA are folded in the AND arrays (OR arrays) to allow signals to be input (output) at both the top and bottom of the physical array. Last, pairs of rows in the OR array are folded to allow product term output signals from a split AND array to enter from both the left and right sides of the OR array. An example of PLA folding follows.

Example 10.1. Design a minimum-size PLA to realize the functions $Y_1 = A\bar{B} + AC + D$, and $Y_2 = \bar{A}B + \bar{B}C + D$

Solution. A direct implementation requires eight input lines for the four variables and their complements, plus two output columns, and five product lines, for a total size of $5R \times 10C = 50N$. The PLA is shown in Fig. 10.21a.

Since the PLA outputs are independent of $\bar{C}$ and $\bar{D}$, these columns could be omitted from the AND plane, reducing the size to $5R \times 8C = 40N$. Further examination shows that if the last two rows of the PLA are interchanged, then input pairs $A, \bar{A}$ and $B, \bar{B}$ can be merged to occupy one column per pair. The reduced PLA has dimensions $5R \times 6C = 30N$ as shown in Fig. 10.21b.

With large PLAs, a systematic approach to PLA-folding is required in order to successfully minimize the chip area and maximize the PLA speed (3,4).

Two columns of a PLA, c_i and c_j, are said to be disjoint if they do not have 1's at the same row in the personality matrix of a PLA. In the AND plane two input lines are disjoint if they do not drive the same product line. In the OR plane two output lines are disjoint if they are not driven by the same product line. Two rows (product lines) are said to be disjoint if they do not have 1's at the same column in the expanded PLA matrix. They are disjoint if they are not both driven by the same input lines, and do not drive the same output lines.

Example 10.2. Three rows of a PLA are $r_1 = 111001$, $r_2 = 000110$, and $r_3 = 111000$. Which rows can be folded together?

Solution. Rows r_1 and r_2, as well as rows r_2 and r_3, are disjoint and can be folded. Rows r_1 and r_3 cannot be folded since they overlap at three column sites.

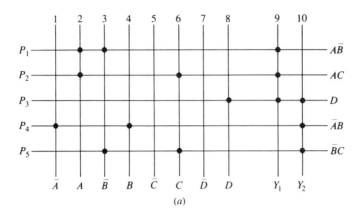

(a)

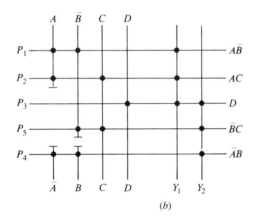

(b)

FIGURE 10.21
A simple PLA implemented (a) directly, and (b) optimized.

Given the expanded or decoded personality matrix, Q, of a PLA, define R_i as the set of rows with 1's at the crosspoints of column c_i, and define C_i as the set of columns with 1's at the crosspoints of row r_i. Columns i and j are disjoint if $C_i \cap C_j = \varnothing$, and rows i and j are disjoint if $R_i \cap R_j = \varnothing$. Interchanging r and c, R and C, has no effect on the discussion, and the approach is the same for both rows and columns.

Example 10.3. Show mathematically which of the rows $r_1 = 111001$, $r_2 = 000110$, and $r_3 = 101000$ of Q can be folded as pairs.

Solution. $C_1 = \{c_1, c_2, c_3, c_6\}$, $C_2 = \{c_4, c_5\}$, and $C_3 = \{c_1, c_3\}$. $C_1 \cap C_2 = \varnothing$, and rows 1 and 2 can be paired. $C_1 \cap C_3 = \{c_1, c_3\}$. Rows 1 and 3 overlap at two column sites and they cannot be paired. $C_2 \cap C_3 = \varnothing$, and rows 2 and 3 can be paired.

An ordered folding pair $\langle c_i, c_j \rangle$ specifies two columns that can be folded, with column c_i above column c_j in the same physical column of the folded PLA. The *column disjoint graph* is an undirected graph whose vertex set, V, represents the columns of the personality matrix and whose edge set, E, is defined as $E = \{c_i, c_j | R_i \cap R_j = \varnothing\}$. The edge set consists of pairs of columns which are disjoint, hence they can be folded.

The procedure for column/row folding consists of constructing the column/row disjoint graph from the expanded personality matrix, finding the connected components of the disjoint graph, and constructing a path for each ordered pair of vertices on the graph (5).

Next, a path with the maximum length among those constructed is taken, in order to extract the ordered folding set from the selected path. If the generated partial ordering is found to be cyclic, the path is deleted and the next longest path is chosen. A linear ordering is obtained from the generated partial ordering, and the folded PLA is generated.

Example 10.4. Give the edge set and the row disjoint graph for the three rows of the previous example.

Solution. Rows 1 and 2 can be folded as a pair, and form an edge in the disjoint graph. So do rows 2 and 3. The edges are $E = \{\{r_1, r_2\}, \{r_2, r_3\}\}$, and the graph is a line from row 1 to row 2 to row 3.

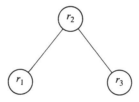

Example 10.5. Column-fold the PLA whose decoded personality matrix is Q, where

$$Q = \begin{bmatrix} 1 & 1 & 0 & 0 & 0 & 0 & 1 & 0 & & 1 & 1 & 0 \\ 1 & 0 & 0 & 0 & 1 & 1 & 0 & 0 & & 1 & 0 & 1 \\ 1 & 1 & 0 & 1 & 1 & 0 & 0 & 0 & & 1 & 0 & 0 \\ 0 & 1 & 1 & 0 & 0 & 1 & 1 & 0 & & 0 & 1 & 0 \\ 0 & 0 & 1 & 0 & 0 & 1 & 0 & 1 & & 0 & 1 & 1 \\ 0 & 1 & 0 & 0 & 0 & 0 & 1 & 0 & & 0 & 1 & 1 \end{bmatrix}$$

Solution. First, compute the row sets, R_i.

For the AND plane

$$R_1 = \{r_1, r_2, r_3\}$$

$$R_2 = \{r_1, r_3, r_4, r_6\}$$

$$R_3 = \{r_4, r_5\}$$

$$R_4 = \{r_3\}$$

$$R_5 = \{r_2, r_3\}$$

$$R_6 = \{r_2, r_4, r_5\}$$

$$R_7 = \{r_1, r_4, r_6\}$$

$$R_8 = \{r_5\}$$

Next determine which columns can be paired. The matrix below is the disjoint matrix for the AND plane. The entries are the row locations common to R_i and R_j.

	R_2	R_3	R_4	R_5	R_6	R_7	R_8
R_1:	r_1, r_3	$\emptyset$	r_3	r_2, r_3	r_2	r_1	$\emptyset$
R_2:		r_4	r_3	r_3	r_4	r_1, r_4, r_6	$\emptyset$
R_3:			$\emptyset$	$\emptyset$	r_4, r_5	r_4	r_5
R_4:				r_3	$\emptyset$	$\emptyset$	$\emptyset$
R_5:					r_2	$\emptyset$	$\emptyset$
R_6:						r_4	r_5
R_7:							$\emptyset$

For the OR plane.

$$R_9 = \{r_1, r_2, r_3\}$$

$$R_{10} = \{r_1, r_4, r_5, r_6\}$$

$$R_{11} = \{r_2, r_5, r_6\}$$

$$R_9 \cap R_{10} = \{r_1\}$$

$$R_9 \cap R_{11} = \{r_2\}$$

$$R_{10} \cap R_{11} = \{r_5, r_6\}$$

The output lines cannot be folded.

Construct the column disjoint graph for the AND plane. Columns 1 and 3, 1 and 8, 2 and 8, 3 and 4, 3 and 5, 4 and 6, 4 and 7, 4 and 8, 5 and 7, 5 and 8, 7 and 8 can be paired. The column disjoint graph is shown in Fig. 10.24. From the graph, the longest path merges columns 2 and 8, 1 and 3, 5 and 7, and 4 and 6. The path is traced on Fig. 10.22 with dark lines linking columns to be folded. The pairs form-ordered sets of two columns each, and the first numbered columns in each set must be on the same edge of the AND plane. They will be chosen to be located above the second column of the pair.

Columns 1 and 3 can be merged as is, but to merge columns 2 and 8, row 5 must be the bottom row. To merge columns 4 and 6, row 3 must be the top row, and

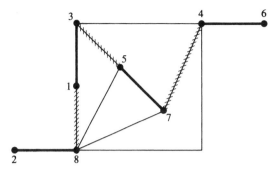

FIGURE 10.22
The column disjoint graph of Example 10.5.

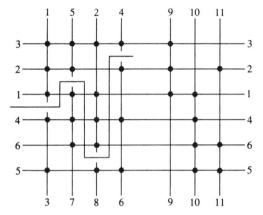

FIGURE 10.23
The PLA of Example 10.5, with rows folded.

to merge columns 5 and 7, row 1 must be the third row. The original rows are then in the sequence 3, 2, 1, 4, 6, 5. The folded PLA is shown in Fig. 10.23.

The original PLA consisted of 6 rows and 11 columns, or 66 crosspoints. The folded PLA consists of 6 rows and 7 columns, or 42 crosspoints, for a net area savings of 36 percent.

10.8.2 Feedback-Reduced PLAs

Consider the carry-out of an adder stage, $C_0 = AB + C_i(A\bar{B} + \bar{A}B)$. Start with the deepest nested level of the function, and feed back the output of each level of nesting to the next higher logic level. The feedback paths do not actually form a loop in the circuit, but form a "coil." The PLA can be reduced greatly in size, but the circuit is much slower due to the multiple loops (6). Feedback reduction is shown in Example 10.6.

Example 10.6. Use feedback reduction to realize the carry-out function $C_0 = AB + C_i(A\bar{B} + \bar{A}B)$, with NAND-NAND PLAs.

Solution. The output of PLA 1 is obtained as $Y_1 = A\bar{B} + \bar{A}B$. This is fed back as an input to PLA 2, whose output is C_0. The result is shown in Fig. 10.24.

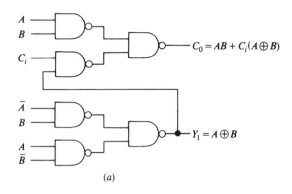

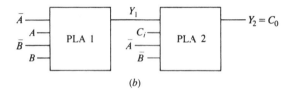

FIGURE 10.24
The two PLAs to be realized. (*a*) Circuit; (*b*) representation.

10.8.3 AND-OR Interface Logic

Often it is desirable to add additional logic between the AND plane and the OR plane of a PLA. A channel of columns between the two planes allows dot-ANDing between product lines as shown in Fig. 10.25. The dot-AND connects two pull-up devices in parallel. In static NMOS PLAs, this connection doubles the effective pull-up width, and requires doubling the widths of all the pull-down devices to maintain inverter ratios. This greatly increases the total area required for the PLA. A suitable solution for NMOS PLA design would be to use precharge and evaluate transistors to design a dynamic PLA. CMOS PLAs avoid this problem. Note the similarity of this structure and the DLA structure.

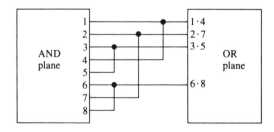

FIGURE 10.25
A dot-AND channel between an AND-plane and an OR plane.

10.9 SUMMARY

The parallel-gate structure of the AND and OR planes is best suited to PLAs which have large fan-ins. Ripple PLAs are not useful for systems with large numbers of inputs and implicants (products), but they can be used for systems with few inputs and implicants. Ripple PLAs are simpler and faster than gated PLAs and can drive successive stages during the same clock period.

PLA generation tools take input in boolean algebra and enable design engineers to implement changes quickly and easily, with little impact upon the layout of the rest of the logic circuitry.

Domino logic requires only one clock phase, but it can have charge-sharing problems. Making the capacitance of the output node much larger than any internal node capacitances minimizes charge-sharing. Using weak pull-up devices to "staticize" domino logic eliminates charge leakage at the output of each logic gate.

In complementary CMOS, NAND gates are preferred to NOR because the faster n-channel devices are in series.

Area, speed, and power are critical parameters for large PLA designs. The PLA should be reduced as much as possible, after which the physical layout can be done by a CAD PLA generator. Partitioning inputs into minterms or max-terms can minimize the AND plane, and is usually limited to two variables at a time.

During phase 1 a gated PLA can be precharged while the input register loads the new inputs. During phase 2 the PLA then evaluates the signals which ripple through the AND and OR planes to the state register. The OR-plane outputs can be fed back to the AND plane to create a finite-state machine, while the input register prevents races. The PLA is a two-level SOP realization. Arbitrarily deep SOP functions can be realized by Weinberger arrays (7). Software for a Weinberger generator similar to present PLA generators is discussed by Ullman (8).

Whether a PLA is generated by hand or by a computer, there are certain steps that should be done. Poly lines can be truncated at the last active term to reduce line capacitances. Except for the smallest PLAs, metal must be used for power and ground lines. If the PLA is very large, the power and ground lines must be widened to prevent metal migration.

Direct implementation of a sum-of-products realization of a function often leads to a very large PLA with few interconnecting transistors. This is referred to as a sparse PLA, and it wastes chip area. PLA folding and sharing techniques tend to minimize the number of unused crosspoints and reduce the size of the PLA, which in turn reduces propagation delays.

Multiple AND- and OR-planes allow folding to create a denser PLA. The row breaks and column breaks of a folded PLA allow more implicants on a single row and more outputs on a single column than are obtained with the original PLA structure. This results in a more compact external routing than that of the original sparse PLA.

PLAs are inherently low-performance circuits due to the nature of their layout. Long polysilicon gate lines have high capacitance and high resistance. Long metal lines for array outputs also have high capacitance. If polysilicon lines were purely capacitive, the drivers could be widened, but the combination of large resistance and large capacitance seriously degrades signals, regardless of driver size. The use of refractory-polysilicon and/or a double-metal process can significantly improve system performance.

PLA connect cells are required to interface the AND and OR planes, and change signal paths from metal to poly. A large AND plane presents a heavy input capacitance to the OR plane. Sense amplifiers inserted between the two planes can greatly speed up switching.

OR planes are usually smaller than AND planes, but if they have many columns, the outputs of the AND plane have to be driven through superbuffers also. Output pull-ups may require a larger ratio to compensate for voltage drops in long poly lines. This adds some delay.

The PLA designer must consider input and output latches and precharge circuitry as well as the basic AND and OR planes, since this peripheral circuitry along with its interconnects also plays an important role in layout design. For example, the OR-plane dimensions of a PLA may be limited by the pitch of the output latches, whereas the AND-plane dimensions of a PLA may be limited by the pitch of the OR plane. There are advantages and disadvantages to each PLA structure, and the design engineer must learn to choose the PLA best suited to each particular application.

Coherent noise is a major concern in all PLA arrays. Coherent noise is created by coupling between adjacent lines, by crossing groups of lines, by the resistance of diffused and polysilicon lines and by current spikes due to precharging. Alternating NMOS and PMOS is appealing, but this logic is extremely susceptible to capacitive coupling noise.

REFERENCES

1. C. M. Gerveshi, "Comparisons of CMOS PLA and Polycell Representations of Control Logic," *Proceedings of the 23rd ACM/IEEE Design Automation Conference*, June 29–July 2, 1986, pp. 638–642.
2. L. A. Glasser and D. W. Dobberpuhl, *The Design and Analysis of VLSI Circuits*, Addison-Wesley Publishing Company, Reading, Mass., 1985, pp. 375–377.
3. G. D. Hachtel, A. R. Newton, and A. L. Sangiovanni-Vincentelli, "An Algorithm for Optimal PLA Folding," *IEEE Trans. on Computer-Aided Design of Integrated Circuits and Systems*, vol. CAD-1, 1982, pp. 63, 76.
4. J. L. Lewandowski and C. L. Liu, "A Branch and Bound Algorithm for Optimal PLA Folding," *Proceedings of the IEEE 21st Design Automation Conference*, Albuquerque, New Mexico, June, 1984, pp. 426–433.
5. A. S. Y. Hwang, R. W. Dutton, and T. Blank, "A Best-First Search Algorithm for Optimum PLA Folding," *IEEE Transactions on Computer-Aided Design*, vol. CAD-5, no. 3, July 1986, pp. 433–442.
6. A. B. Glaser, "A Feedback Reduced PLA," MIT Technical Report, 1982.
7. A. Weinberger, "Large Scale Integration of MOS Complex Logic: A Layout Method," *IEEE Journal of Solid-State Circuits*, December 1967, p. 182.
8. J. D. Ullman, *Computational Models in VLSI*, Computer Science Press, Rockville, Maryland 1983.

PROBLEMS

10.1. Use values of resistance and capacitance from Table 10.1, and a gate time constant of 0.5 ns to verify the maximum line lengths of Table 10.1.

10.2. Design an 8-input AND gate using: (*a*) four 2-input NAND gates driving a 4-input NOR gate, and compare its speed to an 8-input AND gate if the 4-input NOR gate has a delay of eight time units. (*b*) Repeat part *a* for two 4-input NOR gates driving a 2-input NAND gate.

10.3. Four input signals are decoded to give the minterms of AB and of CD. Input F is not decoded with another literal.

    (*a*) How would one realize the implicant $A\bar{B}D\bar{F}$ with and without input partitioning?

    (*b*) Repeat part *a* for the implicant $\bar{A}C\bar{D}$.

10.4. Design a decoded PLA to realize a 2-bit adder with a carry-out. The lower two bits are A, B, the higher two bits are C, D, and the outputs are S_1, S_2, and $\bar{C}_0$.

10.5. Column-fold the PLA whose expanded personality matrix is shown below. Calculate R, C, N, and S.

$$Q = \begin{bmatrix} 1 & 0 & 0 & 0 & 0 & 0 & 1 & 1 & & 1 & 0 \\ 1 & 1 & 0 & 0 & 1 & 0 & 0 & 0 & & 1 & 0 \\ 0 & 1 & 0 & 1 & 1 & 0 & 0 & 0 & & 1 & 0 \\ 0 & 0 & 1 & 1 & 0 & 0 & 0 & 1 & & 0 & 1 \\ 0 & 0 & 1 & 0 & 0 & 1 & 0 & 1 & & 0 & 1 \\ 0 & 0 & 1 & 0 & 0 & 1 & 1 & 0 & & 0 & 1 \end{bmatrix}$$

10.6. Row-fold the PLA of Prob. 10.5, and reduce it as much as possible. Calculate R, C, N, and S and compare this PLA to that of Prob. 10.5.

10.7. Fold the PLA shown in Fig. 9.27, and reduce it as much as possible. Calculate R, C, N, and S.

10.8. Sketch a typical signal path for one product line of a domino PLA with inputs, $\bar{A}$, A, $\bar{B}$, and B, driving an output line with one pull-down.

10.9. Design an AOI PLA with a 4-input AND-plane realized in NAND-NAND form. Can you precharge using phase 1 and phase 1-BAR?

10.10. List the 16 possible product-line values of a PLA if the inputs A and B are not decoded and if they are decoded. Assume the PLA is realized with NOR/NOR logic.

10.11 Sketch the AND-plane of a PLA that realizes the function $Y = ABDE + ACDE + A\bar{B}F + ACF + \bar{B}DFG + \bar{C}DFG$. How much area is saved if B and C inputs are decoded? Include the decoder area.

10.12. Do a SPICE transient simulation of a simple 4-input mostly NMOS AND gate (a NOR gate with complemented inputs), and the circuit of Fig. 10.2*b* without evaluation transistors. Compare rise times and fall times of the two circuits.

10.13. Do a SPICE transient simulation of the sense amplifier of Fig. 10.10 and determine the propagation delays for switching the sense amplifier. The input line to the amplifier can be modeled as a resistance of 1 kΩ in parallel with a capacitance of 300 fF.

CHAPTER
11

MULTILEVEL MINIMIZATION

11.1 INTRODUCTION

Two-level logic representations are special cases of multilevel representations, and a logic design approach should include multilevel synthesis in order to obtain better area and/or speed reduction. There are boolean networks which are much smaller when represented in multilevel format. A common example is a parity checker, designed with exclusive-OR gates.

The multilevel representation of the parity checker can be in the recursive form $A \oplus (B \oplus (C \oplus D))$, or in the tree form $(A \oplus B) \oplus (C \oplus D)$. Both representations require $n - 1$ exclusive-OR gates for n inputs. As a canonical SOP expansion the function requires many more gates. Truth tables grow exponentially with the number of variables involved. The number of minterms and maxterms in a truth table is 2^n, which quickly becomes prohibitively large. The exclusive-OR function is true for half the total number of minterms and the two-level realization of a parity checker requires 2^{n-1} first-level gates.

A multilevel combinational circuit can be specified by a boolean network (BN) which is defined as a binary decision diagram (BDD) or as a directed acyclic graph (DAG). In both the BDD and the DAG, each node has two paths leading from the node corresponding to a true or false value of the node variable. A DAG can be thought of as a merged or reduced BDD.

In the BDD approach, a boolean network is specified by a directed acyclic graph with each node associated with a defining sum-of-products expression and a unique reference variable. The edges of the graph are derived from the SOP expressions and reference variables of the nodes in the network. Nodes of a BN representing primary inputs to the network have no SOP expression. Each node of a BN can be viewed as an incompletely specified, single output boolean function.

Multilevel logic minimization transforms a boolean function into an equivalent representation that can be implemented as a circuit that is smaller, faster, or more testable than a circuit built in an SOP or POS form. The function may also have multiple outputs.

There are two basic approaches to multilevel design: the boolean/algebraic approach and the graph-based approach. The boolean/algebraic method typically represents a function as a DAG and optimization is done by factoring and two-level minimization on each node. In the graph-based approach, a function is represented as a DAG whose nodes represent simple functions, and optimization is done using graph manipulation and data flow algorithms.

The Weinberger array and the gate matrix array are two approaches that lead to a multilevel network solution, and they will be studied first, as an introduction to multilevel synthesis.

11.2 WEINBERGER ARRAYS AND GATE MATRICES

In NMOS design, it is customary to run data and metal horizontally, with control running vertically in polysilicon. In CMOS design, it is often more convenient to run control vertically in metal along with VDD and GND, and only run data horizontally. These two choices are shown in Fig. 11.1. Generally both methods should be investigated to see which busing arrangement yields the better overall area utilization. Frequently, one of the two busing choices requires a smaller number of isolation wells, and is thus the superior circuit design.

The *Weinberger array* (1) is a systematic approach to layout pattern design which originated with metal-gate MOS technology, and yields a high circuit

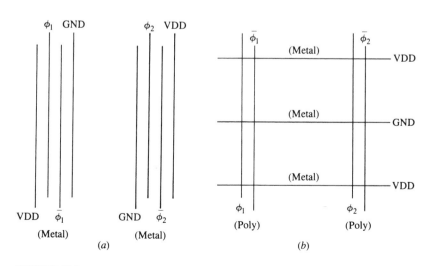

FIGURE 11.1
Floorplans for (*a*) vertical metal clocking and power lines, and (*b*) horizontal metal power lines and vertical polysilicon clock lines.

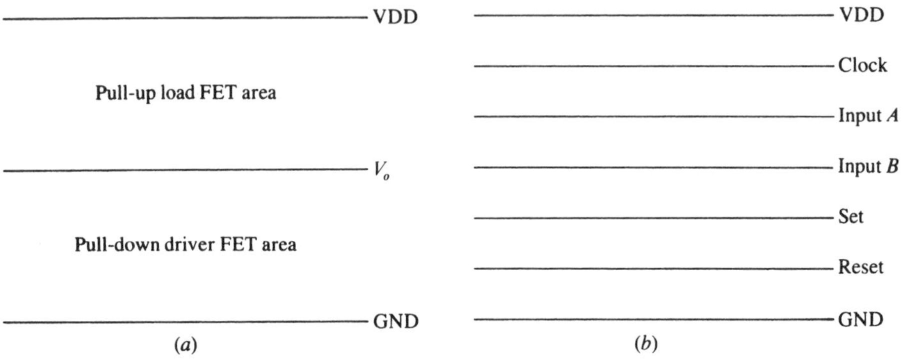

———————————————— VDD   ———————————————— VDD

                                            ———————————————— Clock

Pull-up load FET area

                                            ———————————————— Input *A*

———————————————— V_o ———————————————— Input *B*

                                            ———————————————— Set

Pull-down driver FET area

                                            ———————————————— Reset

———————————————— GND   ———————————————— GND

(*a*)   (*b*)

FIGURE 11.2
(*a*) A simple Weinberger-array layout; (*b*) a clocked SR flip-flop layout.

density. The approach is to lay out lines for VDD and GND rails, with space between for inserting diffused areas to realize the load and driver transistors. The thin oxide layer (thinox) covered by polysilicon produces FETs, whereas the thick field oxide (FOX) is placed where no FET is desired. The pull-up FET is placed in a channel between V_{DD} and V_o, and the pull-down FET is placed in a channel between V_o and GND as shown in Fig. 11.2*a*.

The Weinberger array can easily be enlarged to include clocking and multiple inputs. Such a layout for an SR flip-flop with inputs *A* and *B*, clocking, and direct set and reset capability is shown in Fig. 11.2*b*.

To expand the array to two dimensions, mirror images of the basic pattern can be added above and below the original pattern, alternately sharing GND and VDD. A basic pattern (B.P.) can be mirrored to obtain two basic patterns (Fig. 11.3*a*), laid out in a two-dimensional matrix array of single basic patterns (Fig. 11.3*b*), or laid out in a matrix array of double basic patterns (Fig. 11.3*c*).

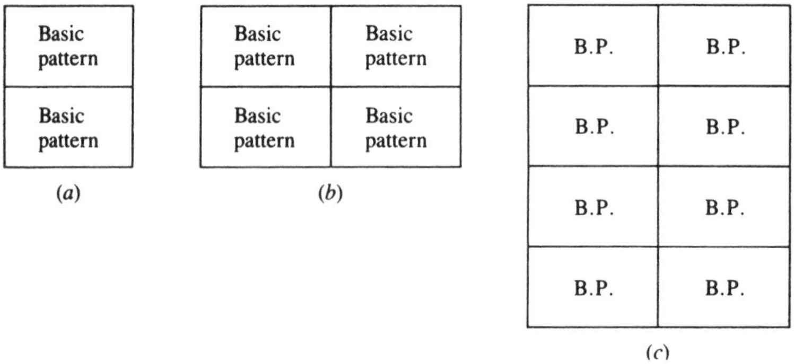

| Basic pattern |
| Basic pattern |

(*a*)

| Basic pattern | Basic pattern |
| Basic pattern | Basic pattern |

(*b*)

B.P.	B.P.
B.P.	B.P.
B.P.	B.P.
B.P.	B.P.

(*c*)

FIGURE 11.3
A basic Weinberger pattern, B.P., augmented by (*a*) mirroring it, (*b*) forming a matrix of B.P.s, or (*c*) forming a matrix of double B.P.s.

The Weinberger array allows NOR-gate logic of arbitrary depth and the devices can be of varying width. The array differs from a PLA in these two respects. The PLA only realizes two levels of logic and all its devices are the same size. In a Weinberger array, a device is formed between two metal columns and signals propagate in rows. The columns are usually metal and the rows are usually polysilicon. Diffusions are run horizontally between two columns to produce FETs. The array is area efficient for NMOS technology.

Example 11.1. Lay out the function $Y = \bar{A}\bar{B} + \bar{C}(D + \bar{E})$ as a multilevel Weinberger array.

Solution. Y can be factored into a multilevel function of NOR gates, as follows:

$$Y = \bar{A}\bar{B} + \bar{C}(D + \bar{E})$$
$$= \overline{A + B(C + \bar{D}E)}$$
$$= \overline{A + \bar{B} + \overline{\bar{C}(D + \bar{E})}}$$
$$= \overline{A + \bar{B} + \overline{C + \bar{D}E}}$$
$$= \overline{A + \bar{B} + \overline{C + \overline{D + \bar{E}}}}$$

The circuit can now be implemented as the four-level NOR array shown in Fig. 11.4a. The gates are labeled α, β, γ, δ. The layout is done in NMOS, with each NOR

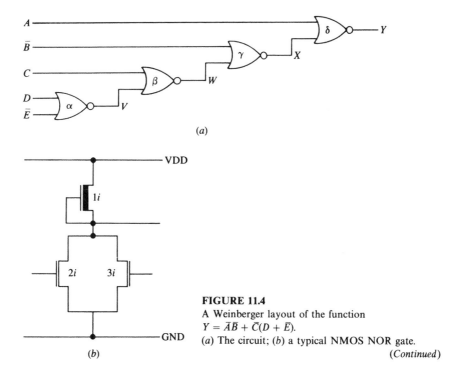

(a)

(b)

FIGURE 11.4
A Weinberger layout of the function
$Y = \bar{A}\bar{B} + \bar{C}(D + \bar{E})$.
(a) The circuit; (b) a typical NMOS NOR gate.
(*Continued*)

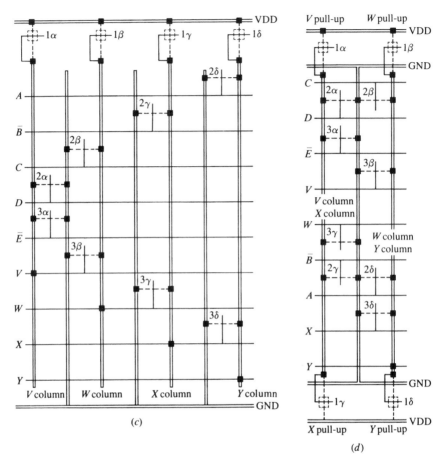

FIGURE 11.4 (*continued*)
A Weinberger layout of the function $Y = \bar{A}\bar{B} + \bar{C}(D + \bar{E})$. (c) A stick layout; (d) an optimized layout.

gate constructed of a pull-up device numbered 1*i*, and two pull-down devices labeled 2*i* and 3*i*, as shown in Fig. 11.4*b*. The layout is shown in Fig. 11.4*c*, with the devices laid out in the sequence shown in Fig. 11.4*a*, and the individual transistors labeled.

The Weinberger array shown in Fig. 11.4*c* is very wasteful of chip real estate. If the pull-up transistors are placed at the top and bottom of the array, and the pull-up metal columns are split appropriately, the size of the array can be greatly reduced. The folded array is shown in Fig. 11.4*d* and requires about one-third the chip area of the unfolded array shown in Fig. 11.4*c*.

The Weinberger array is suitable for NMOS layouts, but it is not suitable for CMOS layout design. A close relative to the Weinberger array that is more suitable for static CMOS is the gate matrix. In a gate matrix, polysilicon lines form the columns of the matrix, with the rows formed by grouping together those FET diffusions which associate with each other in series or in parallel (2,3).

In the Weinberger array logic gates are ordered, whereas in the gate matrix the signals are ordered. An example two-level gate-matrix layout is given below. The gate matrix can also be easily expanded to multilevels of logic.

Example 11.2. Realize the function $Y = AB + CD$ in a gate matrix.

Solution. Y can be realized in NAND-NAND form as

$$Y = AB + CD = \overline{\overline{AB} \cdot \overline{CD}}$$

as shown in Fig. 11.5a. The transistors are laid out in Fig. 11.5b. The gate matrix is given in stick form in Fig. 11.5c, with the transistors numbered as shown in Fig. 11.5b.

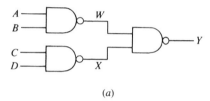

(a)

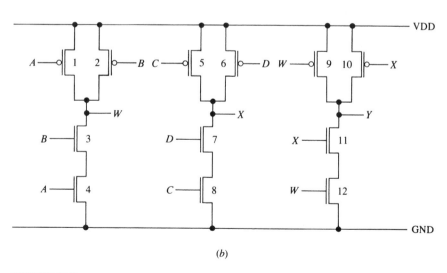

(b)

FIGURE 11.5
A gate-matrix layout of the function $Y = AB + CD$. (a) The circuit; (b) the layout of each NAND gate.

(*Continued*)

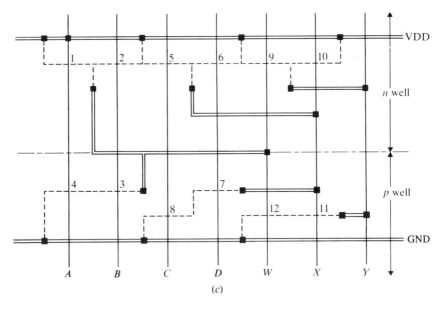

FIGURE 11.5 (*continued*)
A gate-matrix layout of the function $Y = AB + CD$. (*c*) The stick layout.

11.3 MODERN BOOLEAN LOGIC

In multilevel minimization, many boolean definitions and operations not normally covered in an introductory digital design course are required. These terms will be defined as needed. For easy reference, App. B contains an alphabetical listing of the definitions of terms used in the text.

In the synthesis of optimized multilevel, multioutput logic, a technique called *algebraic decomposition* is used. The first step is to determine the factors common to two or more boolean expressions. This is referred to as kernel extraction. The *kernels* of boolean functions are their prime multicube (implicant) divisors, and *kernel intersections* are the kernels that identify common subexpressions in a network. Once the set of kernels is obtained, one must determine the intersection of kernels of one function with the kernels of a second function. Once the kernel intersections are known, one can minimize the multioutput boolean expressions. The lowest-level kernels are expressions in a sum-of-products or product-of-sums form, which can be represented by two-level gates such as AND-OR-INVERT and OR-AND-INVERT.

The second step is to apply algebraic resubstitution and node elimination or flattening. *Resubstitution* requires identifying common subexpressions of a function, and then substituting them into the original function in order to reduce the number of literals. *Flattening* is the elimination of a node by substituting it into its fan-out.

11.4 BOOLEAN CUBES

A *variable* is a symbol representing a coordinate in boolean space (A, B, etc.), and a *literal* is the occurrence of a variable in either true or complemented form. A literal can also be considered to be a variable combined with a *phase*. If the phase of the literal is positive the literal is true, and if the phase is negative the literal is complemented. (A is a literal with positive phase, while $\bar{B}$ is a literal with negative phase.)

Phase assignment is a global procedure that helps simplify multilevel boolean networks. *Phase assignment* determines the phases of all the gates in a network, in order to minimize the total number of inverters required and to define the types of gates needed to implement the function.

> **Example 11.3.** Group the products of the function, Y, according to phase, and implement Y with 3-input AND, OR, NAND, or NOR gates. $Y = ABC + DE + F\bar{G} + \bar{H}\bar{I} + \bar{J}\bar{K}$.
>
> *Solution.* Let $Y = Z_1 + Z_2 + Z_3$. Z_1, with no complemented variables, consists of products ABC and DE, and can be realized with three NAND gates. Z_2, with both true and complemented variables, consists of $F\bar{G}$ and can be realized with two NOR gates, one gate being used to form an inverter. Z_3, with complemented variables only, consists of products $\bar{H}\bar{I}$ and $\bar{J}\bar{K}$, and can be realized with two NOR gates and one OR gate. The three subcircuits are shown in Fig. 11.6. An additional OR gate is needed to form the function Y.

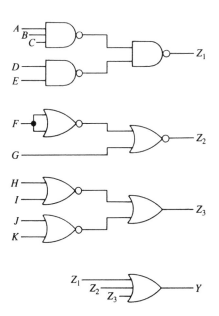

FIGURE 11.6
Realization of function $Y = Z_1 + Z_2 + Z_3$, $Z_1 = ABC + DE$, $Z_2 = F\bar{G}$, $Z_3 = \bar{H}\bar{I} + \bar{J}\bar{K}$.

A *cube* is a conjoint set (product) of literals, C, such that if E is an element of C then $\bar{E}$ is not an element of C. Both phases of a variable cannot occur in the same cube. ($\{A, B, \bar{C}\}$ is a cube while $\{A, B, \bar{B}, C\}$ is not a cube.) Trivial cubes 0 and 1 represent boolean functions 0 and 1, respectively. A cube is an implicant of an expression.

An *algebraic expression* is a cover set of cubes (implicants). The sum-of-products (SOP) written $\{\{A, B, C\}, \{A, C, \bar{D}\}\}$ is the expression $ABC + AC\bar{D}$, consisting of cubes $\{A, B, C\}$ and $\{A, C, \bar{D}\}$. A *nonredundant* expression has no cube that contains another cube, and represents the disjunction of its cubes, i.e., there is no overlap of cubes in a nonredundant expression. $A + AB$ is redundant because $A = A\bar{B} + AB$ contains AB. A *prime implicant* is any cube of a function which is not totally contained in some larger cube of the function. A *prime cube* is a prime implicant and the cubes of a nonredundant expression are the prime implicants of the expression. $Y = AB + CD + AC$ is an algebraic expression, whereas $Z = AB + ABD + CD$ is redundant, and is not an algebraic expression because AB contains ABD. Functions will be assumed to have been first reduced to nonredundant expressions unless otherwise specified.

The *ON-set* of an algebraic expression is the set of cubes S_{ON} for which the expression is true, the *OFF-set* is the set of cubes S_{OFF} for which the expression is false, and the *DC-set*, S_{DC}, is the set of don't care cubes for which the expression is unspecified. Mathematically, $S_{ON} = f^{-1}(1)$, $S_{OFF} = f^{-1}(0)$, and $S_{DC} = f^{-1}(\times)$, where $\times$ represents a don't care literal.

11.5 CUBE REPRESENTATION

In boolean cartesian geometry, a switching variable can be represented by two points at opposite ends of a single line. Two variables can be represented by a plane, with the four boolean values of the two variables (the minterms) forming the vertices of a square. Three variables can be represented by a cube, with the eight minterms of the three variables forming the vertices of the cube (4). These three representations are shown in Fig. 11.7.

A function of n variables consists of a subset of 2^n potential minterms of the function. In an n-dimensional space, 2^n points corresponding to the 2^n potential minterms form the vertices of an n cube (*n-dimensional cube*) or boolean hypercube. There is a one-to-one correspondence between the minterms of n variables and the vertices of the n cube. A 3-dimensional cube (3 cube) is shown in Fig. 11.8, with the vertices representing the function $F(A, B, C)$ whose minterm expansion is $\sum m(0, 2, 3, 4, 7)$.

A function of n variables consists of the set of vertices of the n cube corresponding to the minterms (0 cubes) of the function. The function $G(A, B, C) = \sum m(0, 2, 4, 7)$ is shown in Fig. 11.9. The vertices corresponding to the minterms of G are marked.

Two 0 cubes form a 1 cube if they differ in only one coordinate (variable). Two 1 cubes of G are shown in Fig. 11.9. They are obtained by combining the 0

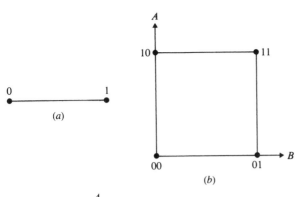

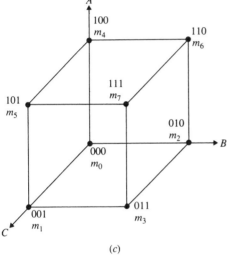

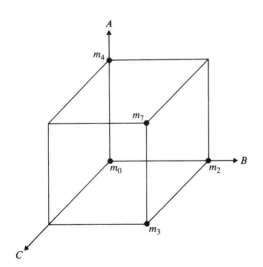

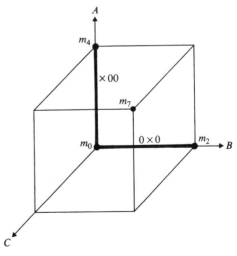

FIGURE 11.7
Cubic representations of a boolean function of
(a) one variable, (b) two variables, and
(c) three variables.

FIGURE 11.8
A cubic representation of the function
$F(A, B, C) = \sum m(0, 2, 3, 4, 7)$.

FIGURE 11.9
A cubic representation of the function
$G(A, B, C) = \bar{A}\bar{C} + \bar{B}\bar{C} + ABC$.

cubes at the vertices of an edge of the 3 cube, and form two edges of the 3 cube. Minterms 0 and 2 combine to give $000 + 010 = 0\times0$, where $\times$ represents the missing variable B, that is, B is now a don't care. Minterms 0 and 4 also combine to give $000 + 100 = \times00$. These two edges of the 3 cube are represented by bold lines in Fig. 11.9. Minterm 7 does not combine and is a prime implicant of G. The function G has been simplified as follows:

$$G(A, B, C) = \sum m(0, 2, 4, 7)$$
$$= \bar{A}\bar{B}\bar{C} + \bar{A}B\bar{C} + A\bar{B}\bar{C} + ABC$$
$$= \bar{A}\bar{C} + \bar{B}\bar{C} + ABC$$

A 2 cube is obtained by combining a set of four 0 cubes whose coordinate values are the same in all but two variables. The 2 cube forms a face of a 3 cube. Consider the function, $H = \sum m(2, 3, 6, 7)$. Minterms 2, 3, 6, 7 combine to form the 2 cube $\times1\times$, shown by the surface or face of the 3 cube which is hatched in Fig. 11.10. This corresponds to reducing the function H as follows:

$$H(A, B, C) = (\bar{A}B\bar{C} + \bar{A}BC) + (AB\bar{C} + ABC)$$
$$= \bar{A}B + AB = B$$

A 4 cube can be represented as shown in Fig. 11.11. Minterms (0 cubes) form the 16 vertices of the 4 cube, 1 cubes, obtained by combining two 0 cubes, form the edges of the hypercube, 2 cubes, obtained by combining two 1 cubes (four 0 cubes); form the faces of the 3 cubes, and 3 cubes form subvolumes of the 4 cube. Representations of hypercubes of higher order than 4 cubes cannot be drawn in a two-dimensional plane.

Figure 11.11 shows the function $J(A, B, C, D) = \sum m(2, 4, 5, 6, 7, 8, 10, 12)$. Minterms 8 and 12 combine to give edge $A\bar{C}\bar{D}$ ($1000 + 1100 = 1\times00$), minterms

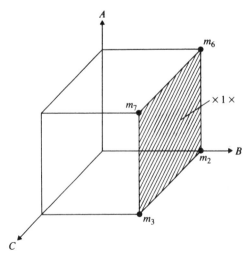

FIGURE 11.10
A cubic representation of the function
$H(A, B, C) = B$.

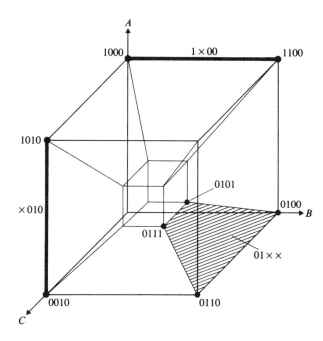

FIGURE 11.11
A four-dimensional hypercube representing the function
$J(A, B, C, D)$
$= \sum m(2, 4, 5, 6, 7, 8, 10, 12).$

2 and 10 combine to give edge $\bar{B}C\bar{D}$ ($0010 + 1010 = \times 010$), and minterms 4, 5, 6, and 7 combine to form surface $\bar{A}B$ ($0100 + 0101 + 0110 + 0111 = 010\times + 011\times = 01\times\times$). The function, J, reduces to

$$J(A, B, C, D) = A\bar{C}\bar{D} + \bar{B}C\bar{D} + \bar{A}B$$

In Fig. 11.9, the prime implicants of the function represented are the 0 cube $ABC = 111$ and the 1 cubes $\bar{A}\bar{C} = 0\times0$, $\bar{B}\bar{C} = \times00$, the prime implicant of the function represented in Fig. 11.10 is the 2 cube $B = \times1\times$, and the prime implicants of the function in Fig. 11.11 are the 1 cubes $A\bar{C}\bar{D} = 1\times00$, $\bar{B}C\bar{D} = \times010$, and the 2-cube $\bar{A}B = 01\times\times$.

11.6 ALGEBRAIC DECOMPOSITION

The familiar Karnaugh map (5) and Quine-McCluskey (6,7) methods of reducing a function to a minimum sum-of-products are two procedures for combining 0 cubes (minterms) into larger or higher-dimension cubes, and then selecting the minimal number of prime cubes needed to realize the function. The problem of minimizing two or more functions simultaneously is much more complicated and requires tools not necessary in minimizing a single boolean function. The new tools needed are defined and discussed below.

The support of an expression is the set of variables that are elements of the cubes of the expression. The *support of expression* Y is written sup (Y), where sup $(Y) = \{a | a$ is a cube and either $a \epsilon Y$ or $\bar{a} \epsilon Y\}$. Sup $(AB + \overline{AC}) = \{A, B, C\}$.

Expressions Y and Z have *disjoint support* (no overlap of variables) if $\sup(Y) \cap \sup(Z) = \varnothing$, the null set, and the product YZ is an *algebraic product* or *algebraic expression*. No boolean operations are required to obtain an algebraic product. Otherwise YZ is a *boolean product*. If $Y = AB + AC$ and $Z = EF + H$, then YZ is an algebraic product because $\sup(Y) \cap \sup(Z) = \varnothing$, and Y and Z have disjoint support. If $Y = AB + AC$ and $X = DE + A$, then XY is not an algebraic product because $\sup(X) \cap \sup(Y) = A$. $(A + B)(C + D) = AC + AD + BC + BD$ is an algebraic product, while $(A + B)(A + C) = A + BC$ and $(A + B)(\bar{B} + C) = A\bar{B} + AC + BC$ are boolean products.

The factored form of an expression is the most useful for multilevel logic, and replaces the SOP and POS forms, which give minimum two-level logic solutions. The factored form is defined recursively. A literal is a factored form, a sum of factored forms is a factored form, and a product of factored forms is a factored form. A factored form is an SOP of an SOP of an SOP, etc.

Factored forms are not always unique. $ABC + ABD + CD = AB(C + D) + CD = ABC + (AB + C)D$. The minimum factored form contains the least number of literals. In the above example, $ABC + (AB + C)D$ has 7 literals, while $AB(C + D) + CD$ has 6 literals and is the minimum factored form.

If XY is an algebraic product in an expression Z, either X or Y contains two or more cubes, and Z has no other algebraic product that contains XY, then XY is a *prime product* of Z. If $Z = GH + K$, then GH is a prime product of Z, while GM is not contained in Z and is therefore not a prime product of Z.

11.7 ALGEBRAIC AND BOOLEAN DIVISION

Let Y be the set of elements y_i and Z be the set of elements z_j. The product of the two expressions is the set of all the elements in either Y or Z, made nonredundant using the standard Boolean absorption theorem, $A + AB = A$. $YZ = \{y_i \cup z_j | y_i \epsilon Y$ and $z_j \epsilon Z\}$. If $Y = \{A, B, C\}$ and $Z = \{B, D, E\}$ then $YZ = \{A, B, C, D, E\}$ since $ABC \cap BDE = ABCDE$.

The quotient Q of Y/Z is the largest set of cubes Q such that $Y = QZ + R = (Y/Z)Z + R$, where R is the remainder. If QZ is restricted to an algebraic product, Y/Z is a unique algebraic quotient. Otherwise Y/Z is a nonunique boolean product. If Q is not the null set and Q can be obtained using algebraic division, then Z and Q are algebraic divisors of Y. Otherwise Z and Q are boolean divisors of Y.

Example 11.4. Find the quotient and the remainder of X divided by Y, and by Z, where $X = AD + BCD + E$, $Y = A + BC$, and $Z = A + B$. Are the divisions algebraic or boolean?

Solution. The quotient of $X/Y = ((A + BC)D + E)/(A + BC)$ is D and the remainder is E. This is algebraic division. The quotient of $X/Z = ((A + B)(A + C)D + E)/(A + B)$ is $(A + C)D$, and the remainder is E. This is boolean division.

11.8 KERNELS AND COKERNELS OF AN EXPRESSION

Kernel extraction, intersection, and phase assignment are very important algebraic operations in multilevel synthesis and optimization of combinational networks. The synthesis of a complex boolean expression into multilevel logic is done by obtaining and selecting those kernels that reduce the area of the network. These kernels become new "nodes" or subfunctions of the network, and the process is repeated until no more literal (area) reduction is possible.

Let C_i and C_j be cubes and let the cube C_{ij} denote the conjunction of the maximal set of literals present in both C_i and C_j. C_{ij} is defined as the literal intersection of cubes C_i and C_j. (If $C_i = ABC$ and $C_j = ACD$, then $C_{ij} = AC$).

Let C be the set of cubes whose literals constitute the literal intersections of two or more cubes of an algebraic expression F. For each cube C_i of the set C, define the *algebraic division* of F by C_i as K_i. K_i is said to be a *kernel* of F, and C_i is the corresponding *cokernel*. Since C_i is the literal intersection of cubes of F, no subcube may be factored out of each of the cubes of K_i.

A *primary divisor* is a cube or a subexpression that divides F. The primary divisors of a function F are the set $D(F)$, where $D(F) = \{F/C \mid C \text{ is a cube}\}$. The kernels of F are the set $K(F)$, where $K(F) = \{G \mid G \epsilon D(F) \text{ and } G \text{ is cube-free}\}$. An expression F is said to be cube-free if no cube divides the expression evenly. The kernels of F are the cube-free primary divisors of F. The cube C used to obtain the kernel F/C is called the cokernel of K, and $C(F)$ is the set of cokernels of F.

The kernels are used to find subexpressions common to two or more expressions. *Weak division* of F by G is defined as the largest set of cubes common to the result of dividing the numerator F by each cube of the denominator G. If $(F/G)G = F$ then G divides F evenly. $F_1 = (AB + CD)$ has two cubes in it and F_1/AB has a remainder CD, while F_1/CD has a remainder AB. Neither cube divides F_1 evenly, therefore it is a cube-free expression. $F_2 = ABC$ is a cube and $F_2/ABC = 1$. A cube-free expression must have more than one cube in it.

A kernel that contains no kernels other than itself is said to be of level 0. A kernel is of level n (a *level-n kernel*) if the highest kernel contained in it is of level $n - 1$. Given a function $Y = AE + AF + BCE + BCF + BDE + BDF + G$, factor Y to obtain $Y = (A + B(C + D))(E + F) + G$. $K^0 = C + D$ is a kernel of level 0, $K^1 = A + B(C + D)$ is a level-1 kernel, and Y itself is a level-2 kernel. Once the level-0 kernels of all the functions have been assertained, a method of determining the intersections, $I(K)$, among kernels of different functions must be found.

Example 11.5. Find the kernels and cokernels of the function F, where $F = ABDE + ABDG + EH$.

Solution. $F = ABD(E + G) + EH = ABDG + E(ABD + H)$. $F/ABD = E + G$ with a remainder EH, and $F/E = ABD + H$ with a remainder $ABDG$. $C = \{ABD, E\}$, the kernels of F are $E + G$ and $ABD + H$, and the respective cokernels are ABD and E.

Two functions F and G have a multiple-cube common divisor if and only if the intersection of a kernel from F and a kernel from G has more than one cube (8). This provides a method of detecting whether two or more expressions have any common algebraic divisors other than single cubes.

To ascertain this, compute the set of kernels for each logic expression and form nontrivial (more than one term) intersections among kernels from different functions. One doesn't need to compute the set of all algebraic divisors for each expression to see if there are common multiple-cube divisors, since the set of kernels is smaller than the set of all algebraic divisors. Also, if the intersection set of all kernels consists of single cubes or is empty, then one need only look for common divisors consisting of single cubes (8).

Example 11.6. Find the kernel intersection of functions,

$$F_1 = AB(C(D + E) + F + G) + H \quad \text{and} \quad F_2 = AI(C(D + E) + F + J) + K$$

Solution. By inspection the kernels of F_1 are $K_1 = D + E$ and $K_2 = C(D + E) + F + G$. The kernels of F_2 are $K_3 = D + E$ and $K_4 = C(D + E) + F + J$. The kernel intersection set is $N = A(C(D + E) + F)$, and the functions can be written as: $F_1 = B(N + AG) + H$ and $F_2 = I(N + AJ) + K$.

11.9 KERNEL DETERMINATION

A tabular method of computing the kernels and cokernels of an expression F is shown below by means of an example (9). The function to be factored is $F = ABC + ABD + BCD + ACD$. The procedure consists of first listing all the cubes of the function in both rows and columns, and then comparing each cube to each of the remaining cubes to find the largest common cube, as follows:

	ABC	ABD	BCD	ACD
ABC	*			
ABD	AB	*		
BCD	BC	BD	*	
ACD	AC	AD	CD	*

The table has generated smaller cubes common to two or more of the original cubes of the function. Form a new table for these cubes.

	AB	BC	BD	AC	AD	CD
AB	*					
BC	B	*				
BD	B	B	*			
AC	A	C	$\emptyset$	*		
AD	A	$\emptyset$	D	A	*	
CD	$\emptyset$	C	D	C	D	*

The cokernels of F are the set of cubes $C = \{AB, BC, BD, AC, AD, CD, A, B, C, D\}$.

Next, the function F is divided by each cokernel to obtain the kernels of the function.

$$C_1 = AB \qquad \frac{F}{AB} = C + D = K_1$$

$$C_2 = BC \qquad \frac{F}{BC} = A + D = K_2$$

$$C_3 = BD \qquad \frac{F}{BD} = A + C = K_3$$

$$C_4 = AC \qquad \frac{F}{AC} = B + D = K_4$$

$$C_5 = AD \qquad \frac{F}{AD} = B + C = K_5$$

$$C_6 = CD \qquad \frac{F}{CD} = A + B = K_6$$

$$C_7 = A \qquad \frac{F}{A} = BC + BD + CD = B(C + D) + CD = K_7$$

$$C_8 = B \qquad \frac{F}{B} = AC + AD + CD = A(C + D) + CD = K_8$$

$$C_9 = C \qquad \frac{F}{C} = AB + BD + AD = D(A + B) + AB = K_9$$

$$C_{10} = D \qquad \frac{F}{D} = AB + BC + AC = C(A + B) + AB = K_{10}$$

The level-0 kernels of the function are: $C + D$, $A + D$, $A + C$, $B + D$, $B + C$, and $A + B$; the level-1 kernels are $B(C + D) + CD$, $A(C + D) + CD$, $D(A + B) + AB$, and $C(A + B) + AB$.

11.10 ALGEBRAIC AND BOOLEAN RESUBSTITUTION

Algebraic resubstitution uses algebraic division to reduce the number of literals in a function. Let $X = AC + AD + BC + BD + EF$, and $Y = A + B$. Y is a divisor of X, and X can be simplified to $X = (A + B)(C + D) + EF = Y(C + D) + EF$. The literal count for the functions X and Y has been reduced from $10 + 2 = 12$ to $5 + 2 = 7$, an elimination of 5 literals.

Boolean resubstitution uses boolean division to substitute one function into another function and reduce the number of literals in the function. Boolean resubstitution is generally better than algebraic resubstitution, but it usually takes more machine time (8).

Let $X = (AB + CD)\bar{E}\bar{F} + (AB + EF)\bar{C}\bar{D} + (CD + EF)\bar{A}\bar{B}$, and $Y = AB + CD + EF$. With the aid of boolean algebra, X can be simplified to $X = (AB + CD + EF)(\bar{A}\bar{B} + \bar{C}\bar{D} + \bar{E}\bar{F}) = Y(\bar{A}\bar{B} + \bar{C}\bar{D} + \bar{E}\bar{F})$. The literal count for X and Y has dropped from $18 + 6 = 24$ to $7 + 6 = 13$, a saving of 11 literals. If Y had been the expression $(\bar{A} + \bar{B})(\bar{C} + \bar{D})(\bar{E} + \bar{F}) = \overline{AB + CD + EF}$ then X would reduce to $\bar{Y}(\bar{A}\bar{B} + \bar{C}\bar{D} + \bar{E}\bar{F})$, which is the same reduction in literals.

To decide whether it is advisable to use resubstitution, divide one function, X, by another function, Y, or its complement, $\bar{Y}$. Express the function in terms of Y or $\bar{Y}$ and see if literals are saved.

Example 11.7. Use algebraic resubstitution to reduce two functions, $Y_1 = AC + AD + AE$, and $Y_2 = BC + BD + BE$.

Solution. Define a new function, $Y_3 = C + D + E$. Then $Y_1 = AY_3$ and $Y_2 = BY_3$. The literal count has been reduced from 12 to 7.

The converse of algebraic or boolean resubstitution is the reduction of literal count by eliminating nodes. This is sometimes referred to as "flattening" the function. Again, a simple check will reveal whether literals are saved or not.

Example 11.8. Use node-elimination to flatten the functions $Y_1 = CD\bar{Y}_3$, $Y_2 = DE\bar{Y}_3$, $Y_3 = CDE$.

Solution. $\bar{Y}_3 = \bar{C} + \bar{D} + \bar{E}$. Therefore, $Y_1 = CD(\bar{C} + \bar{D} + \bar{E}) = CD\bar{E}$ and $Y_2 = DE(\bar{C} + \bar{D} + \bar{E}) = \bar{C}DE$. The literal count has decreased from 9 to 6.

11.11 BOOLEAN TREES

Multilevel logic can be synthesized by mapping the function or functions into one or more trees. This can be done by extracting the kernels of the functions, or by the use of Shannon's expansion theorem. Both methods will be considered.

11.11.1 Tree Mapping by Kernel Extraction

Tree-mapping techniques transform an optimized boolean network into a forest of trees. Each tree is rooted either in a primary output or in a multi fan-out gate. A multilevel function can be represented by a tree as follows (10). Each node of the tree is either an OR gate, represented by a plus sign at the node, or an AND gate, represented by an AND dot at the node. Tree mappings of the functions $Y_1 = AB + CD$, and $Y_2 = (A + B)(C + D)$ are given in Fig. 11.12. In multilevel logic, each common kernel selected becomes the root of a new tree.

In the tree graph, a branch connects node i to node j if the output of node i is part of the support of node j (if $Y_i \in \sup(F_j)$). Primary inputs to a tree are the leaves and primary outputs are the roots. Each node in a boolean network is a completely specified boolean function represented by an SOP form and a factored form.

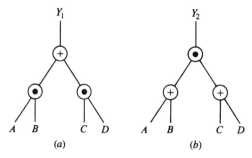

FIGURE 11.12
Tree mappings of (a) $Y_1 = AB + CD$, and (b) $Y_2 = (A + B)(C + D)$.

Example 11.9. The SOP representation of a function Y_1 is $Y_1 = ABC + AB\bar{D} + E\bar{F} + \bar{F}\bar{G} + \bar{F}H$. Factor Y_1 and give a tree mapping of the function.

Solution. The cokernels of Y_1 are found to be $C_1 = AB$ and $C_2 = \bar{F}$. The kernel of AB is $K_1 = Y_1/AB = C + \bar{D}$, and the kernel of $\bar{F}$ is $K_2 = Y_1/\bar{F} = E + \bar{G} + H$. The factored form of Y_1 is thus $Y_1 = AB(C + \bar{D}) + \bar{F}(E + \bar{G} + H)$. This maps into the tree shown in Fig. 11.13.

Algebraic resubstitution gives $Y_1 = ABK_1 + \bar{F}K_2$, $K_1 = C + \bar{D}$, $K_2 = E + \bar{G} + H$. Multilevel synthesis of boolean functions gives a covering of the function tree, subdividing it into two-level gates.

Example 11.10. Give a tree mapping of $\bar{Y}_1$, the complement of the function Y_1 in Example 11.9.

Solution. $\bar{Y}_1 = (\bar{A} + \bar{B} + \bar{C}D)(F + \bar{E}G\bar{H})$. This maps into the tree shown in Fig. 11.14. The kernels of $\bar{Y}_1$ are $K_3 = \bar{A} + \bar{B} + \bar{C}D$ and $K_4 = F + \bar{E}G\bar{H}$, and algebraic resubstitution gives $\bar{Y}_1 = K_3K_4$.

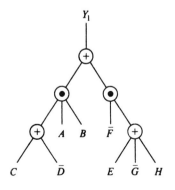

FIGURE 11.13
Tree for $Y_1 = AB(C + \bar{D}) + \bar{F}(E + \bar{G} + H)$.

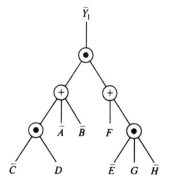

FIGURE 11.14
Tree for $\bar{Y}_1 = (\bar{A} + \bar{B} + \bar{C}D)(F + \bar{E}G\bar{H})$.

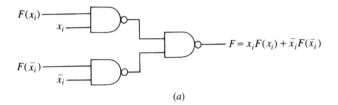

$$F = x_i F(x_i) + \bar{x}_i F(\bar{x}_i)$$

(a)

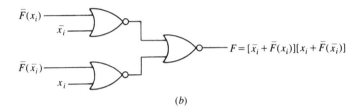

$$F = [\bar{x}_i + \bar{F}(x_i)][x_i + \bar{F}(\bar{x}_i)]$$

(b)

FIGURE 11.15
An expanded function F, represented (a) in NAND-NAND logic, and (b) in NOR-NOR logic.

11.11.2 Tree Mapping by Shannon's Theorem

A function is said to be *positive unate* (*negative unate*) in x_i if $F(x_1, x_2, \ldots, x_n)$ is a logic expression with x_i only uncomplemented (complemented). The function, $F = AB + B\bar{C}\bar{D} + \bar{A}BC + AC\bar{D}$ is positive unate in B, negative unate in D, and *binate* (nonunate) in A and C. A positive (negative) unate function is a function which is positive (negative) unate in all its variables. A *unate function* is one which is either positive unate or negative unate in each of its variables. $Y = ABC + AB\bar{D} + E\bar{F} + \bar{F}G + \bar{F}H$ is positive unate in variables A, B, C, E, G, and H, and negative unate in variables D and F. The function Y is a unate function and has a unique minimum POS and minimum SOP realization.

A function F that is binate in a variable x_i of its cover can be expanded about that variable by Shannon's theorem (11) to give $F = x_i F(x_i) + \bar{x}_i F(\bar{x}_i)$. Element x_i is referred to as the splitting variable, $F(x_i)$ is the *positive-phase cofactor* of F with respect to x_i, and $F(\bar{x}_i)$ is the *negative-phase cofactor* of F with respect to x_i. The function can be implemented in NAND-NAND logic as shown in Fig. 11.15a.

The complement of the function can be written in the form

$$\bar{F} = [\bar{x}_i + \bar{F}(x_i)][x_i + \bar{F}(\bar{x}_i)]$$

and it can be implemented in NOR-NOR logic as shown in Figure 11.15b.

The tree mapping of a function is obtained by recursively expanding the function by Shannon's theorem until a full binary tree is generated. This amounts to decomposing the function into unate cofactors.

Example 11.11. Obtain a binary tree representation of the function $F = ABD + A\bar{B}\bar{C} + \bar{A}B\bar{C} + \bar{A}\bar{B}CD$.

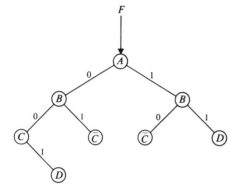

FIGURE 11.16
A binary tree representation of the function $F = A(BD + \bar{B}\bar{C}) + \bar{A}(B\bar{C} + \bar{B}CD)$.

Solution. Expanding in alphabetical order, one obtains $F_A = BD + \bar{B}\bar{C}$, and $F_{\bar{A}} = B\bar{C} + \bar{B}CD$. Expanding F_A, $F_{AB} = D$ and $F_{A\bar{B}} = \bar{C}$. Expanding $F_{\bar{A}}$, $F_{\bar{A}B} = \bar{C}$, and $F_{\bar{A}\bar{B}} = CD$. The expanded function can be written in factored form as $F = A(BD + \bar{B}\bar{C}) + \bar{A}(B\bar{C} + \bar{B}CD)$. The tree is shown in Fig. 11.16.

11.12 BINARY DECISION DIAGRAMS AND DIRECTED ACYCLIC GRAPHS

A *binary decision diagram* (BDD) is a *directed acyclic graph* (DAG) with two paths directed away from itself, one for the node asserted true and one for the node asserted false. Binary decision diagrams were proposed by Akers (12) in 1978 and directed acyclic graphs were proposed by Bryant (13) in 1986, both as alternative approaches to truth-table solutions. These approaches define a digital function in terms of a diagram which represents the function, and contains the information necessary to implement the function. Nodes of the BDD are either variables or subfunctions. Ultimately, nodes will be reduced to single variables. The root of the tree is the function to be implemented, and the leaves are either zeros or ones. The diagram is entered at the arrow pointing to the function realized by using that node as a root. The value of the node variable is indicated on the two branches leaving the node, and the nodes are directed downward.

Some simple examples of BDD representations of AND, OR, and EOR combinational circuits are shown in Fig. 11.17. To read the BDD for the AND operation, if A is false, $Y = 0$. This is the path from A to the left, marked with a value of A equal to 0, and terminating in a value of the function Y equal to 0. If A is true, the right branch from node A is taken (labeled with a 1), and the decision is transferred to B. Y is false if A is true and B is false, and Y is true if A is true and B is true.

The BDD for the inclusive-OR operation is read in the same fashion. If A is true then Y is true, and if A is false then the value of Y depends upon the value of B. In the EOR diagram, if A is true and B is true then Y is false, while if A is false then Y is true if B is true and false if B is false.

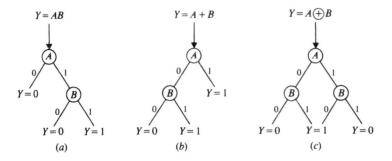

FIGURE 11.17
Binary decision diagrams of the functions (a) AB, (b) $A + B$, and (c) $A \oplus B$.

Representations of sequential edge-triggered delay, toggle, and J-K flip-flops are shown in Fig. 11.18. These BDDs are read in the same manner as the combinational network diagrams of Fig. 11.17. The characteristic equation of each flip-flop is given as the function to be realized. In these diagrams, Q^+ is the state of the flip-flop after the next clock pulse, P. D is the input data to the delay FF, T is the input to the toggle FF, J and K are inputs to the J-K FF.

BDDs can be generated by combining the basic operations shown in Fig. 11.17, and expanding the function. Consider the function $F = A + BC$. Represent the OR of A with BC to obtain the graph of Fig. 11.19a, then expand the AND of B with C to obtain the graph of Fig. 11.19b. A function of any complexity can be expanded in this manner. If the diagram is entered at BC in Fig. 11.19b, the exit leaf will be a value of BC, while if the diagram is entered at node F, the exit leaf will be a value of F.

If the function to be realized is given in the form of a truth table, one can construct a diagram as shown in Fig. 11.20. The function shown in Fig. 11.20 is a binary decision tree, and can be obtained by the Shannon expansion theorem as discussed in Sec. 11.11.2. BDDs share many properties with *binary decision trees*,

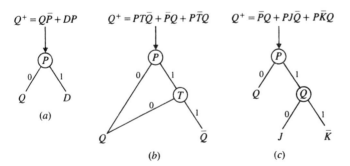

FIGURE 11.18
Binary decision diagrams of the clocked flip-flops (a) delay, (b) toggle, and (c) J-K.

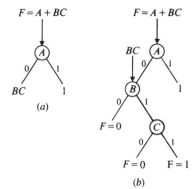

$F = A + BC$

$F = A + BC$

(a)

BC

$F = 0$

$F = 0$ $F = 1$

(b)

FIGURE 11.19
The binary decision diagram implementation for (a) $F = A + BC$, BC a node, and (b) $F = A + BC$, BC expanded.

but they differ from the binary decision tree in that a node in a BDD can have more than one branch directed into it. This occurs when the tree is simplified.

A BDD is obtained from the truth table or equivalently from the minterm expansion of the function. The exclusive-OR of three inputs, A, B, and C, consists of minterms 1, 2, 4, and 7. The binary tree representation of the function is shown in Fig. 11.21a.

Nodes 5 and 6 of the tree have the same output values and can be combined into one node labeled 5,6 in Fig. 11.21b. Nodes 4 and 7 also have the same output values for the function and can be combined into one node labeled 4,7 in Fig. 11.21b. The BDD is now in its reduced form. Each node has two output branches as in the tree, but nodes 4,7 and 5,6 have two input branches, as do the leaves 0 and 1.

From every node of a BDD there is only one active path from the function to the output corresponding to a given input vector. For the exclusive-OR of Fig. 11.21b, and an input vector $ABC = 101$, the path from F to output 0 is shown in bold lines in Fig. 11.22a.

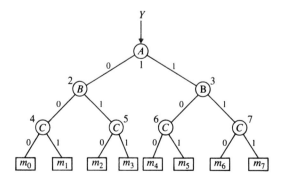

FIGURE 11.20
Realizing a function as a binary tree.

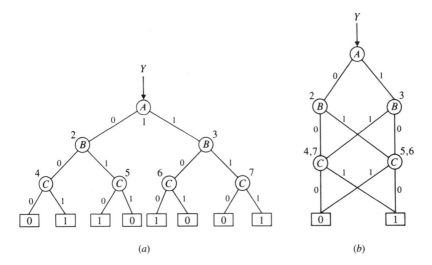

FIGURE 11.21
Realization of the function $Y = A \oplus B \oplus C$. (a) The binary tree; (b) the tree reduced to the BDD.

There are four input vectors which will result in $F = 0$, and four that result in $F = 1$. The number of paths from the function to an output can be obtained by assigning a number to each output branch which is equal to the sum of the numbers on all the input branches. For the EOR function of Fig. 11.22a, there is only one input to node A, hence the outputs of node A are assigned the number 1. Since both nodes B have one input their output lines are labeled 1 also. There

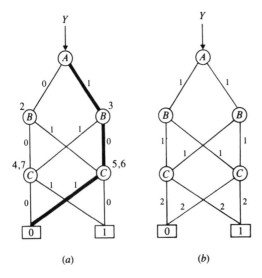

(a)   (b)

FIGURE 11.22
The BDD of Fig. 11.21 for (a) an input vector, $ABC = 101$, and (b) counting the paths to an output.

are two inputs of weight 1 entering nodes C, however, and the node-C outputs are assigned the number 2. This is shown in Fig. 11.22b. Both the true and the false output leaves have two inputs of weight 2 each, and there are four paths from F to a true or to a false output. The true output paths yield the SOP solution consisting of minterms 1, 2, 4, and 7, viz.,

$$F = \bar{A}B\bar{C} + \bar{A}\bar{B}C + A\bar{B}\bar{C} + ABC = \sum m(1, 2, 4, 7)$$

while the four paths to a false output give the POS solution, consisting of maxterms 0, 3, 5, and 6.

$$F = (A + B + C)(A + \bar{B} + \bar{C})(\bar{A} + B + \bar{C})(\bar{A} + \bar{B} + C) = \prod M(0, 3, 5, 6)$$

Consider next the function whose minterm expansion is 0, 2, 6, and 7. The binary tree representation of this function is shown in Fig. 11.23a. Examination of the tree shows that nodes 4 and 5 have the same outputs and can be merged. When this is done node B is seen to be redundant and it can be removed, as shown in Fig. 11.23b. Also, the output of gate 6 is zero and the output of gate 7 is one regardless of the value of C. In both cases C is superfluous and can be deleted from the diagram. When these three reductions are applied, one obtains the BDD shown in Fig. 11.23c. The function realized in the BDD is $F = \bar{A}\bar{C} + AB$, which is the result obtained by reducing the function to a minimum SOP form.

The implicants obtained by the BDD method are not necessarily prime implicants, but each different path must have at least one branch that is different from the branches used in any alternative solution. This guarantees that the implicants obtained are disjoint and they are essential in the sense that each minterm is covered by one and only one implicant.

Consider the function $Y = AB + D = \sum m(1, 3, 5, 6, 7)$. The binary tree is shown in Fig. 11.24a. The BDD is simplified by noting that nodes 4 and 5 have the same outputs and can be merged. This makes node 2 redundant. Node 7 is redundant also, since $Y = 1$ regardless of the value of D. Finally, since the outputs of nodes 5 and 6 are the same, they can be merged into one node, giving the BDD shown in Fig. 11.24b and c. From Fig. 11.24d it is seen that there are three paths to a true output and two paths to a false output.

The true output is seen to be

$$Y = AB + A\bar{B}D + \bar{A}D = A(B + \bar{B}D) + \bar{A}D = A(B + D) + \bar{A}D = AB + D$$

The false output is

$$\bar{Y} = A\bar{B}\bar{D} + \bar{A}\bar{D} = (\bar{A} + A\bar{B})\bar{D} = (\bar{A} + \bar{B})\bar{D} = \bar{A}\bar{D} + \bar{B}\bar{D}$$

Neither the true nor the false output is given in terms of prime implicants, although the implicants obtained from the graph can be seen to be disjoint.

The ordering of the input variables can sometimes make a difference in the size of the BDD. The function $AB + D$ is symmetric in inputs A and B, and reordering these inputs gives the same diagram. Expand the function letting D be

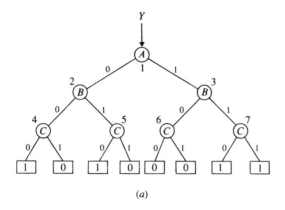

(a)

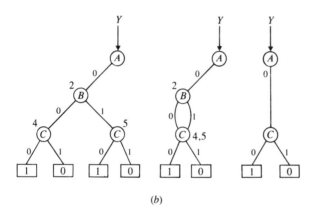

(b)

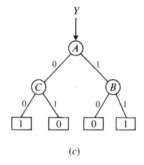

(c)

FIGURE 11.23
Realization of the function, $Y(A, B, C) = \sum m(0, 2, 6, 7)$. (a) The binary tree; (b) reducing the tree; (c) the BDD.

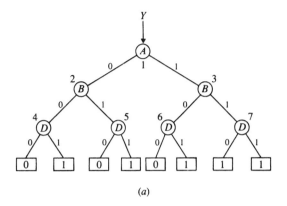

(a)

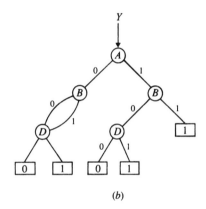

(b)

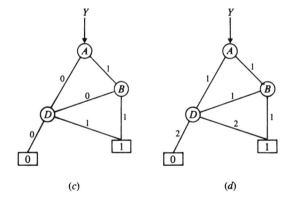

(c)   (d)

FIGURE 11.24
Realization of the function $Y = AB + D$. (a) The binary tree; (b) reducing the tree; (c) the BDD; (d) counting the paths to an output.

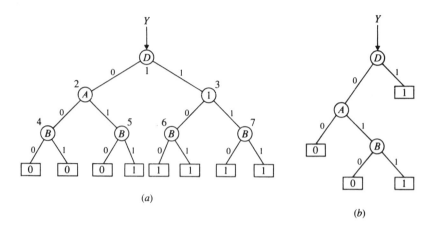

FIGURE 11.25
The BDD for the function $Y = AB + D$, with D the most significant bit. (a) The binary tree; (b) BDD.

the most significant bit, and one obtains $Y = AB + D = \sum m(3, 4, 5, 6, 7)$. The BDD for this representation is shown in Fig. 11.25. There are now two paths to a true output and two paths to a false output, yielding the functions

$$Y = AB + D \qquad \text{and} \qquad \bar{Y} = \bar{D}\bar{A} + \bar{D}A\bar{B} = \bar{D}(\bar{A} + \bar{B})$$

Y is seen to consist of two prime implicants while $\bar{Y}$ is seen to consist of one prime implicant and a second term, $A\bar{B}\bar{D}$ which can be reduced to a prime implicant. There isn't much difference in the function represented by the BDD in Fig. 11.24 and the BDD in Fig. 11.25.

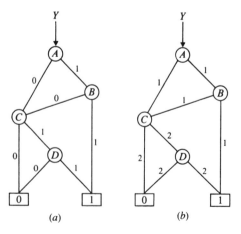

FIGURE 11.26
Realization of the function $Y = AB + CD$. (a) The BDD; (b) the number of paths to an output.

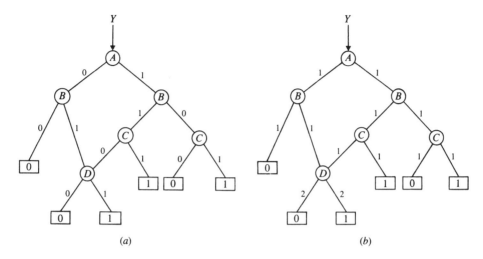

FIGURE 11.27
Realization of the function $Y = AC + BD$. (a) The BDD; (b) the number of paths to an output.

The function $Y = AB + CD$, with the literals taken in alphabetical order, is implemented in a BDD in Fig. 11.26, with the function realized in the form

$$Y = AB + \bar{A}CD + A\bar{B}CD \quad \text{and} \quad \bar{Y} = \bar{A}\bar{C} + A\bar{B}\bar{C} + \bar{A}C\bar{D} + A\bar{B}C\bar{D}$$

The function $Y = AC + BD$, with its literals taken in alphabetical order, is implemented in a BDD in Fig. 11.27, and realized in the form

$$Y = \bar{A}BD + A\bar{B}C + ABC + AB\bar{C}D \quad \text{and} \quad \bar{Y} = A\bar{B}\bar{C} + AB\bar{C}\bar{D} + \bar{A}B\bar{D} + \bar{A}\bar{B}$$

(It is left as an assignment to show that Fig. 11.27 is the correctly reduced binary tree for the function $AC + BD$.) Had the ordering of literals in Fig. 11.27 been taken as A, C, B, D, the outcome would have been a diagram equivalent to that in Fig. 11.26. In the order taken Fig. 11.27 yields a much more complicated BDD.

As a final example of binary decision diagrams, consider the three functions represented by the boolean equations

$$Z_1 = AC + AD + BC + BD = (A + B)Y$$

$$Z_2 = CE\bar{F} + DE\bar{F} = YE\bar{F}$$

$$Z_3 = BC + BD + \bar{G} = BY + \bar{G}$$

where $Y = C + D$.

The network is shown in Fig. 11.28a. From examination of the network one can obtain the BDDs for Z_1, Z_2, Z_3, and Y, as shown in Fig. 11.28b, c, d, and e. Upon combining these diagrams one obtains the multioutput solution graph shown in Fig. 11.29.

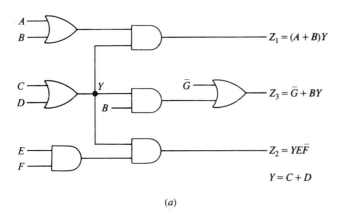

$$Z_1 = (A + B)Y$$

$$Z_3 = \bar{G} + BY$$

$$Z_2 = YE\bar{F}$$

$$Y = C + D$$

(a)

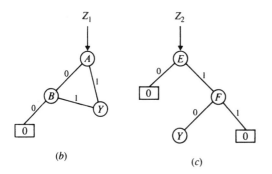

(b)   (c)

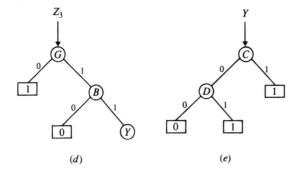

(d)   (e)

FIGURE 11.28
Realization of a multioutput network with BDDs. (a) The network; (b) the BDD for Z_1; (c) the BDD for Z_2; (d) the BDD for Z_3; (e) the BDD for Y.

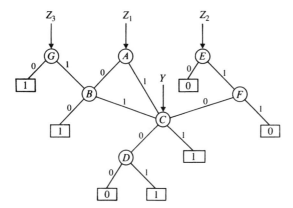

FIGURE 11.29
The BDD for the multioutput network of Fig. 11.28.

11.13 IF-THEN-ELSE OPERATORS

The *if-then-else* (ITE) operator is a universal operator which directly represents arbitrary networks of 2-input gates (13,14). In a BDD the if-part is always a single variable. In a DAG the if-part may consist of arbitrary expressions.

The if-then-else operator can replace the standard boolean operations of ANDing, ORing, and INVERTing. The ITE operators corresponding to several simple boolean functions are shown in Table 11.1.

If-then-else diagrams of AB, $A + B$, and $A \oplus B$ are shown in Fig. 11.30; diagrams of $AB + \bar{A}C$ and ABD are shown in Fig. 11.31; and diagrams of $C(D + E)$ and $AB(D + E)$ are shown in Fig. 11.32.

TABLE 11.1

AB	if A then B else FALSE
$A + B$	if A then TRUE else B
$A \oplus B$	if A then $\bar{B}$ else B
ABD	if (if A then B else FALSE) then D else FALSE
$AB + \bar{A}C$	if A then B else C
$C(D + E)$	if C then (if D then TRUE else E) else FALSE
$AB(D + E)$	if (if A then B else FALSE) then (if D then TRUE else E) else FALSE

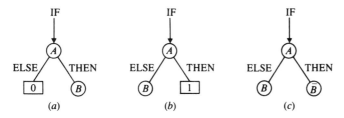

FIGURE 11.30
If-then-else diagrams of (a) AB, (b) $A + B$, and (c) $A \oplus B$.

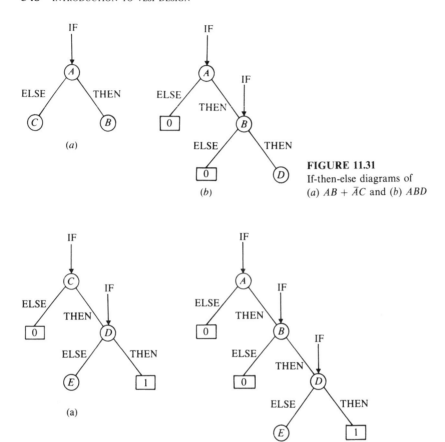

FIGURE 11.31
If-then-else diagrams of
(a) $AB + \bar{A}C$ and (b) ABD

FIGURE 11.32
If-then-else diagrams of (a) $C(D + E)$ and (b) $AB(D + E)$

11.14 SUMMARY

Weinberger arrays and gate matrices lead to multilevel logic implementations, and analytical tools to synthesize multilevel logic are necessary.

A large effort is currently being expended in the construction of software algorithms which will synthesize multilevel circuits with one or more outputs; a special case of two-level multioutput circuits being the PLA. This chapter is devoted to multilevel and multioutput optimization, and offers an introduction to the techniques being investigated for implementation with computer-aided design of VLSI.

The basic technique discussed is called algebraic decomposition, and begins with the determination of the kernels and cokernels of a multilevel boolean function, or the kernels and cokernels common to two or more boolean functions.

In multioutput synthesis, the kernel intersections determine which factors are common to two or more output functions. A common factor of two or more functions can be implemented with one gate feeding two or more outputs.

Binary decision diagrams, directed acyclic graphs, and if-then-else graphs are also very useful in the synthesis of multilevel logic.

The goal of this chapter is to acquaint the reader with the basics of modern boolean logic and switching theory research and applications.

REFERENCES

1. A. Weinberger, "Large Scale Integration of MOS Complex Logic: A Layout Method," *IEEE J. Solid-State Circuits*, vol. SC-2, February 1967, pp. 182-190.
2. A. D. Lopez and H. F. S. Law, "A Dense Gate Matrix Layout Method for MOS VLSI," *IEEE J. Solid-State Circuits*, vol. SC-15, August 1980, pp. 736-740.
3. S. Devadas and A. R. Newton, "Topological Optimization of Multi-Level Array Logic," *IEEE Transactions on Computer Aided Design*, vol. CAD-6, November 1987, pp. 915-941.
4. F. J. Hill and G. R. Peterson, *Introduction to Switching Theory and Analog Design*, 2d ed., John Wiley & Sons, New York, N.Y., 1974, chap. 7.
5. M. Karnaugh, "The Map Method for Synthesis of Combinational Logic Circuits," *Transactions of the AIEE*, vol. 72, pt. 1, 1953, pp. 593-598.
6. W. V. Quine, "The Problem of Simplifying Truth Functions," *American Mathematics Monthly*, vol. 59, no. 8, 1952, pp. 521-531.
7. E. McCluskey, "Minimization of Boolean Functions," *Bell System Technical Journal*, vol. 35, no. 5, 1956, pp. 1417-1444.
8. R. K. Brayton, R. Rudell, A. Sangiovanni-Vincentelli, and A. R. Wang, "MIS: A Multiple-Level Logic Optimization System," *IEEE Transactions on Computer-Aided Design*, CAD-6, November 1987, pp. 1062-1081.
9. G. D. Hatchtel and M. R. Lightner, "A Tutorial on Logic Synthesis: Algebraic Decomposition," *IEEE Conference on CAD*, ICCAD-88, Santa Clara, Calif., Nov. 7, 1988.
10. M. C. Lega, "Mapping Properties of Multi-Level Logic Synthesis Operations," *Proceedings of the IEEE Conference on Computer Design*, ICCD 88, Rye Brook, New York, Oct. 3-5, 1988, pp. 257-261.
11. C. E. Shannon, "The Synthesis of Two-Terminal Switching Circuits," *Bell System Technical Journal*, vol. 28, no. 1, 1949.
12. S. B. Akers, "Binary Decision Diagrams," *IEEE Transactions on Computers*, vol. C-27, no. 6, June 1978, pp. 509-516.
13. R. E. Bryant, "Graph-Based Algorithms for Boolean Function Manipulation," *IEEE Transactions on Computers*, vol. C-35, no. 8, August 1986, pp. 677-691.
14. K. Karplus, "Using If-Then-Else DAGs for Multi-Level Logic Minimization," *Proceedings of the 1989 Decennial Caltech Conference*, March 20-22, 1989, pp. 101-117.

PROBLEMS

11.1. A CMOS NAND-NAND circuit, clocked by CMOS transmission gates, is shown in Fig. P11.1 Do a stick layout of the NAND-NAND circuit with the metal running vertically as shown in Fig. 11.1a. Figure 11.1a is on page 319.

11.2. Repeat Prob. 11.1 with the metal running horizontally as shown in Fig. 11.1b.

11.3. Do a Weinberger stick drawing of the function $Y = \overline{A + \overline{B} + C}$.

11.4. Do a gate-matrix stick drawing of the function $Y = AB + C\overline{D}$.

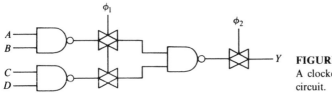

FIGURE P11.1
A clocked CMOS NAND-NAND circuit.

11.5. Do a Weinberger stick drawing of the function Y, where $Y = \overline{\overline{A} + X}$, $X = \overline{B + W}$, and $W = \overline{C} + D$.

11.6. Do a gate-matrix stick drawing of the function $Y = ABC + AD$.

11.7. Do a Weinberger stick drawing of the function Y, where $Y = \overline{\overline{A} + B + X}$ and $X = \overline{C + \overline{D} + \overline{E}}$.

11.8. Do a gate-matrix stick drawing of the function $Y = AB + BC + AC$.

11.9. Which of the following products are cubes? (a) $ABC\overline{D}$, (b) $AB\overline{C}C$, (c) $A\overline{B}BD$, and (d) ABD.

11.10. Group the products of F by phase. $F = ABC + ABD + \overline{A}\overline{B} + A\overline{B}CD + \overline{A}D + CD + \overline{A}\overline{C}$.

11.11. Find the ON-set, OFF-set, and DC-set of cubes of H, if $H(A, B, C, D)$ is the set of minterms 0, 1, 5, 6, 8, 9, and 14 plus don't care minterms 4 and 12.

11.12. Find the terms of Y that are 0 cubes, 1 cubes, and 2 cubes, if $Y(A, B, C, D) = \overline{A}\overline{B}\overline{C}D + A\overline{B}C + BD$.

11.13. Find the prime cubes of the function $Z(A, B, C, D) = AD + \overline{A}BD + A\overline{C}\overline{D} + ABD + A\overline{B}\overline{C}\overline{D}$.

11.14. Find the support of the functions. $X = ABC + \overline{A}BD + \overline{B}D$, $Y = BC + FG + HJ + K$, and $Z = EF + G$.

11.15. Find the support of XY, XZ, and YZ of Prob. 11.14.

11.16. $U = AB + CD$, $V = EF + GH$, and $W = EF + JK$. Examine UV, UW, and VW and determine which are algebraic expressions and which are not.

11.17. Which of the expressions of Prob. 11.15 are algebraic?

11.18. Find the kernels and cokernels of $Y = DEX + DE\overline{W} + GZ + \overline{H}Z + \overline{F}Z$.

11.19. Find the kernels and cokernels of the function X, where $X = ADF + AEF + BDF + BEF + CDF + CEF + G$.

11.20. (a) Find all the kernels of X, where $X = (A(B + C) + D)(E\overline{G} + G(\overline{E} + F) + (B + C)(H + I))$.
(b) Repeat for $Y = AE + AF + BCE + BDE + BCF + BDF + G$.

11.21. (a) Use decomposition and algebraic resubstitution to reduce the total literal count of the two functions $F_1 = AC + AD + AE$ and $F_2 = BC + BD + BE$. By how much is the literal count reduced?
(b) Repeat for $X_1 = AE + AF + BE + BF$, $X_2 = AE + AF + CE + CF$, and $X_3 = BE + BF + DE + DF$.

11.22. (a) Use decomposition and algebraic resubstitution to reduce the total literal count of $Z_1 = BE + \overline{A}E + \overline{A}CD + BCD$ and $Z_2 = \overline{A}B + A\overline{B}$
(b) Repeat for $X = AC + AD + BC + BD + E$ and $Y = A + B$.

11.23. Realize as much as possible of the function $Y = ABC + DEF + GHK + L\bar{M}\bar{N} + PQR + \bar{S}\bar{T}U + \bar{V}\bar{W}\bar{X}$ with AND-OR-INVERT gates, if the AND gates and OR gates are restricted to three inputs each, and all the input literals are to have positive phase. The function can be realized by two AOI gates, three NOR gates, and one NAND gate, for a total gate count of 6. (*Hint:* Group cubes by unateness, and use DeMorgan's law to change literals of negative phase to positive phase.)

11.24. Find the intersections of kernels $K_1 = ABC + CDE + FG$, $K_2 = ABC + CDE + FH$, and $K_3 = CDE + FG + FH$.

11.25. Find the kernel intersection of the functions $Y_1 = AB(C(D + E) + F + G) + H$ and $Y_2 = AK(C(D + E) + F + J) + L$.

11.26. (*a*) Find the kernels and cokernels of the majority function $F = ABC + ABD + BCD + ACD$.

(*b*) Sketch a realization of F.

CHAPTER
12

TESTABILITY
OF VLSI

12.1 INTRODUCTION

The time required to perform fault simulation and test-vector generation continues to increase as VLSI dimensions shrink, and better testing techniques are
required. This leads to a philosophy of design, operation, and verification in
which system reliability and testability must be considered at an early stage of the
design process. Computer-aided testing is essential to VLSI design in order to
increase the effectiveness of existing models and algorithms, and produce a chip
that is capable of being tested thoroughly and easily in a reasonable time period.

Surface-state density, gate-oxide thickness, channel length, channel width,
and channel doping all strongly influence device parameters and require constant
monitoring. Testability is required for evaluating both functionality and reliability, and some very successful techniques aimed at enhancing the testability of a
circuit have been devised in recent years.

Pattern generation and fault simulation are often based on simple fault
models of "stuck-at" nodes or gate inputs, short-circuits between nodes, or the
critical-path algorithm. A node is said to be stuck at zero (one) if it remains in a
low (high) state regardless of the logic value asserted.

Testing involves measurement or comparison, done to determine performance characteristics. A node is said to be controllable if the tester is able to set the value of the node to either logic 0, 1, or high-impedance. A node is observable if the tester is able to observe the value of the node level. Some of the key control points in a circuit are: clock, set, and clear inputs to storage latches; data select inputs to multiplexers and demultiplexers; and enable and read/write inputs to memory devices.

A defect is any source of circuit failure which is not system-related, but is caused by the physical structure of the materials used in the IC fabrication and the geometric relationships among these materials. Basic circuit defects include junction leakage, high contact resistance, metal voids that cause open circuits, unwanted short circuits between conductors, and leakage through dielectric layers.

Some of the sources of defects are starting material defects, ambient particulates, processing gases, water and processing chemicals, handling mistakes and incorrect procedures, thermal and mechanical stress, and layer-to-layer misalignment. Defect test structures allow the characterization of those defects which cause circuit failures.

Combinational logic is relatively easy to test by applying sets of input signals to the circuit and comparing the outputs with calculated outputs, and the problem of testing combinational logic is well understood.

Sequential networks are more difficult to test because the outputs depend on both the present inputs and the internal state of the network. To test sequential networks they must be converted into combinational networks. It is necessary to ensure that all registers are clocked and checked, and modifications required for testability must not interfere with the normal operation of the circuit. This might require inserting multiplexers in the circuit in order to electrically isolate parts of the circuit for testing purposes.

Breaking the normal feedback path of a sequential network establishes a logical path for which inputs can be defined and outputs observed. Internal state information can then be sampled by loading a serial register from the state register and shifting the information out via the serial data output, so that it may be observed. The serial data inputs and outputs can be cascaded to make long chains of state information available with a minimum number of connections.

Device specifications establish critical timing parameters such as setup times, hold times, and minimum pulsewidths, as well as the high and low temperature limits. The generation of a set of test vectors that exercise the chip as completely as possible in a reasonable amount of time, can be speeded up if the vectors can be expressed in an algorithmic form instead of being hand-entered.

12.2 SHADOW REGISTER AND SCAN DESIGN

A technique called *serial-shadow register diagnostics* converts a sequential network into a combinational network, by adding a duplicate or shadow of the state register and a multiplexer which can break the feedback path by selecting the shadow register. The shadow shift register is tested by shifting data through its serial ports, after which it can be used to test other parts of the circuitry. State information is loaded into the serial register, and it can be transferred into the internal state register by selecting the multiplexer and clocking the state register. This technique allows any internal state to be set to a desired value in a simple, quick, and systematic manner, by establishing a logical path for which inputs can be controlled and outputs observed. This reduces the serial network to a combinational network. The circuit is shown in Fig. 12.1.

In the *scan-path approach*, the logic network is transformed into a shift register and tested. If all the flip-flops can be controlled and observed, then the test generation process reduces to the testing of a combinational logic network, as in the serial shadow technique. A modified D-type master-slave flip-flop with two-phase nonoverlapping clocking is taken as the basic memory element. It is augmented by a multiplexer consisting of two 2-input AND gates (3 transistors each), one 2-input OR gate (3 transistors), and one inverter (2 transistors) for a total of 11 additional transistors inserted in the data path.

The mode-select input chooses either the normal or scan mode as shown in Fig. 12.2. The same master and slave clocks are used in scan and normal modes and the slave clock can be generated locally from the master clock, so that only one clock signal need be routed over the whole chip. This can eliminate many timing problems.

Implementing testability by either serial scan, random scan, or built-in test all require extra hardware that introduces additional delay. In Fig. 12.1, the multiplexer introduces at least one propagation delay (designed as an AOI structure), and the output of each flip-flop is connected to the scan input of the

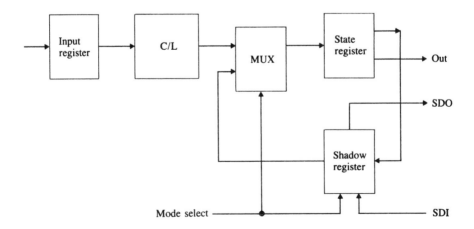

FIGURE 12.1
The serial shadow register circuit.

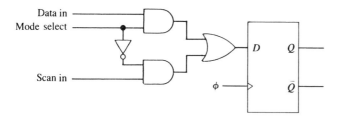

FIGURE 12.2
A scan register flip-flop.

next flip-flop in the scan-register chain, resulting in extra capacitive loading due to scan wiring at the flip-flop outputs. These additional delays can be minimized by proper design.

To provide a hazard-free and race-free sequential design while maintaining reasonable design flexibility, construct all memory elements in D-type master-slave flip-flops, and allocate one input pin for implementing either the scan or normal mode of operation. Normal input and output pins can be used for scan-in and scan-out signals of the shift register.

To assure the scan-testability of a sequential circuit, all flip-flops should be connected in a shift register, and each shift register should have a primary input and a primary output in the scan mode. Normal primary inputs and outputs may be used or shared for this purpose. When in the scan mode, the output of a flip-flop or scan-out primary output should be a function of only the preceding flip-flop output or scan-in primary input of the shift register.

A test pattern for a fault may contain don't care states, and two patterns can be merged into one as long as the corresponding bits are identical or align with a don't care. The test patterns obtained are compacted to give a smaller set of patterns. A test pattern of alternating ones and zeros, shifted through every flip-flop of the scan register, is sufficient to detect faults in the shift path and in the master-slave flip-flops.

12.3 COUNTER TESTABILITY

A 16-stage ripple counter requires $2 \times 2^{16} = 131{,}072$ vectors to toggle every node in the counter by assigning one vector per clock transition. If the package has excess pins, use them to access internal nodes for testing purposes. Breaking a 16-bit counter into two 8-bit sections allows the insertion of a multiplexer controlled by a test signal, TEST, that can feed the clock input directly to the second 8-bit section, reducing the number of counter-testing clock cycles by a factor of 2^8. (From 2×2^{16} to 2×2^8 clock pulses needed.)

Break the circuit into four parts and only $2 \times 2^4 = 32$ vectors are required to count from 0000 to 1111, and back to 0000. A circuit for doing this is shown in Fig. 12.3. Mode select connects the clock to each section in parallel. Mode select

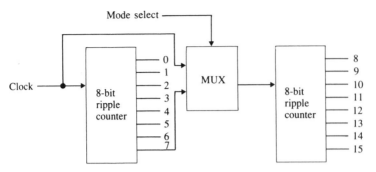

FIGURE 12.3
Circuitry to reconfigure a ripple counter and facilitate testing.

must remain low when the counter goes from 1111 to 0000, in order to verify the carry from bit 4 to bit 5.

To check a clear line requires counting from 0000 to 1111 twice, therefore doubling the number of vectors to 64. If there is a set line in the counter, the counter can be set and then cleared, thus reducing the number of needed test vectors to 32 plus 2, or 34.

12.4 TESTING STUCK-AT FAULTS

As both devices and separations between signal lines continue to shrink, new types of failure modes are introduced such as data-dependent or neighboring-interaction faults. Electrical failures caused by physical failure mechanisms can be grouped into three categories: open circuits, short circuits, and stuck-at faults. *Stuck-at faults* can be stuck-on faults or stuck-open faults, and are caused by overstress breakdown and ionic contamination.

Stuck-on faults cause the FET to remain conducting regardless of the gate input voltage, and are often undetectable. The test pattern for a stuck-on fault creates a path between VDD and GND within the faulty logic gate, and the output takes on a votage level between GND and VDD.

Many interconnect failures are due to short circuits between metal and diffusion lines or breaks in metal/polysilicon crossovers. FET failures are often due to gate-to-drain or gate-to-source short circuits, open drain or source contacts, or gate-to-substrate short circuits. Some of these faults are very difficult to detect, whereas some can be modeled as stuck-at faults. The testing of stuck-at faults is important and can be accomplished by the application of appropriate input test vectors. A system's sensitivity to stuck-at faults is close to 100 percent provided logical redundancy has not been designed into the system. Physical design for testability is just as important as logical design for testability in order to detect all failures.

A CMOS NAND gate with a stuck-open fault is shown in Fig. 12.4. If a test vector, TV_1, of 00 is input to the NAND gate, the output will go high because the

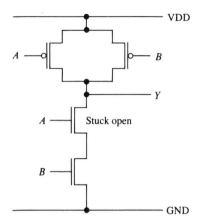

FIGURE 12.4
A CMOS NAND gate with a stuck-open fault in the NMOS pull-down network.

pull-ups connect the output to VDD. If this is followed by a second test vector, TV_2, of 11, the output is in a high-impedance state because both pull-ups and the stuck-open device are off. The test-vector sequence $TV_1 = 00$, $TV_2 = 11$ will detect the stuck-open fault in this network.

The test vectors for *stuck-open faults* and *stuck-on faults* are derived as follows:

1. Provoke the fault by applying an input 0 to the NPN transistor (1 to the PNP transistor) that is stuck on, or an input 1 to the NPN transistor (O to the PNP transistor) that is stuck off.

2. Sensitize a path to which the transistor under test belongs, allowing the signal to propagate from the fault to the output.

3. Ensure that the output changes only as a function of the given signal change, by allowing no other paths between the appropriate supply rail and the output.

A CMOS gate with a stuck-on fault is shown in Fig. 12.5. The four test vectors shown in Table 12.1 will potentially test for a stuck-on fault at the indicated device in Fig. 12.5.

Not all test vectors will work properly, however. Due to the stuck-on fault shown in Fig. 12.5, both the n network and the p network may conduct. The output voltage then depends on the resistances involved. For the resistances

TABLE 12.1

Test vector	Inputs				Faulty output	Correct output
	A	B	C	D		
TV_1	0	1	0	0	0	1
TV_2	0	1	0	1	0	1
TV_3	0	1	1	0	‘0	1
TV_4	0	0	1	1	1	1

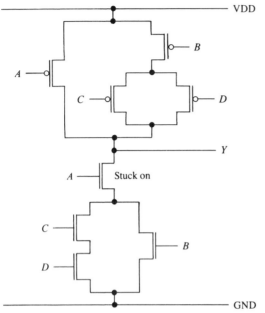

FIGURE 12.5
A CMOS gate with a stuck-on fault.

shown in Fig. 12.6, the output due to TV_1, TV_2, or TV_3 is 2.22 V, while the output due to TV_4 is 2.73 V. If the inverter recognizes 2.73 V as a logic 1, and 2.22 V as a logic 0, then TV_4 fails to detect the fault while the other three test vectors detect the fault.

A faulty CMOS circuit becomes equivalent to an NMOS network in the presence of a stuck-on PMOS device between the positive rail and the output. Only the current consumption differs from the normal amount and only methods based on measuring current can detect such a fault. A built-in current (BIC) tester, implemented in standard CMOS, has been reported in the literature (1). The circuit consists of a differential amplifier and a circuit breaker.

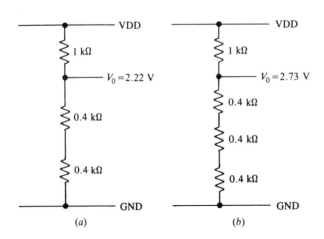

FIGURE 12.6
Equivalent resistive network (a) for test vectors TV_1, TV_2, TV_3, and (b) for test vector TV_4.

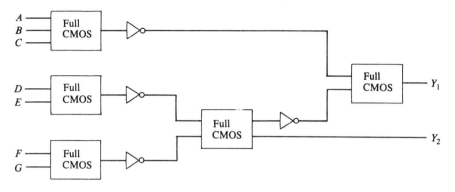

FIGURE 12.7
Full complementary MOS designed with inverters at the outputs of each level of logic.

If test vectors are derived carefully they may test simultaneously for stuck-open and stuck-on faults in fully complementary networks (2). One method of fault-testing requires the design of an inverting buffer after every nonprimary output logic gate as shown in Fig. 12.7, and the addition of blocking pull-up and pull-down FETs to each logic gate as shown in Fig. 12.8. C_1 and C_2 are called control inputs. Other inputs are functional or data inputs. For normal operation, $C_1 = 0$, $C_2 = 1$, and the control inputs are both closed switches. The resulting circuit has no undetectable stuck-on faults, and easily detectable stuck-open faults (3).

Detecting a stuck-open fault in a conventional or fully complementary CMOS gate requires two patterns. The first, or initializing, input is applied to charge or discharge the gate output. The second, or testing, input is applied to change the value of the output node through the faulty FET. This two-vector test must be robust in the sense that stray circuit delays must not affect the validity of the test.

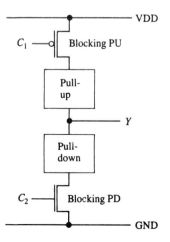

FIGURE 12.8
Pull-up and pull-down circuitry with two control inputs.

The output of a fully complementary CMOS gate can be initialized to 0 if all its inputs are set to 1; the output node can be initialized to 1 if all the inputs are set to 0. Thus, an all-1 or an all-0 pattern will initialize the gate for the detection of stuck-open faults. In Fig. 12.7, if all primary inputs are set to 0 (1), then each gate outputs a 1 (0). The inverters connected between the outputs of each gate of level i and the inputs of gates of level $i + 1$ force all the secondary gate inputs to be 0 (1) also. Hence, the inputs to every gate other than the inverters are initialized to 0 (1), and the outputs of every gate other than the inverters are forced to 1 (0). This method will automatically test domino logic because the inverters are already present at the output of each domino gate.

The fundamental meta-rule for testing is that a test exists if, and only if, the correct and faulty circuits are not equivalent. Logical redundancy must be avoided. A node is logically redundant if all the output values of the circuit are independent of the binary value of the node for all input combinations or state sequences. Logical redundancy is used to mask static hazard conditions. It is not possible to make a primary output value-dependent on the value of the redundant node, and certain fault conditions at the node cannot be detected. Thus, the fault condition may either reintroduce the hazard condition it was meant to eliminate, or it may mask the subsequent detection of a second fault at a nonredundant node.

Partitioning a circuit into several segments for testing purposes can reduce the amount of effort considerably. If a circuit consisting of 100 devices is partitioned into four subcircuits of 25 devices each, testing can be done approximately $4^2 = 16$ times faster. If one partitioned segment is revised after original testing, only this part need be retested. This saves still more time.

Asynchronous logic uses stored-state latches and global feedback but the state-transitions are governed by the sequence of changes of the primary inputs. There is no system clock to determine the next state of the system. Asynchronous circuits are fast since they are governed only by the propagation delays of the gates and interconnects. Race conditions can be designed out of asynchronous circuits, but faults can reintroduce races, and critical races with the outcome unknown can cause serious problems during fault simulation. For these reasons synchronous logic is preferred.

Global feedback paths complicate both test generation and fault diagnosis, and the feedback loops must be broken and controlled. It is also desirable to be able to initialize all storage registers in order to know their starting states.

If a test vector tests for a stuck-on fault of the n network (p network), it also tests for the corresponding stuck-open fault of the p network (n network). The converse is not true: vectors that test for stuck-open faults do not necessarily test for the complementary stuck-on faults.

Full CMOS realizations have complementary n and p networks. If the pull-up is realized in a sum-of-products (SOP) form, then the pull-down is in the form of an SOP-BAR form; while if the pull-up is realized in a product-of-sums (POS) form, then the pull-down is in the form of a POS-BAR form.

The same function can be represented by either pull-up in conjunction with

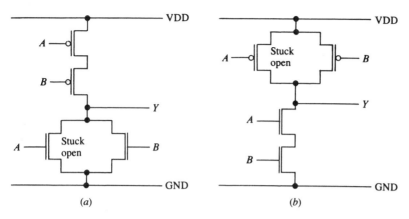

FIGURE 12.9
Faulty CMOS circuits that become sequential circuits. (*a*) NOR; (*b*) NAND.

either pull-down as was discussed in Chap. 7. If a simple, valid test set does not exist for determining the presence of a stuck-open fault for either AND-OR or OR-AND CMOS realizations, one should investigate the hybrid CMOS realization consisting of a POS or OR-AND pull-up and an SOP-BAR or AND-OR pull-down, and vice versa.

Classical algorithms for test-pattern generation are based on the assumption that a faulty combinational circuit remains both combinational and digital. However, in static NMOS and CMOS, stuck-open faults may transform a combinational circuit into a sequential one as shown in Fig. 12.9. Table 12.2 shows that the faulty circuit becomes dependent upon the past value of the output when the input is $AB = 10$ for the mostly NMOS NOR case or 01 for the mostly PMOS NAND case.

CMOS faults may result in a correct logical behavior with wrong timing. If the resistance of the PMOS pull-up is larger than the resistance of the NMOS pull-down, then a permanently conducting pull-up changes a CMOS inverter into an NMOS inverter.

Domino CMOS is easier to test than conventional CMOS because most stuck-open faults are tested during the precharge and evaluation phases of

TABLE 12.2

Inputs		NOR output		NAND output	
A	B	Y (true)	Y (faulty)	Y (true)	Y (faulty)
0	0	1	1	1	1
0	1	0	0	1	Y
1	0	0	Y	1	1
1	1	0	0	0	0

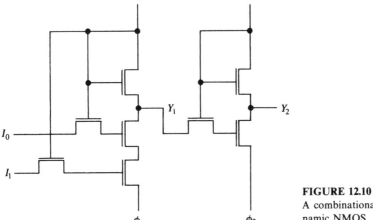

FIGURE 12.10
A combinational network in dynamic NMOS.

operation. Stuck-on faults are harder to detect, since both the NMOS and the PMOS networks may conduct. The resistance of a MOSFET varies with its operating point, but for simplicity one can assume it to be the normal on-resistance of the device when it is stuck on.

The next higher level of sophistication is the dynamic NMOS gate, which uses an n-channel device for the pull-up, as shown in Fig. 12.10. The dynamic NMOS gate can be regarded as a conventional pull-down network with the terminals connected to the same clock, phase 1. The output Y_1 is precharged on phase 1, while the input nodes are conditionally charged by the pass-transistor network. When the clock transitions to phase 2, the precharge transistor and all the pass transistors are turned off, holding the node values on the pass-transistor network, which are the inputs to the combinational-logic network.

The combinational logic conditionally discharges the output, which is the complement of the transmission function, as it was for the domino gate. The inputs to the gate are blocked during phase 2 when the output of the gate is valid. It requires at least two nonoverlapping clocks to build a combinational network of dynamic NMOS gates.

There is no fault that changes a combinational dynamic MOS circuit into a sequential one, although there are some faults within domino circuits which will result in a decrease in circuit speed.

12.5 BOOLEAN DIFFERENCES

The *boolean difference* is an algebraic technique for developing test patterns for combinational circuits. It is a method of determining the primary inputs required to force a function to be sensitive to a particular input variable. The boolean difference is an exact method of generating test vectors, as opposed to some techniques of path sensitization by trial and error (4).

The boolean difference of a function Y with respect to variable X is defined as

$$\frac{dY}{dX} = Y_x(0) \oplus Y_x(1) \qquad (12.1)$$

where $Y_x(0)$ is the value of Y when $X = 0$, and $Y_x(1)$ is the value of Y when $X = 1$. If an output Y is sensitized to a variable X and if variable X is toggled then output Y should toggle. If the output does toggle $Y_x(0)$ and $Y_x(1)$ will differ and $dY/dX = 1$.

Example 12.1. Given the function $Y(A, B, C) = \bar{A}\bar{B}C + A\bar{B}\bar{C} + ABC$, find dY/dC, and show that the value of the function Y depends upon the value of variable C when $A = 1$ or when $B = 0$. Evaluate Y when $A = 1$ and when $B = 0$.

Solution. $Y_C(0) = Y(A, B, 0) = A\bar{B}$ and $Y_C(1) = Y(A, B, 1) = \bar{A}\bar{B} + AB$. The boolean difference is:

$$\frac{dY}{dC} = Y_C(0) \oplus Y_C(1) = A\bar{B} \oplus (\bar{A}\bar{B} + AB)$$

$$= A\bar{B}(A + B)(\bar{A} + \bar{B}) + (\bar{A} + B)(\bar{A}\bar{B} + AB)$$

$$= A\bar{B} + \bar{A}\bar{B} + AB$$

$$= A + \bar{B}$$

If $A = 1$ or if $B = 0$, then Y depends upon C. $Y(1, B, C) = \bar{B}\bar{C} + BC$, $Y(1, B, 1) = B$, and $Y(1, B, 0) = \bar{B}$. When $A = 1$, Y changes when C changes, regardless of the value of B.

$Y(A, 0, C) = \bar{A}C + A\bar{C}$, $Y(A, 0, 1) = \bar{A}$ and $Y(A, 0, 0) = A$. When $B = 0$, Y changes when C changes, regardless of the value of A.

To develop a set of test vectors for a function with a primary input stuck at 1 (stuck at 0), a path must be sensitized that will exercise the fault when that variable is set to 0 (1). Mathematically, $\bar{X} \, dY/dX = 1$ will test for an X stuck-at-1 fault, and $X \, dY/dX = 1$ will test for an X stuck-at-0 fault.

Example 12.2. Find the test vectors that will exercise a stuck-at-0 and a stuck-at-1 fault for input B in Fig. 12.11.

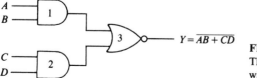

$Y = \overline{AB + CD}$

FIGURE 12.11
The AOI circuit of Example 12.2 with $Y = \overline{AB + CD}$.

Solution. $Y(A, B, C, D) = \overline{AB + CD}$, and

$$Y_B(0) = Y(A, 0, C, D) = \overline{CD} = \bar{C} + \bar{D}$$

$$Y_B(1) = Y(A, 1, C, D) = \overline{A + CD} = \bar{A}(\bar{C} + \bar{D})$$

The boolean difference is

$$\frac{dY}{dB} = Y_B(0) \oplus Y_B(1) = \overline{CD} \oplus (\overline{A + CD})$$

$$= CD(\overline{A + CD}) + \overline{CD}(A + CD)$$

$$= CD[\bar{A}(\bar{C} + \bar{D})] + (\bar{C} + \bar{D})(A + CD) = A\bar{C} + A\bar{D}$$

$$B\frac{dY}{dB} = AB\bar{C} + AB\bar{D} = 1$$

and the vectors that test for B stuck at 0 are $110\times$ and $11\times0 = 1100$, 1101, and 1110. These are the test vectors that sensitize a path from B to Y by forcing the output of gate 2 to 0. The correct response when $AB = 11$ is $Y = 0$, and the faulty response with B stuck at 0 is $Y = 1$.

$$\bar{B}\frac{dY}{dB} = A\bar{B}\bar{C} + A\bar{B}\bar{D} = 1$$

and the vectors that test for B stuck at 1 are $100\times$ and $10\times0 = 1000$, 1001, and 1010. These are the vectors that sensitize a path from B to Y by again forcing the output of gate 2 to 0. The correct response when $AB = 10$ is $Y = 1$, and the faulty response with B stuck at 1 is $Y = 0$. The only difference between the two sets of test vectors is that the value of B changes in going from the first set of vectors to the second set.

Example 12.3. Consider the majority function of three variables, $Y(A, B, C) = AB + AC + BC$, shown in Fig. 12.12. In this function each variable appears as an input to two distinct AND gates, and a test vector must be able to test each input separately. To test input C

$$Y_C(0) = Y(A, B, 0) = AB \quad \text{and} \quad Y_C(1) = Y(A, B, 1) = AB + A + B = A + B.$$

$$\frac{dY}{dC} = Y_C(0) \oplus Y_C(1) = AB \oplus (A + B)$$

$$= \overline{AB}(A + B) + AB(\overline{A + B})$$

$$= (\bar{A} + \bar{B})(A + B) + AB(\bar{A}\bar{B}) = \bar{A}B + A\bar{B}$$

For C stuck at 0

$$C\frac{dY}{dC} = \bar{A}BC + A\bar{B}C = 1$$

$$TV_1 = 011 \quad \text{and} \quad TV_2 = 101$$

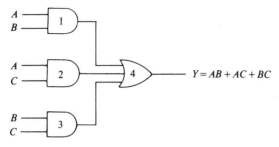

$$Y = AB + AC + BC$$

FIGURE 12.12
The 3-input majority function circuit of Example 12.3.

For C stuck at 1

$$\bar{C}\frac{dY}{dC} = \bar{A}B\bar{C} + A\bar{B}\bar{C} = 1$$

$$TV_3 = 010 \quad \text{and} \quad TV_4 = 100$$

For test vectors $TV_1 = 011$ and $TV_2 = 101$, the correct output is 1 and the erroneous output when C is stuck at 0 is 0. TV_1 tests input C at gate 3 for a stuck-at-0 fault, while TV_2 tests input C at gate 2 for a stuck-at-0 fault.

For test vectors $TV_3 = 010$ and $TV_4 = 100$, the correct output is 0 and the erroneous output is 1. TV_3 tests input C at gate 3 for a stuck-at-1 fault, and TV_4 tests input C at gate 2 for a stuck-at-1 fault.

The above technique can also be applied to nonprimary inputs of a circuit. The chain rule of differentiating can be applied to obtain test vectors for secondary inputs (5).

The chain rule states that if line Y depends upon line M, which in turn depends upon line N, then the boolean difference of Y with respect to N is

$$\frac{dY}{dN} = \frac{dY}{dM}\frac{dM}{dN}$$

This can be generalized to sensitize a path of arbitrary depth.

Example 12.4. Apply the chain rule to the circuit of Figure 12.13 to find test vectors for A stuck at 1 and A stuck at 0.

Solution. Using the chain rule

$$V = A + B \qquad \text{and} \qquad \frac{dV}{dA} = B \oplus 1 = \bar{B}$$

$$W = VC \qquad \text{and} \qquad \frac{dW}{dV} = 0 \oplus C = C$$

$$X = W + DE \qquad \text{and} \qquad \frac{dX}{dW} = DE \oplus 1 = \overline{DE} = \bar{D} + \bar{E}$$

$$Y = XF \qquad \text{and} \qquad \frac{dY}{dX} = 0 \oplus F = F$$

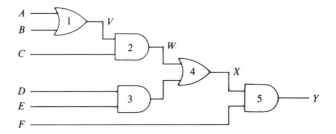

FIGURE 12.13
The circuit of Example 12.4, with $Y = [(A + B)C + DE]F$.

and the vectors that test A for a stuck-at-0 fault are 1010×1 and 101×01.

$$\frac{dY}{dA} = \frac{dY}{dX}\frac{dX}{dW}\frac{dW}{dV}\frac{dV}{dA} = \bar{B}C\bar{D}F + \bar{B}C\bar{E}F$$

$$A\frac{dY}{dA} = A\bar{B}C\bar{D}F + A\bar{B}C\bar{E}F$$

and the vectors that test A for a stuck-at-0 fault are 1010×1 and 101×01.

$$\bar{A}\frac{dY}{dA} = \bar{A}\bar{B}C\bar{D}F + \bar{A}\bar{B}C\bar{E}F$$

and the vectors that test A for a stuck-at-1 fault are 0010×1 and 001×01. As can be seen from Fig. 12.13, $F = 1$ enables gate 5, either $D = 0$ or $E = 0$ disables gate 3 and enables gate 4, $C = 1$ enables gate 2, and the path from A to V to W to X to Y is sensitized.

12.6 PLA TESTABILITY

PLAs are attractive building blocks for implementing VLSI logic because of their regular structure which allows automatic layout generation and minimization, and their ability to implement boolean functions in such a way that they can be easily changed without requiring major changes in the PLA layout.

The PLAs must be easily testable. Path-oriented test-pattern generation algorithms fail because, when a faulty signal has to be propagated through the AND plane, the probability of choosing the right path is quite low due to the high fan-out of the input lines. The same thing happens as a result of the high fan-in of the product terms when a logic-0 signal has to be backtracked from the OR plane through the AND plane.

Optimization of programmable logic devices is one of the most thoroughly studied areas in logic simplification, and testing of PLAs and related circuits is vital to VLSI design (6,7).

To facilitate the testing of PLAs, fault models more accurate than stuck-at models are required. PLAs can also be augmented to simplify testing. Activating only one product line at a time eliminates multiple fan-ins, and masking faults are eliminated by inverting each bit line independently of the other bit lines.

Bit lines are controlled by the inputs of the PLA, and control of product lines can be achieved through a shift register, each cell of which controls one product line. The pitch of a register cell is normally much greater than the pitch between two product lines, and it is difficult to incorporate these registers within the PLA. Shift registers also interfere with PLA folding, which leads to additional routing problems or additional hardware. Individual product lines can be activated by adding extra inputs to the AND array of the PLA (6).

In modeling PLAs, the *crosspoint defect* (also called a *contact-fault defect*) approach is superior to a stuck-at approach. A crosspoint is the site of a potential transistor when programming the PLA, and a crosspoint defect can be due to the absence of a desired FET or to the presence of an undesired FET.

One of the simplest and earliest schemes for testing PLA designs is shown in Fig. 12.14 (8). A product line, bold line P_p, is added to give odd parity to the number of AND devices on each input line (AND-plane column), and an output line, bold line Y_p, is added to give odd parity to the number of OR devices on each product line (row). The solid dots in Fig. 12.14a represent the PLA crosspoint interconnects and the hollow dots are the crosspoint interconnects added to achieve odd parity.

Control circuitry to activate one true or complemented input line at a time is shown in Fig. 12.14b. Parity checkers are needed to test product-line and output-line parity. A shift register is used to activate one product line at a time.

This augmented PLA can test all single stuck-at faults and single crosspoint faults by applying an independent input sequence and observing the outputs, PC_1 and PC_2, of the two parity checkers. By modifying the above PLA it can be converted to a PLA with built-in self-test capability (9).

A *built-in self test* (BIST) for large CMOS PLAs with folded product lines was reported in 1988 (10). Two input control circuits and two extra product lines are required if the AND plane is folded. One extra product line gives odd parity to columns whose inputs enter the PLA and whose outputs leave the PLA at the bottom of the PLA, while the other product line gives odd parity to columns folded on top of these, with inputs entering and outputs leaving from the top of the PLA. One extra output line is still necessary to establish the parity of the output columns. Product-line (row) folding is not allowed in this approach.

For a PLA implemented in a sum-of-products form, a stuck-at fault may cause the disappearance of a literal from an implicant, or an implicant from a function. It can also cause the function to be forced true or false, depending upon the location of the fault as shown in Fig. 12.15.

Crosspoint defects in a PLA can cause four different errors. A *growth error* is said to occur when a missing device in the AND plane causes a literal to

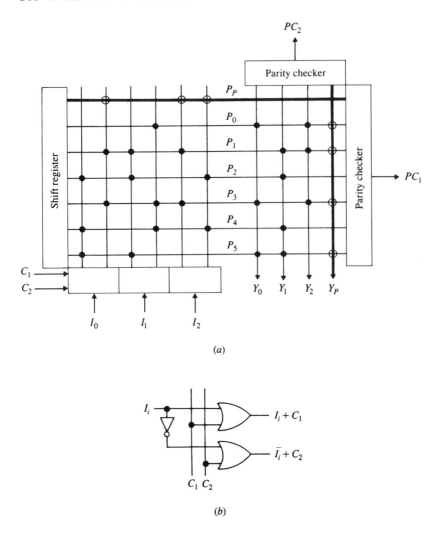

FIGURE 12.14
A PLA augmented for odd parity of the number of crosspoints in the AND and OR planes.

disappear from an implicant, and the implicant to grow. A *shrinkage error* occurs when an extra FET in the AND plane causes a literal to appear in an implicant, and shrink it. A *disappearance error* is due to a missing device in the OR plane, causing an implicant to vanish from a function, and an *appearance error* is due to an extra device in the OR plane, which causes an undesired implicant to appear in a function.

Redundancy can mask stuck-at faults, making them undetectable. The presence of undetectable crosspoint faults is due to the overlap of implicants such

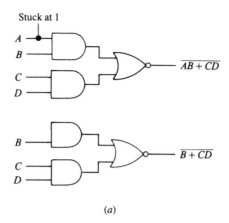

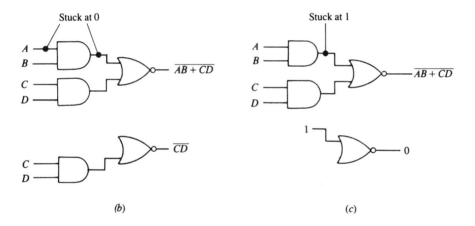

FIGURE 12.15
Examples of stuck-at faults causing the disappearance of (a) a literal or (b) an implicant, or (c) forcing the function to 0.

that two implicants cover the same minterm, making shrinkage of one minterm undetectable.

To design for testability, consider that the product line of a NOR-NOR PLA is high if, and only if, each pull-down is OFF; while the product line of a NAND-NAND PLA is low if, and only if, each pull-down is ON. For a PLA product line p_i, controlled by inputs A, B, and C to be high in a NOR-NOR realization $p_i = \bar{A}\bar{B}\bar{C}$, while in a NAND-NAND PLA $p_i = \bar{A} + \bar{B} + \bar{C}$ or $\bar{p}_i = ABC$.

Define the *main test vector* or *root test vector* to be that test vector which keeps p_i low for the NAND-NAND PLA, and keeps p_i high for the NOR-NOR PLA. This vector is 000 for the NOR-NOR PLA product line, and 111 for the NAND-NAND PLA. Define *auxiliary test vectors* as those that pull the NAND-NAND product line low, or the NOR-NOR product line high. There is one auxiliary vector for each input, and the *j*th auxiliary test pattern is obtained by complementing the *j*th bit of the main test vector.

Since NAND-NAND is the logical dual of NOR-NOR, only one case need be examined, the results applying to the other case by interchanging all 0's and 1's in the test pattern. The NOR-NOR PLA will be examined for testability in the following discussion.

To test the NOR-NOR PLA product line with inputs *A*, *B*, and *C*, the main or root test vector is 000, and the auxiliary test vectors are 001, 010, and 100. If one or more inputs are stuck at zero, it will fail to pull the product line low when it is exercised. A missing-crosspoint error acts as a stuck-at-0 fault, and will also be detected by these test vectors. A stuck-at-1 fault will keep the product line low when it should go high, and an extra-crosspoint fault acts as a stuck-at-1 fault.

Table 12.3 shows the correct and erroneous results for product line $p_1 = ABC$, when input *A* is stuck at 1 or stuck at 0. With input *A* stuck at 1, the product line remains low regardless of the value of *A*, while *A* stuck at 0 does not distinguish between test vectors 000 and 100.

To obtain a complete set of test vectors that will detect both stuck-at and crosspoint faults, one product line at a time must be isolated and tested. Two product lines that differ in only one bit are said to have a *Hamming distance* of 1, and if they differ in two bits they have a Hamming distance of 2. A single error on a product line changes one of its bits, which in turn changes its distance by 1.

If all other product lines are of Hamming distance 2 or more from the line under test, the above procedure of obtaining a root or main test vector, and complementing bits to obtain the remaining test vectors, will uniquely test every product line of the PLA for single faults. If this is not true of the PLA, extra inputs can be added to make each product line of distance 2 or more from every other product line.

Define the *characteristic matrix*, C, as that part of the personality matrix, Q, which corresponds to the AND plane only. Recall from the definition of a PLA

TABLE 12.3

Inputs			A stuck-at-one		A stuck-at-zero	
A	*B*	*C*	Y (true)	Y (faulty)	Y (true)	Y (faulty)
0	0	0	1	0	1	1
0	0	1	0	0	0	0
0	1	0	0	0	0	0
1	0	0	0	0	0	1

personality matrix in Chap. 9 that, in the AND plane: element $q_{ij} = 0$ if a FET connects product line p_i to input x_j, $q_{ij} = 1$ if a FET connects p_i to input $\bar{x}_j$, and q_{ij} is a don't care ($\times$) if neither input connects to p_i. In the OR plane: $q_{ij} = 1$ if p_i connects to output y_j, and zero otherwise.

For the PLA shown in Fig. 12.16, the personality matrix and characteristic matrix are

$$Q = \begin{bmatrix} 1 & 0 & \times & 1 & 0 \\ \times & 1 & 1 & 1 & 1 \\ 1 & 0 & 0 & 0 & 1 \\ 0 & 1 & \times & 1 & 0 \end{bmatrix} \qquad C = \begin{bmatrix} 1 & 0 & \times \\ \times & 1 & 1 \\ 1 & 0 & 0 \\ 0 & 1 & \times \end{bmatrix}$$

To find the required test vectors, define the *select set*, s_i, of product line p_i, as the set of all input vectors that activate line p_i. For a NOR-NOR PLA the s_i are the values of the ith row of matrix C, while for a NAND-NAND PLA the s_i are the complements of the elements of the ith row of C.

Thus, for the PLA of Fig. 12.16 to be realized in NOR-NOR form, the s_i are: $s_1 = \{100, 101\}$, $s_2 = \{011, 111\}$, $s_3 = \{100\}$, and $s_4 = \{010, 011\}$. For the same PLA to be realized in NAND-NAND form, the s_i are: $s_1 = \{011, 010\}$, $s_2 = \{100, 000\}$, $s_3 = \{011\}$, and $s_4 = \{100, 101\}$.

An input vector is a main test vector, TV_{1i}, of product line p_i, if TV_{1i} is an element of s_i as defined above, and the minimum Hamming distance of TV_{1i} to all other elements s_j of the PLA is 2. The Hamming distances generate the *distance matrix*, D, whose elements are given by the vector-wide exclusive-OR of TV_{1i} and s_j, or

$$d_{ij} = \sum_{j=1}^{n} TV_{1i} \oplus s_j = \sum_{j=1}^{n} TV_{1i}\bar{s}_j + s_j \overline{TV_{1i}}$$

The exclusive-ORs of 1 with $\times$, and of 0 with $\times$, are zero, since don't care terms are distance zero from both a 1 and a 0. Also, the elements of the principle

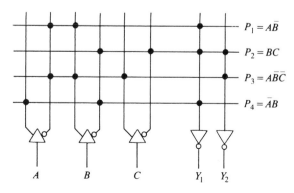

FIGURE 12.16
A symbolic PLA to be tested.

diagonal of matrix D represent the distance of TV_{ii} from itself. Since this distance is irrelevant to the test, either let the elements TV_{ii} have a distance, d_{ii}, of 2 or instruct the program to ignore the principal diagonal of the matrix. The PLA is testable if every element of matrix D that is not on the principal diagonal is at least 2, and if the original PLA is not testable, it must be augmented by the addition of input lines until all the $d_{ij} \geq 2$.

For a NOR-NOR realization of the PLA of Fig. 12.16, a possible set of test vectors is 100, 111, 100, and 010. Two test vectors are identical in this set, and p_1 and p_3 cannot be separately tested. TV_1 can be chosen to be 101, since this is also an element of the set, s_1, but it is only of distance 1 from $s_3 = 100$. The PLA is not testable as is, and must be augmented by at least one additional input variable.

Proceeding in the above manner, calculations of the elements d_{ij} show that the above PLA must be augmented with two input lines to be testable. To increase the distance of all product lines, add two inputs that have each product line at least distance 1 from each other. Counting in binary will do this. However, the original product lines p_1 and p_3 were of distance zero. To guarantee a Hamming distance of two after augmentation, one can assign either 00 as input to one product line and 11 to the other line, or one can assign 01 to one product line and 10 to the other. The augmented personality matrix Q_2, with 00 assigned to row 1 and 11 assigned to row 3 is given by:

$$Q_2 = \begin{bmatrix} 0 & 0 & 1 & 0 & \times & 1 & 0 \\ 0 & 1 & \times & 1 & 1 & 1 & 1 \\ 1 & 1 & 1 & 0 & 0 & 0 & 1 \\ 1 & 0 & 0 & 1 & \times & 1 & 0 \end{bmatrix}$$

where the two columns to the left of the line are the additional input lines. The select set is now:

$$s_1 = 0010\times \qquad s_2 = 01\times 11 \qquad s_3 = 11100 \qquad s_4 = 1001\times$$

A suitable set of test vectors is

$$TV_{11} = 00101 \qquad TV_{12} = 01011 \qquad TV_{13} = 11100 \qquad TV_{14} = 10010$$

The minimum distance of the above set of test vectors with respect to each other is 3. This will guarantee a minimum distance of 2 for each of the s_j that have one don't care term.

The first two rows of the D matrix are obtained as follows:

$$d_{11} = \text{(by definition)} = 2 \qquad d_{21} = (01011) \oplus (0010\times) = 3$$

$$d_{12} = (00101) \oplus (01\times 11) = 2 \qquad d_{22} = \text{(by definition)} = 2$$

$$d_{13} = (00101) \oplus (11100) = 3 \qquad d_{23} = (01011) \oplus (11100) = 4$$

$$d_{14} = (00101) \oplus (1001\times) = 3 \qquad d_{24} = (01011) \oplus (1001\times) = 2$$

TABLE 12.4

Test vector	TV_{1i}	TV_{2i}	TV_{3i}	TV_{4i}
Main	00101	01011	11100	10010
Auxiliary	00100	01010	11101	10011
Auxiliary	00111	01001	11110	10000
Auxiliary	00001	01111	11000	10110
Auxiliary	01101	00011	10100	11010
Auxiliary	10101	11011	01100	00010

The distance matrix for the augmented PLA is:

$$D = \begin{bmatrix} 2 & 2 & 3 & 3 \\ 3 & 2 & 4 & 2 \\ 2 & 3 & 2 & 3 \\ 3 & 3 & 3 & 2 \end{bmatrix}$$

Since every element in D is at least 2, the augmented PLA is now testable for single error detection. A set of 24 test vectors which form an exhaustive test set that will give 100 percent fault coverage with respect to stuck-at and missing/extra crosspoint faults is given in Table 12.4, and the PLA is shown in Fig. 12.17.

If a product line is a subproduct of another product line, then the distance of these two lines is 0, and at least two extra inputs are required to test these two product lines. Extra product lines are more cost-effective than extra input lines because they have no I/O connections to the outside world, and it is advantageous to exchange extra inputs for extra product lines whenever possible.

To add extra product lines, expand the product terms in the personality

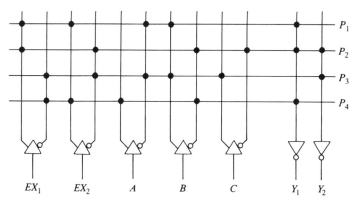

FIGURE 12.17
The expanded or augmented testable PLA from Fig. 12.16.

matrix by replacing each line that has a don't care term with two lines without don't cares. For the PLA discussed above, the expanded personality matrix is

$$
Q_{EXP} = \begin{bmatrix}
1 & 0 & 0 & 1 & 0 \\
1 & 0 & 1 & 1 & 0 \\
0 & 1 & 1 & 1 & 1 \\
1 & 1 & 1 & 1 & 1 \\
1 & 0 & 0 & 0 & 1 \\
0 & 1 & 0 & 1 & 0 \\
0 & 1 & 1 & 1 & 0
\end{bmatrix}
$$

Examination of Q_{EXP} shows that rows 1 and 5 can be combined to give 10011, and rows 3 and 7 can be combined to give 01111. The resulting matrix is now

$$
Q_{NEW} = \begin{bmatrix}
1 & 0 & 0 & 1 & 1 \\
1 & 0 & 1 & 1 & 0 \\
0 & 1 & 1 & 1 & 1 \\
1 & 1 & 1 & 1 & 1 \\
0 & 1 & 0 & 1 & 0
\end{bmatrix} = \begin{bmatrix}
1 & 0 & 0 & 1 & 1 \\
1 & 0 & 1 & 1 & 0 \\
\times & 1 & 1 & 1 & 1 \\
0 & 1 & 0 & 1 & 0
\end{bmatrix}
$$

The new matrix should be examined for testability.

Extra crosspoint devices represent less that 0.5 percent of faults mapped from physical failures, and PLA-folding eliminates many sites of possible extra devices. Thus, a vector need not uniquely select one product line if the collective output response of the other selected product terms does not have a 1 where line P has a 1 (11). The deselection of a product line does not require a Hamming distance of 2 if the product line is unique to a given output line.

Consider the PLA whose personality matrix is given below. Label the product lines 1, 2, and 3, from top to bottom, and label the output lines 1, 2, and 3, from left to right.

$$
Q = \begin{bmatrix}
1 & \times & \times & 0 & \times & 1 & 1 & 1 & 1 \\
0 & \times & 0 & \times & 0 & 1 & 0 & 1 & 0 \\
0 & \times & 0 & 0 & 0 & 0 & 1 & 1 & 0
\end{bmatrix}
$$

$TV_0 = 100001$ is a satisfactory main test vector for product line 1, even though complementing the first bit to obtain $TV_1 = 000001$ can also select both product lines 2 and 3. (Product line 2 is selected if the line is correct, and product line 3 is selected if its LSB is a 1.) Output line 3 is controlled only by product line 1, and activating either or both of the other two product lines with a test vector will have no effect upon output line 3. All entries of Hamming distance 1 in the distance matrix that correspond to this case can be changed to 2. The OR-plane matrix must be examined to determine when these cases occur.

A second case considered by Khakbaz and Bozorgui-Nesbat is shown with the following personality matrix (11). The rows and columns are labeled as above.

$$Q = \begin{bmatrix} 1 & \times & \times & 0 & \times & 1 & 1 & 1 & 0 & 0 & 0 \\ \times & 0 & \times & \times & 0 & 1 & 0 & 0 & 1 & 1 & 0 \\ 1 & \times & 0 & 0 & 0 & \times & 0 & 0 & 0 & 1 & 1 \end{bmatrix}$$

Test vector $TV_0 = 100001$ selects all three product lines, but it tests all the connections of product line 1 in the OR plane. Output lines 1 and 2 can both be used to test product line 1. All entries of Hamming distance 0 that correspond to the above case can be changed to 2.

TV_0 does not qualify as a main test vector for the other two product lines because of the partial masking due to crosspoint connections in output line 4. Product lines 2 and 3 can be tested with this main test vector by monitoring output lines 3 and 5, respectively, but output line 4 requires a different main test vector.

12.7 PLA PERFORMANCE ESTIMATION

All PLAs, whether static or dynamic, NMOS or CMOS, are similar in structure. The loadings of the input lines, word lines, and output lines define the speed at which the PLA operates. As the number of transistors in the circuit increases, the number of gates which an input latch must drive also increases. The same is true of the precharge circuitry which pulls up the transistor drains, and the critical case is generally when the logic state causes a heavily loaded word line to be discharged through a single device.

PLAs must be designed for propagation-delay testability, where the propagation delay of a PLA is defined as the time lapse between the change in a signal at the input line and the corresponding change in a signal at the output line.

In a NOR-NOR PLA, the AND-plane and the OR-plane pull-downs are in parallel throughout the matrix. The delays of the output inverters are a function of the loading of the output lines, and can be treated separately from the PLA structure, as can the two-phase clocking of the input and output.

This reduced PLA (sans clocking and output inverters) can be tested by applying all possible input pattern sequences of test vectors, and measuring the responses of the output lines. This is very time-consuming and expensive.

Assume that the low-level voltage of either a product line or an output line is independent of the number of active pull-downs on that line. Then, rising-output delay depends upon the delay of pull-up devices of some product lines and upon the delay of some OR-plane pull-down devices, and the worst-case rising-output delay occurs when a single pull-up and a single pull-down cause the delay. Falling-output delay depends upon the delay of the output line pull-up device and upon the delay of some of the AND-plane pull-down devices, and the worst-case falling-output delay occurs when the output pull-up and only a single AND-plane pull-down cause the delay.

The worst-case rising or falling delays associated with each output line are equal to the sum of the delays of a pull-up device and a pull-down device. Testing the propagation delays of all the appropriate pull-up/pull-down pairs will be sufficient to determine the worst-case propagation of the PLA. The appropriate pull-up/pull-down pairs are determined as follows:

For a rising output, the pull-up belongs to a product line, p_i, and the pull-down is located at the intersection of p_i and an output line Y_j; while for a falling output, the pull-up is associated with output line Y_j and the pull-down is tied to product line p_i in the AND-plane, and there is a pull-down at the intersection of Y_j and p_i.

To test for worst-case rising-output delay, first deactivate all the product lines, then activate only one product line at a time until all product lines are tested. To test for worst-case falling-output delay, deactivate all product lines except one, which is activated. Deactivate that line using a single AND-plane pull-down located on the line. Repeat these steps until all the product lines are tested.

A step input can be applied to a standard size CMOS inverter and the propagation delay, t_p, can be measured for a rising and a falling output waveform. From this and knowledge of the capacitive load on the node, one can calculate either the effective resistance, R_{eff}, or the effective source/sink current, I_{eff}, as the output swings through a voltage change $V_{oH} - V_{oL}$. The gate output voltage change, $V_{oH} - V_{oL}$, is the logic swing, LS, $t_{pd} = 0.7\tau$, $t_{\text{rise}} = 2.2\tau_{pLH}$, and $t_{\text{fall}} = 2.2\tau_{pHL}$. Hence

$$t_{pd} = 0.7\tau = 0.7 R_{\text{eff}} C$$

$$R_{\text{eff}} = \frac{t_{pd}}{0.7C}$$

$$I_{\text{source}} = C\frac{\Delta V}{\Delta t} = C\frac{LS}{t_{\text{rise}}} \quad \text{or} \quad I_{\text{sink}} = C\frac{LS}{t_{\text{fall}}}$$

The operating temperature of the inverting transistors must also be known. A device dissipating 1.5 mW of heat, with a case thermal resistance of 20° C/mW, surrounded by an ambient at a temperature of 70°C, will be operating at a device temperature of $70 + 20(1.5) = 100$°C, about 80°C above room temperature. If the device has a propagation delay of t_p at room temperature, the delay when operating at 100°C might be as much as 50 percent longer, or $1.5t_p$.

12.8 DESIGN SIMULATION

VLSI circuits are large complex systems and, due to oversights and design errors, there is a negligible probability that a circuit will work the first time. Typical errors include *missing connections, logic inversions, short circuited wires, charge-sharing errors* that simulators don't catch, *noise-margin problems* which are hard to resolve, *sneak paths,* and *incorrect specifications.*

To facilitate simulation and testing, circuits should be partitioned functionally rather than structurally. The circuit then has easily identifiable subsystems that are controllable from the chip inputs and observable from the chip outputs, and it is relatively easy to write test vectors that exercise each subsystem individually.

One should use synchronous logic only, and provide a means for initializing the network. Long divider chains and counters can be broken up into separately controllable sections. Designing for testability means that a design contains readily accessible control and observation paths to all functional units. Poor control will increase test-generation time and test-program size. Generating a set of test vectors is a critical design step, and is usually the final specification of the device.

Low-level and intermediate modules should be simulated first and under worst-case conditions, before attempting chip-level simulation. When worst-case testing, it must be kept in mind that devices that run faster than predicted can violate internal set-up and hold times, and can be just as bad as devices running too slowly.

Proper evaluation of test coverage gives a complete test set and ensures that the vectors are compatible with, and properly formatted for, the automatic test equipment available. To guarantee that each node is controllable with a given set of test vectors, the set of test patterns must cause every node in the network to change state at least once.

12.9 MISCELLANEOUS TEST TECHNIQUES

A simple test of misregistration in IC processing is accomplished with the layout of Fig. 12.18. For a misregistration in the x direction of ΔX, the resistance of the left-hand and right-hand resistors is given by

$$R_{\text{left}} = \frac{R_s L}{W + \Delta X} \quad \text{and} \quad R_{\text{right}} = \frac{R_s L}{W - \Delta X}$$

where R_s is the sheet resistance of the resistor of nominal length L and nominal width W. Solve for ΔX

$$\Delta X = \frac{R_s L}{2} \left(\frac{1}{R_{\text{left}}} - \frac{1}{R_{\text{right}}} \right)$$

W does not appear in the equation, and misregistration is independent of processing variations such as etching and outdiffusion because their effects occur equally at both edges.

Under normal operating conditions, the main sources of leakage current in a FET are due to diode junction leakage and leakage along the surface of the active region. Diode leakage current can be minimized by reducing the defect density of the material, while surface leakage current is controlled by the subthreshold characteristics of the FET. A subthreshold transfer curve is shown in

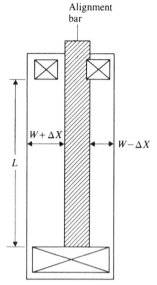

Alignment
bar

$W + \Delta X$

$W - \Delta X$

L

FIGURE 12.18
Geometry for measurement of misregistration.

Fig. 12.19, from which

$$I_D = I_0 \exp \left[\frac{V_{GS} - V_{TH}}{\eta V_T} \right]$$

where V_{TH} is the threshold voltage when $I_D = I_0$, V_T is the thermal voltage kT/q, and η is approximately 2 for very low current. For zero gate bias:

$$I_D = I_0 \exp \left[\frac{-V_{TH}}{\eta V_T} \right]$$

The leakage current is determined by the threshold voltage, V_{TH}, and the

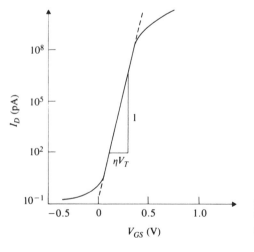

I_D (pA)

10^8

10^5

10^2

10^{-1}

1

ηV_T

-0.5 0 0.5 1.0

V_{GS} (V)

FIGURE 12.19
The subthreshold slope is used to calculate the leakage current.

subthreshold slope, $1/\eta V_T$. The threshold voltage decreases with decreasing channel length due to the short channel effect and decreases as the temperature increases. The subthreshold slope changes with temperature but is not a function of channel length. Threshold voltage has a substantial effect on the leakage current of a FET (12,13).

The *kerf* is the region between chips where the dicing saw cuts. In Fig. 12.20, the squares represent individual circuit chips. The space between these chips is the kerf. Test structures for extensive device and process characterization can be placed in this region where they do not affect the number of chips per wafer, or test structures can be uniformly placed throughout the wafer, as shown in Fig. 12.20. Kerfs are preferred to discrete test chips because they do not reduce the number of usable chips per wafer.

Kerf-testing is affected by the number of test I/O pads required and the ease of making a probe card. Groups of $2 \times N$ pad arrays can be conveniently arranged in the kerf in such a manner that the tester does not require a large number of probes. N is determined by the tester, which "steps" along the kerf, testing each group of $2 \times N$ test pads independently. A kerf with 2×5 pads is shown in Fig. 12.21. The test structures are between the pads (not shown in Fig. 12.21), and connected to a pair of pads. One set of kerfs per chip should be sufficient, leaving two segments of the kerf for optical image and alignment aids, and any special structures that might be desired.

The kerf width is a function of the maturity of the process technology. Initially a wide kerf is required to handle an extensive assortment of test structures, whereas a well-defined process only requires the tracking of a few key parameters such as capacitances, contact resistances, and sheet resistances. Kerf widths as small as 200 microns allow sufficient test structures to characterize a stable process.

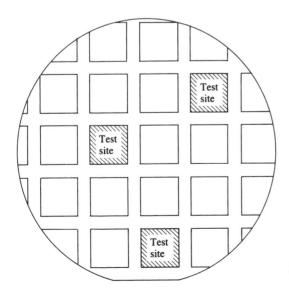

FIGURE 12.20
Typical test-site locations on a wafer.

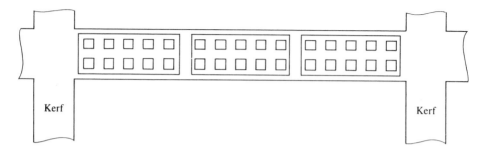

FIGURE 12.21
Kerf designed with 2 × 5 test pads.

Device parameters are extracted from a matrix of short- and long-channel devices as well as wide- and narrow-channel devices, in order to test short-channel and narrow-channel effects of each depletion or enhancement device. Each transistor to be tested should have the same number of squares from both the source and drain contacts to the channel edges, in order to have identical source and drain series resistance for each transistor type.

If multiple test devices are connected common-gate and common-source, with each drain separate, the number of I/O pads required is kept to a minimum. N devices connected in this manner require only $N + 2$ pads, whereas N devices connected separately require $3N$ pads. The transistors should be larger than minimum geometry because they must be insensitive to process variations if one is to measure parameter information and not test the technology. A variety of device sizes might help eliminate process variations.

Capacitance measurements using standard CV techniques provide information on gate-oxide thickness, flatband voltages, effective doping profiles, concentrations, and mobile-ion densities (14). The FET gate capacitance consists of the gate oxide capacitance, C_{ox}, in series with the silicon depletion-layer capacitance, C_{si}, as shown in Fig. 12.22a.

The inversion-layer charges are minority carriers and take one minority-carrier lifetime to reach the oxide interface. For very low frequencies, equilibrium is reached and the entire gate voltage drops across the oxide region. The capacitance is then C_{ox}. For higher frequencies the inversion-layer charges do not change rapidly enough to affect the capacitance, and the total capacitance is given by $1/C_T = 1/C_{ox} + 1/C_{si}$ as shown in Fig. 12.22b. Capacitors are usually designed to be parallel-plate, but fringing effects can be measured using long thin conductor runs.

Thin-oxide capacitors are susceptible to gate damage due to ion-implanting and reactive ion etching, which can charge the devices to dielectric breakdown. A protective diode to provide a charge leakage path to ground will prevent exessive charge buildup, but the diode must be removed from the capacitor before any CV measurements are taken. This can be done by inserting a narrow metal fuse between the capacitor and the protective diode, which is blown prior to CV testing.

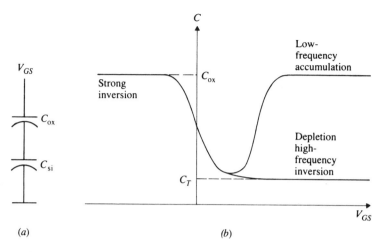

(a) (b)

FIGURE 12.22
Capacitance of a FET. (a) Equivalent circuit; (b) capacitance as a function of gate bias.

Applied potentials should stress the device to the maximum value of both polarities. A pinhole in the oxide can lead to a *pn* junction formed by diffusion through the pinhole which short circuits the channel to a doped polysilicon gate. The tester voltage polarity must be reversible in order to detect the diode characteristic.

Contact resistance must be monitored for each contact level and can be measured with a four-point probe and the structure shown in Fig. 12.23. Current

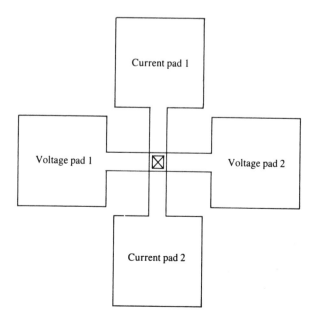

FIGURE 12.23
Contact-resistance monitor.

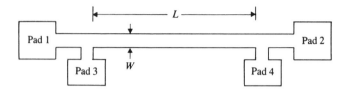

FIGURE 12.24
Geometry for the measurement of sheet resistance.

is fed through two probes and the voltage across the other two probes is monitored. Contact resistance is defined as the ratio of voltage measured to current applied.

Discrepancies in measurements of contact resistance taken at two or more bias currents can be due to parasitic currents which affect the accuracy of the measurements. A long string of contacts in series gives a better overall picture of contact reliability and resistance. Minimum contact dimensions test the technology whereas larger contact dimensions minimize errors due to defects unrelated to the contact levels under examination.

Sheet resistance can be monitored by a simple structure such as that shown in Fig. 12.24. A current I is forced from PAD_1 to PAD_2 and the voltage drop from PAD_3 to PAD_4 is measured. Then the resistance from PAD_3 to PAD_4 is

$$R = \frac{V}{I} = \frac{R_S L}{W}$$

where R_S is the sheet resistance to be determined.

The length can be large enough to neglect errors in L, but width errors need to be determined in order to calculate R_S. Metal layers have very low sheet resistance, but sheet resistance should be monitored for all polysilicon and diffusion layers. If the sheet-resistance circuitry is zigzagged and placed under probe pads no additional space is required for it.

Structures to measure image size for each mask level can be placed on the kerf and must be placed over topography similar to that in the product chip in order to produce comparable results. Patterns too small for optical imaging can be measured with a scanning electron microscope. Two examples of optical patterns are shown in Fig. 12.25. The positive-image-size monitor is used for subtractive processes such as lift-off metal, while a negative-image-size monitor is used for additive processes such as polysilicon and active areas.

When the process is subtractive, the extensions on the bottom patterns of the positive monitor get wider while the widths of the openings on the top pattern get narrower. The reverse happens for additive processes. The bias is measured by visibly aligning the top and bottom edges of the pattern. Optical overlay monitors can also be used to determine mask-to-mask registration by comparing two patterns from different masking steps.

As dimensions continue to shrink, oxide integrity becomes more critical. Large numbers of FETs connected in parallel and placed in the kerf can be used to monitor gate-oxide defects. The devices are constructed to have source, drain,

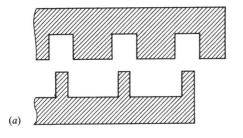

(a)

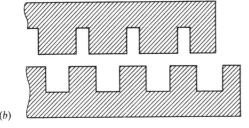

(b)

FIGURE 12.25
Optical image size monitors.
(a) Positive monitor;
(b) negative monitor.

gate, and substrate contacts that are wired in parallel. Large gates can give defect information also.

Thin-oxide defects are monitored by measuring the gate-to-drain, gate-to-source, and gate-to-substrate leakage currents. The test structure contains poly-silicon gates bounded by both diffusion and recessed oxide, and can be used with large planar capacitors to determine thin-oxide defect levels. Perimeter defects, due to gate overlap of the diffusion region, can be measured as can area defects.

The average number of *area defects* equals the defect density multiplied by the critical area, and the average number of *perimeter defects* equals the perimeter defect density multiplied by the critical perimeter. It seems reasonable to assume that these two failure mechanisms are independent, in which case the average number of defects, T, is given by

$$T = AD_A + PD_P$$

where A is the critical area, D_A is the area defect density, P is the critical perimeter, and D_P is the perimeter defect density.

Poisson statistics apply when defects are distributed randomly across a wafer (15). Assuming a Poisson distribution, the test yield can be expressed in terms of an average number of defects as

$$Y = e^{-T}$$

The test yield is defined as the fraction of structures that are good. For the planar capacitor with no diffusion perimeter the yield Y_A is

$$Y_A = e^{-AD_A} \qquad \text{and} \qquad D_A = -\frac{\ln Y_A}{A}$$

while the test yield, Y_{AP}, for the gate string is

$$Y_{AP} = e^{-(AD_A + PD_P)}$$

$$D_P = \frac{1}{P}(-AD_A - \ln Y_{AP})$$

$$= \frac{1}{P}(\ln Y_A - \ln Y_{AP})$$

D_A and D_P can be determined once the yields are obtained. A third thin-oxide capacitor can be used to verify the previous calculations.

Since performance is dependent upon the gate overlap capacitance, a gate-overlap Miller capacitor can be employed with a dual purpose. The area and perimeter of this capacitance, along with the area and perimeter defect densities determined above, can be used to predict the test yields of the Miller capacitor. If the predicted test yield agrees with the actual measured test yield, then the assumption of two independent failure types is reasonable.

To monitor grossly oversized contacts and/or excessive overlay error a diffusion-to-metal contact chain as shown in Fig. 12.26 can be used. Metal sense lines are placed a minimum distance (as specified in the design rules) from the contact edge on each side of the chain.

The contact chain is first tested for continuity. If it is continuous the sense lines are tested for short circuiting to the chain. If the chain is not continuous a test structure failure occurred and no useful information can be obtained.

Short circuits will occur when the contacts are oversized and/or the overlay from metal to contacts is out of specification. To eliminate false readings, the metal space between the sense lines and the metal links of the chain can be larger than the minimum value allowed. The structure shown in Fig. 12.26 will detect gross overlay errors in both the X and Y directions.

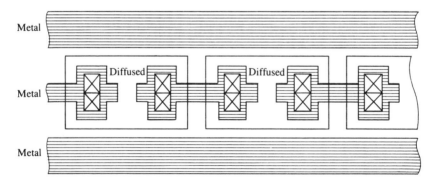

FIGURE 12.26
Structure for testing overlay error.

12.10 SUMMARY

The advent of VLSI has precipitated a revolution in the way electrical engineers design and test circuitry. The density of transistors on an IC chip has doubled about each year for two decades. Testability is inversely proportional to the complexity of a circuit, and the continual scaling down of feature sizes stretches the limits of both inspection and testing equipment and techniques. The higher operating speeds which accompany reduced feature size further complicate testing.

The increases in gate count, pin count, and performance which accompany the shrinkage of VLSI designs require the formulation of sophisticated approaches to circuit design and testing. This in turn requires testability to be designed into the system throughout the various design levels in order to allow verification or validation of the design at each stage of development.

The design engineer must think about testing from the beginning of the design. If testing is not kept in mind throughout the entire circuit design the chip will probably be untestable. The design engineer must consider what test vectors are needed, what output signals are expected, what to do if the desired output signals do not occur, and what tests can be performed. Special hardware is generally required to do the testing, and extra circuitry is often required to ensure testability.

The development of computer-aided design and testing tools and techniques allows the implementation of these new methodologies, and has led to devising new techniques for enhancing the testability of a circuit. There are three general approaches to testing: the use of special validation wafers inserted between regular wafers whose entire areas are devoted to test patterns; test dice which replace some ICs in a few strategic locations on the wafer; and the use of test structures placed on the kerf area between circuits.

Due to the large silicon area required, validation wafers are ideally suited to process development and characterization of new fabrication lines, while using kerf areas for test structures is very satisfactory when dealing with mature, well-defined, and relatively trouble-free processes which do not require large statistical samples.

Test dies are best suited for many process monitoring applications which fall between the above two extremes. Test dies must provide sufficient data to debug process-related problems and provide statistical data on worst-case variations of important process parameters. Test structures should use as few probe pads as possible. This is often accomplished by multiplexing or demultiplexing between logic functions and pads.

VLSI design can be divided into various levels such as system architecture, high-level internal design, logic design, circuit design, and actual mask layout. Some sort of simulator or test program should be associated with each level, to verify the design at that level. Software that can transition through all the levels is referred to as a silicon compiler. Ideally, the silicon compiler can start with the top-level system design, proceed through all the intermediate steps, and output correct masks.

An understanding of failure mechanisms and testing procedures is vital to the successful design of VLSI circuits. Functional failures of VLSI circuits are caused by process-induced defects which often have very complex physical characteristics and may be different from the simplistic defects assumed by the fault-models discussed in this chapter.

Soft errors are those due to transient failures, such as hole-electron pair generation by alpha-particle bombardment. They are very difficult to detect and fault-modeling is useless. Single-bit error detecting and correcting can be used to minimize soft errors.

A future trend in VLSI design is self-testing. With over one million transistors on a single chip, it is feasible to throw in an extra 10 percent or 100,000 transistors for testing purposes.

REFERENCES

1. D. B. I. Feltham, P. J. Nigh, L. R. Carley, and W. Maly, "Current Sensing for Built-In Testing of CMOS circuits," *IEEE International Conference on Computer Design*, ICCD'88, Rye Brook, N.Y., Oct. 3–5, 1988, pp. 454–457.
2. D. Baschiera and B. Courtois, "Testing CMOS: A Challenge," *VLSI Design*, vol. 10, October 1984, pp. 58–62.
3. D. L. Liu and E. J. McCluskey, "Designing CMOS circuits for Switch-Level Testability," *IEEE Design & Test of Computers*, August 1987, pp. 42–49.
4. B. W. Johnson, *Design and Analysis of Fault Tolerant Digital Systems*, Addison-Wesley Publishing Company, Reading, Mass., 1989, pp. 481–488.
5. A. C. Chiang, I. S. Reed, and A. V. Banes, "Path Sensitization, Partial Boolean Difference, and Automated Fault Diagnosis," *IEEE Transactions on Computers*, vol. C-21, February 1972, pp. 189–195.
6. S. Bozorgui-Nesbit and E. J. McCluskey, "Lower Overhead Design for Testability of Programmable Logic Arrays," *Proceedings of the 1984 IEEE International Test Conference*, Philadelphia, Pa., November 1984, pp. 856–865.
7. S. Bozorgui-Nesbit and E. J. McCluskey, "Design for Delay Testing of Programmable Logic Arrays," *Proceedings of the International Conference on Computer-Aided Design*, ICCAD-84 Santa Clara, Ca., November 1984.
8. H. Fujiwara and K. Kinoshita, "A Design of Programmable Logic Arrays with Universal Tests," *IEEE Transactions on Computers*, vol. C-30, no. 11, November 1981, pp. 823–828.
9. R. Treuer, H. Fujiwara, and V. Agarwal, "Implementing a Built-In Self-Test PLA Design," *IEEE Design & Test of Computers*, vol. 2, no. 2, April 1985, pp. 37–48.
10. R. Dandapani, R. K. Gulati, and D. K. Goel, "Built-In Self-Test for Large Embedded CMOS Folded PLAs," *Proceedings of the International Conference on Computer-Aided Design*, ICCAD-88, Nov. 7–10, 1988, pp. 236–239.
11. J. Khakbaz and S. Bozorgui-Nesbat, "Minimizing Extra Hardware for Fully Testable PLA Design," *Proceedings of the ACM IEEE 22d Design Automation Conference*, 1985, pp. 102–104.
12. S. M. Sze, *Physics of Semiconductor Devices*, 2d ed., John Wiley, New York, N.Y., 1981.
13. L. Vadasz and A. S. Grove, "Temperature Dependence of MOS Transistor Characteristics below Saturation," *IEEE Transactions on Electron Devices*, ED-13, 1966, p. 863.
14. W. C. Till and J. T. Luxon, *Integrated Circuits: Materials, Devices, and Fabrication*, Prentice-Hall, Inc., Englewood Cliffs, N.J., 1982, pp. 202–205.
15. M. A. Mitchell, "Defect Test Structures for Characterization of VLSI Technologies," *Solid State Technology*, May, 1985, pp. 207–213.

PROBLEMS

12.1. Given effective resistances of 18 kΩ/sq for n-type material and 36 kΩ/sq for p-type material, typical gate capacitances of 5 fF for a minimum geometry gate ($2\lambda \times 2\lambda$), a contact capacitance of 15 fF for an area of $4\lambda \times 4\lambda$, metal and polysilicon line capacitances of 0.3 fF per λ of line length, calculate the fall time for one pair of bits of two 32-bit numbers, laid out as shown in Fig. P12.1 with a pitch of 50λ between bits. Each transistor gate has an aspect ratio of 1/2.

12.2. A scan-register flip-flop is shown in Fig. P12.2.
(a) How many extra transistors are required to implement scan testing?
(b) Estimate the worst-case delay of this flip-flop.

12.3. Find the test vectors that test for stuck-at-1 and stuck-at-0 faults at input A of gate 1 of the circuit given in Fig. P12.3.

12.4. Devise two test vectors to observe the stuck-open fault at transistor P_2 in Fig. P12.4.

12.5. Devise a robust test for a stuck-open fault at FET N_2 in Fig. P12.4.

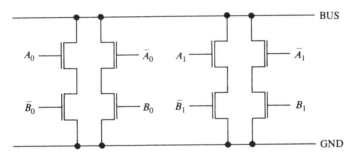

FIGURE P12.1
Circuit diagram of a pair of bits on a bus line.

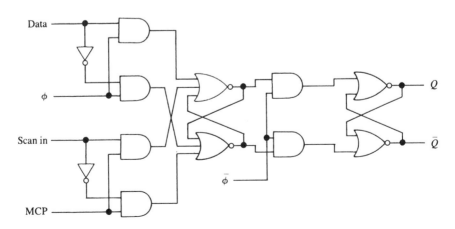

FIGURE P12.2
Scan-register flip-flop.

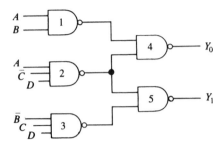

FIGURE P12.3
Two-level, two-output circuit.

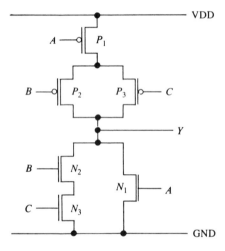

FIGURE P12.4
A CMOS circuit with a stuck-open fault at P_2.

12.6. Show that if all input literals can be set to 1 or 0, a nonredundant gate as shown in Fig. P12.6 can be tested for stuck-open faults. The PMOS gate whose input is A is stuck open. Find two test vectors that are robust.

12.7. Show that the test vectors given will detect the stuck-on fault in Fig. P12.7.

TV	C_1	C_2	A	B	C	D	Y(true)	Y(faulty)
1	0	1	1	0	1	0	1	× *
2	1	1	1	0	1	0	1	0

*TV_1 creates a short circuit from VDD to GND in the faulty circuit, and the output, Y, is between VDD and GND potential.

12.8. (a) Draw the Karnaugh maps for output Y_2 of the circuit in Fig. P12.8a, subject to faults caused by either an undesired transistor at crosspoints X_1, X_2, or X_4, or a missing transistor at crosspoints X_3 or X_5. Only one faulty crosspoint at a time appears in the PLA.
(b) Find the crosspoint faults that produce the Karnaugh maps shown in Fig. P12.8b for output Y_2.

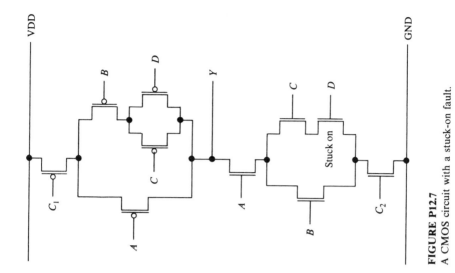

FIGURE P12.7
A CMOS circuit with a stuck-on fault.

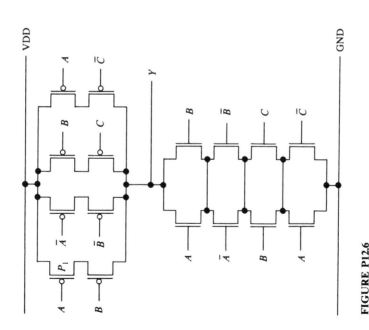

FIGURE P12.6
A nonredundant CMOS gate with a stuck-open fault at P_1.

389

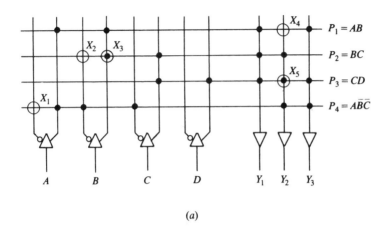

(a)

(b)

FIGURE P12.8
(a) A PLA with crosspoint faults; (b) Karnaugh maps of the PLA of Fig. P12.8a with crosspoint faults.

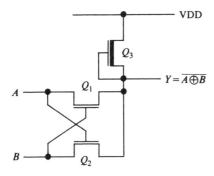

FIGURE P12.9
A simple ENOR gate.

12.9. The ENOR gate shown in Fig. P12.9 can be tested for stuck-off faults with three test vectors. Find them.

12.10. Show that the original PLA in Fig. P12.10 is untestable.

12.11. (*a*) Use the test vectors below to find the distance matrix of the augmented PLA in Fig. P12.10, and show that they can be used as main test vectors for the PLA.

$$TV_{10} = 01100 \qquad TV_{20} = 11011 \qquad TV_{30} = 11101$$

$$TV_{40} = 01010 \qquad TV_{50} = 10111$$

(*b*) List all the test vectors required to test the PLA.

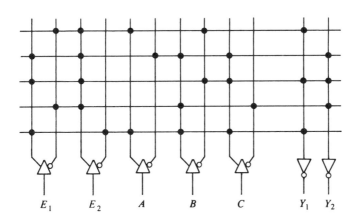

FIGURE P12.10
A PLA with 3 inputs and 2 outputs, augmented by input lines E_1 and E_2.

THE
pn
JUNCTION

A.1 THE *pn* STEP JUNCTION IN EQUILIBRIUM

Under conditions of thermodynamic equilibrium, a potential ϕ_0 exists across a *pn* junction due to the electric field of the ionized impurity atoms in the space-charge region (depletion region) of the junction. The electric field in this depletion region and the voltage across the depletion region can be obtained from Poisson's equation. Once the voltage across the junction is known, the junction capacitances can be calculated.

Epitaxial, implanted, and shallow-diffused junctions have a doping impurity concentration per cross-sectional area that approaches the profile of a simple step junction.

For a step junction, the approximate charge density distribution is as shown in Fig. A.1. Starting with Poisson's equation [Eq. (A.1)] one can obtain the equations for potential, electric field, and depletion-region width of the *pn* junction

$$\nabla^2\phi = -\frac{\rho_v}{\epsilon} \tag{A.1}$$

If one assumes fringing effects at the boundaries of the depletion region are

393

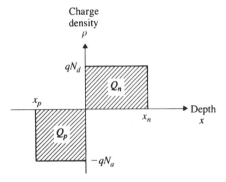

FIGURE A.1
Approximate charge density distribution across a
pn junction.

negligible, the problem reduces to a simple second-order differential equation in the variable x, namely

$$\frac{d^2\phi}{dx^2} = -\frac{qN_d}{\epsilon} \tag{A.2}$$

Upon separating the variables, integrating, and recalling that $E = -\text{grad } \phi$, one obtains the electric field E. If the integration is carried out over the n-type segment of the depletion region, from $x = 0$ to $x = x_n$

$$\frac{d\phi}{dx} = -\frac{qN_d}{\epsilon}(x + C_1) = -E_n \tag{A.3}$$

The boundary condition is that the electric field, E_n, vanishes at $x = x_n$. The electric field in the n region is thus

$$E_n = \frac{qN_d}{\epsilon}(x - x_n) \qquad \text{for} \qquad 0 \le x \le x_n \tag{A.4}$$

The electric field in the p region is obtained in the same manner by substituting $-qN_a$ for the charge density, integrating from $x = x_p$ to $x = 0$, and applying the boundary condition that the electric field in the p region vanishes at $x = x_p$

$$E_p = -\frac{qN_a}{\epsilon}(x + x_p) \qquad \text{for} \qquad x_p \le x \le 0 \tag{A.5}$$

The electric field must be continuous across the metallurgical interface at $x = 0$. All electric flux lines cross this boundary, therefore the magnitude of the electric field is a maximum at $x = 0$, and the field itself is the most negative there since it points in the negative x direction

$$E_{\text{max}} = E(0) = -\frac{qN_d x_n}{\epsilon} = \frac{qN_a x_p}{\epsilon} \tag{A.6}$$

q/ϵ can be cancelled on both sides of Eq. (A.6), to give

$$N_d x_n = -N_a x_p \tag{A.7}$$

Equation (A.7) is a statement of charge balance. The ionized charge on one side of the depletion region is equal in magnitude to the ionized charge on the other side of the metallurgical junction.

Refer to Eq. (A.3) which gives the derivative of the junction potential. Integrating Eq. (A.3) from $x = 0$ to x_n, one obtains the potential drop across the n side of the junction

$$\frac{d\phi}{dx} = -\frac{qN_d}{\epsilon}(x - x_n)$$

$$\phi = -\frac{qN_d}{\epsilon}\left(\frac{x^2}{2} - x_n x + C_2\right) \tag{A.8}$$

Choose the potential to be 0 at $x = 0$, the metallurgical interface, and the voltage drop across the n region is given by

$$V_n = \frac{qN_d x_n^2}{2\epsilon} \tag{A.9}$$

From symmetry, the voltage drop across the p region is obtained by replacing charge density qN_d by charge density $-qN_a$

$$V_p = -\frac{qN_a x_p^2}{2\epsilon} \tag{A.10}$$

The built-in diffusion potential of the step junction is

$$\phi_0 = V_n - V_p = \frac{q}{2\epsilon}[N_d x_n^2 + N_a x_p^2] \tag{A.11}$$

To obtain the voltage drop across the depletion region as a function of the depletion-region width requires some algebra. From the charge-balance equation one can solve for x_n as a function of x_p

$$N_d x_n = -N_a x_p \quad \text{and} \quad x_n^2 = \left(\frac{N_a^2}{N_d^2}\right)x_p^2 \tag{A.12}$$

Substitute this into Eq. (A.11) for ϕ_0, and

$$\phi_0 = \frac{q}{2\epsilon}\left[N_d\left(\frac{N_a^2}{N_d^2}\right)x_p^2 + N_a x_p^2\right]$$

$$= \frac{qN_a}{2\epsilon N_d}(N_a + N_d)x_p^2 \tag{A.13}$$

One can now solve for x_p and x_n as functions of ϕ_0 and the ionized impurity concentrations, N_a and N_d

$$x_p = -\sqrt{\frac{2\epsilon\phi_0 N_d}{qN_a(N_a + N_d)}} \tag{A.14}$$

$$x_n = \sqrt{\frac{2\epsilon\phi_0 N_a}{qN_d(N_a + N_d)}} \tag{A.15}$$

The depletion-region width, x_d, can be obtained from Eqs. (A.14) and (A.15)

$$x_d = x_n - x_p = \sqrt{\frac{2\epsilon\phi_0}{q(N_a + N_d)}} \left[\sqrt{\frac{N_d}{N_a}} + \sqrt{\frac{N_a}{N_d}} \right]$$

$$= \sqrt{\frac{2\epsilon\phi_0}{q(N_a + N_d)}} \frac{N_a + N_d}{\sqrt{N_a N_d}}$$

The depletion-region width is thus found to be

$$x_d = \sqrt{\frac{2\epsilon\phi_0(N_a + N_d)}{qN_a N_d}} \tag{A.16}$$

The maximum electric field occurs at $x = 0$, and from Eqs. (A.6) and either (A.14) or (A.15) is given by

$$E_{MAX} = E(0) = -\sqrt{\frac{2qN_a N_d \phi_0}{\epsilon(N_a + N_d)}} \tag{A.17}$$

A.2 THE STEP JUNCTION UNDER EXTERNAL BIAS

The above equations were derived under the assumption of thermodynamic equilibrium. A positive external bias across the pn junction opposes the built-in potential, while a negative bias across the junction aids the built-in potential. Thus, if an external bias is represented by V (V positive is forward bias, and V negative is reverse bias), the above equations are modified by replacing ϕ_0 by $\phi_0 - V$. When this is done

$$x_p = -\sqrt{\frac{2\epsilon N_d}{qN_a(N_a + N_d)}} \sqrt{\phi_0 - V} \tag{A.18}$$

$$x_n = \sqrt{\frac{2\epsilon N_a}{qN_d(N_a + N_d)}} \sqrt{\phi_0 - V} \tag{A.19}$$

$$x_d = \sqrt{\frac{2\epsilon(N_a + N_d)}{qN_a N_d}} \sqrt{\phi_0 - V} \tag{A.20}$$

The maximum electric field under an external bias is given by

$$E_{MAX} = E(0) = -\sqrt{\frac{2qN_a N_d}{\epsilon(N_a + N_d)}} \sqrt{\phi_0 - V} \tag{A.21}$$

$$E_{MAX} = -\frac{qN_a N_d}{\epsilon(N_a + N_d)} x_d \tag{A.22}$$

Usually the source and drain diffusions have a much higher conductivity than the substrate (or well) material. For *n*-channel devices, $N_d \gg N_a$, and the above equations reduce to

$$\phi_0 = \frac{qN_a x_p^2}{2\epsilon} \tag{A.23}$$

$$x_p = -\sqrt{\frac{2\epsilon(\phi_0 - V)}{qN_a}} \tag{A.24}$$

$$x_n = \sqrt{\frac{2\epsilon N_a(\phi_0 - V)}{qN_d^2}} \tag{A.25}$$

$$x_d = \sqrt{\frac{2\epsilon(\phi_0 - V)}{qN_a}} \tag{A.26}$$

$$E_{\text{MAX}} = \sqrt{\frac{2qN_a(\phi_0 - V)}{\epsilon}}$$

$$= -\frac{qN_a x_d}{\epsilon} \approx -\frac{qN_a x_p}{\epsilon} = -\frac{\rho_v}{\epsilon} \tag{A.27}$$

APPENDIX
B

THE ALGEBRA OF MODERN BOOLEAN LOGIC

Much of the work being done in VLSI design and in the writing of software algorithms uses properties and definitions of boolean operations not taught in an introductory text on boolean and switching logic.

The following terms were found necessary to the discussion of PLA folding, multilevel decomposition, and testing in the text. The definitions are in alphabetical order.

Algebraic division. If the quotient of an expression is obtained by algebraic division, then the quotient and the divisor are algebraic divisors of the function. $A + B$ and $C + D$ are algebraic divisors of $(A + B)(C + D)$. Algebraic division is also called weak division.

Algebraic expression. An algebraic expression or function is a cover set of cubes. The sum-of-products is an algebraic expression consisting of the cover set of cubes or products.

Algebraic product. The product of two or more algebraic expressions which have disjoint support. $F = (A + B)(C + D)$ is an algebraic product because $(A + B) \cap (C + D) = \varnothing$.

Algebraic resubstitution. The use of algebraic division to substitute one function into a larger function in order to reduce the number of literals in a function. If $Y = A + B(C + D)$, and $Z = C + D$, then Y reduces to $A + BZ$.

Binate function. A function is binate in any variable that occurs in it with both positive and negative phase. The function $AB\bar{C} + \bar{B}CD + \bar{A}D$ is binate in literals A, B, and C.

Boolean division. If the quotient of an expression is obtained by boolean division, then the quotient and the divisor are boolean divisors of the function. $A + B$ and $A + C$ are boolean divisors of $A + BC$. Boolean division is also called strong division because it is more powerful than algebraic division.

Boolean product. The product of two or more algebraic expressions which do not have disjoint support. $G = (A + B)(A + C) = A + BC$ is a boolean product because $(A + B) \cap (A + C) \neq \varnothing$.

Boolean resubstitution. The use of boolean division to substitute one function into a larger function in order to reduce the number of literals in a function. See algebraic resubstitution.

Cardinality. The cardinality of a set is the number of elements it contains. The set $\{1, 2, 4, 8, 16\}$ has a cardinality of 5.

Cokernel. The cube used to obtain the kernel of an expression. DE is a cokernel of $(A + BC)DE$, and $A + BC$ is the kernel of DE.

Conjunction. The conjunction of A_1, A_2, and A_3 is

$$\bigcap_{i=1}^{3} A_i = A_1 \cdot A_2 \cdot A_3$$

Conjunctive normal form. A conjunctive normal form is a conjunction of disjunctions of literals. This is a product-of-sums representation of a function. The conjuctive normal form of literals P_{ij} is

$$\bigcap_{i=1}^{M} \bigcup_{j=1}^{N} P_{ij}$$

Cover set. A set of cubes which account for all the literals in an algebraic expression.

Cube. A cube is a set or product of literals which is unate in each of its literals. $A\bar{B}$ and $CDEF$ are cubes, $AB\bar{B}CD$ not a cube.

Cube-free expression. An expression is cube-free if no cube divides it evenly. $A + BC$ is cube-free, whereas BC is a cube.

DeMorgan's laws. DeMorgan's laws in set theory can be written as

$$\bigcap_{i=1}^{N} A_i = \overline{\bigcup_{i=1}^{N} \bar{A}_i} \quad \text{and} \quad \bigcup_{i=1}^{M} A_i = \overline{\bigcap_{i=1}^{M} \bar{A}_i}$$

Disjoint support. Two or more functions have disjoint support if they have no overlap of variables in their covers. The sets $\{A, B, C\}$ and $\{D, E, F\}$ have disjoint support because $\{A, B, C\} \cap \{D, E, F\} = \varnothing$.

Disjunction. The disjunction of A_1, A_2, and A_3 is

$$\bigcup_{i=1}^{3} A_i = A_1 + A_2 + A_3$$

If sets A and B are disjoint they have no common literal. Then the conjunction of A and B is $A \cap B = \varnothing$, the null set.

Disjunctive normal form. A disjunctive normal form is a disjunction of conjunctions of literals. This is a sum-of-products form of a function. The disjunctive normal form of literals P_{ij} is

$$\bigcup_{i=1}^{M} \bigcap_{j=1}^{N} P_{ij}$$

Don't-care-set. The don't-care-set is the set of cubes for which an algebraic expression is not specified.

Element of a set. The primitives which compose a set are referred to as the elements of the set. If A is an element of set S, this is written as $A \in S$.

Hypercube. A cube in more than three dimensions. $ABCDE$ is a 5-dimensional hypercube.

Kernel. The kernels of an expression are the cube-free primary divisors of the expression. $A + BC$ is a kernel of $(A + BC)DE$, and DE is the cokernel of $A + BC$.

Level of a kernel. A kernel is of level 0 if it has no kernels except itself. A kernel is of level n if the highest kernel it contains is a kernel of level $n - 1$. $A + B(C + D)$ is a kernel of level 1, containing $C + D$ which is a kernel of level 0.

Literal. Each occurrence of a variable either in true or in complemented form. A literal is a variable with a phase. The expression $AB\bar{C} + \bar{A}B\bar{C} + BD$ consists of four variables, A, B, C, and D, and eight literals.

Multiple-cube common divisor. Two functions have a multiple-cube common divisor if the intersection of a kernel from one function and a kernel from the other function contains more than one cube.

n-cube. An n-dimensional cube or boolean hypercube. Cubes AB, CDE, and $ABCDE$ are 2-cubes, 3-cubes, and 5-cubes, respectively.

Negative-phase cofactor. The negative-phase cofactor of a function F with respect to a literal X is the function obtained by evaluating the function F at $X = 0$.

Negative unate function. A function is negative unate in literal B if each occurrence of B in the function has negative phase. The function $AB + A\bar{C}\bar{D} + B\bar{D}$ is negative unate in literals C and D. A negative unate function contains no literals with positive phase.

Nonredundant expression. A nonredundant expression consists of the set of prime cubes of an expression. $AB + CD$ is nonredundant, whereas $AB + ABC$ is redundant.

OFF-set. The OFF-set is the set of cubes for which an algebraic expression is false. $\bar{F} = \bar{A}\bar{B} + \bar{A}\bar{C} + \bar{B}\bar{C}$ is the OFF-set of $F = AB + AC + BC$.

ON-set. The ON-set is the set of cubes for which an algebraic expression is true. If $F = AB + AC + BC$, then the ON-set for F is $\{\{A, B\}, \{A, C\}, \{B, C\}\}$.

Phase of a literal. If the phase of a literal is positive, the literal is true, and if the phase of a literal is negative, the literal is complemented. Literal A has positive phase, literal $\bar{B}$ has negative phase.

Positive-phase cofactor. The positive-phase cofactor of a function F with respect to a literal X is the function obtained by evaluating the function F at $X = 1$.

Positive unate function. A function is positive unate in literal A if each occurrence of A in the function has positive phase. The function $AB + A\bar{C}\bar{D} + B\bar{D}$ is positive unate in literals A and B. A positive unate function contains no literals with negative phase.

Prime cube. Any cube which is not covered by another cube. It is a prime implicant of an expression. Given cubes AB and ABD, AB is a prime cube and ABD is contained in AB and is not a prime cube.

Prime product. An algebraic product of two or more cubes which is not contained in another algebraic product.

Quotient of a function. The largest set of cubes that can be factored out of an expression. $Q = DE$ is a quotient of $Y = ADE + BCDE + F = (A + BC)DE + F$.

Remainder of a function. That part of an expression which is not in the quotient. $R = F$ is a remainder of $Y = (A + BC)DE + F$ divided by DE.

Set of elements. A set of elements is denoted by brackets. The set, S, consisting of elements A, B, and C, is written $S = \{A, B, C\}$.

Shannon's expansion theorem. Any function F that is binate in variable x_i can be expanded about x_i to obtain the positive-phase and negative-phase cofactors of F with respect to x_i.

Sharp product. $A \# B$ is the sharp product of A and B, and consists of the elements in the set A that are not in the set B. $A \# B = A\bar{B}$ and $B \# A = B\bar{A}$. $\{1, 2, 3\} \# \{3, 4, 5\} = \{1, 2\}$, and $\{3, 4, 5\} \# \{1, 2, 3\} = \{4, 5\}$.

Splitting variable. A splitting variable is any variable used to expand a function into positive-phase and negative-phase cofactors.

Strong division. See boolean division.

Support of an expression. The set of variables that are elements of the cubes of the expression. The support of a function F is written sup (F). If $F = F(A, B, C, D)$, then the support of F is the set $\{A, B, C, D\}$.

Unate function. A function that contains only one phase of each variable. $A\bar{B}D + \bar{B}C + AC$ is a unate function, since variables A, C, and D occur with positive phase only, and variable B occurs with negative phase only.

Variable. Any symbol representing a coordinate in boolean space. The set $S = \{A, B, C, \bar{C}\}$ consists of variables A, B, and C.

Vector AND. $A \cdot B = A \cap B$ is the vector-wide (bitwise) AND of vectors A and B. $(1011) \cdot (1100) = (1000)$.

Vector complement. $\bar{C}$ is the vector-wide (bitwise) complement of C. $(\overline{1011}) = (0100)$.

Vector EOR. $A \oplus B = A \cup B$ is the vector-wide exclusive-OR of vectors A and B. $(1011) \oplus (1100) = (0111)$.

Vector magnitude. The magnitude of a binary vector is the number of ones the vector contains. The magnitude of vector $V = 10110$ is $|V| = 3$.

Vector OR. $A + B = A \cup B$ is the vector-wide (bitwise) OR of vectors A and B. $(1011) + (1100) = (1111)$.

Weak division. See algebraic division.

INDEX